Biomedical
Instrumentation
and Measurements

Biomedical Instrumentation and Measurements

Second Edition

Leslie Cromwell

California State University,
Los Angeles, California

Fred J. Weibell

Veterans Administration
Biomedical Engineering and Computing Center
Sepulveda, California

Erich A. Pfeiffer

Wells Fargo Alarm Services
Engineering Center
Hawthorne, California

Prentice-Hall of India Private Limited
New Delhi - 110 001
1996

This Tenth Indian Reprint—Rs. 125.00
(Original U.S. Edition—Rs. 3014.00)

BIOMEDICAL INSTRUMENTATION AND MEASUREMENTS, 2nd Ed.
by Leslie Cromwell, Fred J. Weibell and Erich A. Pfeiffer

PRENTICE-HALL INTERNATIONAL, INC., Englewood Cliffs.
PRENTICE-HALL INTERNATIONAL (UK) LIMITED, London.
PRENTICE-HALL OF AUSTRALIA PTY. LIMITED, Sydney.
PRENTICE-HALL CANADA, INC., Toronto.
PRENTICE-HALL HISPANOAMERICANA, S.A., Mexico.
PRENTICE-HALL OF JAPAN, INC., Tokyo.
SIMON & SCHUSTER ASIA PTE. LTD., Singapore.
EDITORA PRENTICE-HALL DO BRASIL, LTDA., Rio de Janeiro.

ISBN-81-203-0653-8

The export rights of this book are vested solely with the publisher.

This Eastern Economy Edition is the only authorised, complete and unabridged photo-offset reproduction of the latest American edition specially published and priced for sale only in Bangladesh, Burma, Cambodia, China, Fiji, Hong Kong, India, Indonesia, Laos, Malaysia, Nepal, Pakistan, Philippines, Singapore, South Korea, Sri Lanka, Taiwan, Thailand, and Vietnam.

Reprinted in India by special arrangement with Prentice-Hall, Inc., Englewood Cliffs, N.J., U.S.A.

Tenth Printing (Second Edition)   . . .   . . .   **September, 1996**

Published by Prentice-Hall of India Private Limited, M-97, Connaught Circus, New Delhi-110001 and Printed by Syndicate Binders, B-167, Okhla Industrial Area, Phase I, New Delhi-110020.

Contents

Preface
to the
First Edition

As the world's population grows, the need for health care increases. In recent years progress in medical care has been rapid, especially in such fields as neurology and cardiology. A major reason for this progress has been the marriage of two important disciplines: medicine and engineering.

There are similarities between these two disciplines and there are differences, but there is no doubt that cooperation between them has produced excellent results. This fact can be well attested to by the man or woman who has received many more years of useful life because of the help of a prosthetic device, or from careful and meaningful monitoring during a critical illness.

The disciplines of medicine and engineering are both broad. They encompass people engaged in a wide spectrum of activities from the basic maintenance of either the body, or a piece of equipment, to research on the frontiers of knowledge in each field. There is one obvious common denominator: the need for instrumentation to make proper and accurate measurements of the parameters involved.

Personnel involved in the design, use, and maintenance of biomedical instrumentation come from either the life sciences or from engineering and technology, although most probably from the latter areas. Training in the life sciences includes physiology and anatomy, with little circuitry, electronics, or instrumentation. For the engineer or electronics technician the reverse is true, and anything but a meager knowledge of physiology is usually lacking on the biomedical side.

Unfortunately for those entering this new field, it is still very young and few reference books are available. This book has been written to help fill the gap. It has grown out of notes prepared by the various authors as reference material for educational courses. These courses have been presented at many levels in both colleges and hospitals. The participants have included engineers, technicians, doctors, dentists, nurses, psychologists, and many others covering a multitude of professions.

This book is primarily intended for the reader with a technical background in electronics or engineering, but with not much more than a casual familiarity with physiology. It is broad in its scope, however, covering a major portion of what is known as the field of biomedical instrumentation. There is depth where needed, but, in general, it is not intended to be too sophisticated. The authors believe in a down-to-earth approach. There are ample illustrations and references to easily accessible literature where more specialization is required. The presentation is such that persons in the life sciences with some knowledge of instrumentation should have little difficulty using it.

The introductory material is concerned with giving the reader a perspective of the field and a feeling for the subject matter. It also introduces the concept of the man-instrument system and the problems encountered in attempting to obtain measurements from a living body. An overall view of the physiological systems of the body is presented and then is later reinforced by more detailed explanations in appropriate parts of the text. The physiological material is presented in a language that should be readily understood by the technically trained person, even to the extent of using an engineering-type analysis. Medical terminology is introduced early, for one of the problems encountered in the field of biomedical instrumentation is communication between the doctor and the engineer or technician. Variables that are meaningful in describing the body system are discussed, together with the type of difficulties that may be anticipated.

It should also be noted that although reference works on physiology are included for those needing further study, enough fundamentals are presented within the context of this book to make it reasonably self-sufficient.

All measurements depend essentially on the detection, acquisition, display, and quantification of signals. The body itself provides a source of many types of signals. Some of these types—the bioelectric potentials responsible for the electrocardiogram, the electroencephalogram, and the electromyogram—are discussed in Chapter 3. In later chapters the measurement of each of these forms of biopotentials is discussed. One chapter is devoted to electrodes—the transducers for the biopotential signals.

With regard to the major physiological systems of the body, each segment is considered as a unit but often relies on material presented in the earlier chapters. The physiology of each system is first discussed in general, followed by an analysis of those parameters that have clinical importance. The fundamental principles and methods of measurement are discussed, with descriptions of principles of equipment 'actually in use today. This is done in turn for the cardiovascular, respiratory, and nervous systems. There are certain physical measurements that do not belong to any specific system but could relate to any or all of them. These physical variables, in² cluding temperature, displacement, force, velocity and acceleration, are covered in Chapter 9.

One of the novel ideas developed in this book is the fact that, together with a discussion of the nervous system, behavioral measurements are covered as well as the interaction between psychology and physiology.

The latter chapters are devoted to special topics to give the reader a true overall view of the field. Such topics include the use of remote monitoring by radio techniques commonly known as biotelemetry; radiation techniques, including X rays and radioisotopes; the clinical laboratory; and the digital computer as it applies to the medical profession, since this is becoming a widely used tool.

The final chapter is one of the most important. Electrical safety in the hospital and clinic is of vital concern. The whole field becomes of no avail unless this topic is understood.

For a quick reference, a group of appendices are devoted to medical terminology, an alphabetical glossary, a summary of physiological measurements, and some typical values.

The book has been prepared for a multiplicity of needs. The level is such that it could be used by those taking bioinstrumentation in a community college program, but the scope is such that it can also serve as a text for an introductory course for biomedical engineering students. It should also prove useful as a reference for medical and paramedical personnel with some knowledge of instruments who need to know more.

The background material was developed by the authors in courses presented at California State University, Los Angeles, and at various centers and hospitals of the United States Veterans Administration.

In a work of this nature, it is essential to illustrate commercial systems in common use. In many examples there are many manufacturers who produce similar equipment, and it is difficult to decide which to use as illustrative material. All companies have been most cooperative, and we apologize for the fact that it is not possible always to illustrate alternate examples. The authors wish to thank all the companies that were willing to supply illustrative material, as well as the authors of other textbooks for some borrowed descriptions and drawings. All of these are acknowledged in the text at appropriate places.

The authors wish to thank Mrs. Irina Cromwell, Mrs. Elissa J. Schrader, and Mrs. Erna Wellenstein for their assistance in typing the manuscript; Mr. Edward Francis, Miss Penelope Linskey, and the Prentice-Hall Company for their help, encouragement, and cooperation; and Mr. Joseph A. Labok, Jr., for his efforts in encouraging us to write this book.

Los Angeles, California   LESLIE CROMWELL
                                                           FRED J. WEIBELL
                                                           ERICH A. PFEIFFER
                                                           LEO B. USSELMAN

Preface
to the
Second Edition

It is extremely gratifying to write a book in a relatively new field and achieve the wide acceptance enjoyed by the first edition of Biomedical Instrumentation and Measurements. Many major Biomedical Engineering and BMET programs have adopted the book over the last six years both in the U.S.A. and abroad. The reviews by our professional colleagues have also has been most encouraging and the remarks we have had from them and from students with respect to the "readability" have been a stimulant to the authors.

However, this field is dynamic and has progressed tremendously since the book was written. When the authors and publishers decided that a second edition should be prepared much soul searching was necessary to decide on what changes should be made to improve the work. Obviously everything had to be updated. Fortunately the original edition was written in "building block" style so that this could be achieved with relative ease. Also there were the constructive criticisms of our colleagues around the world to consider.

Perhaps the three major impacts on biomedical engineering in recent years are the tremendous expansion of non-invasive techniques, the sophistication built up in special care units and, along with other fields, the greater use of computers and the advent of microprocessors.

Taking all these facts together, the authors re-studied the book and the field and decided on the direction for the new edition. With respect to criticism, it was obvious, even after early adoptions, that the concept and principles of transducers should be presented earlier in the work. The original Chapters 1 and 2 were combined into a new introductory chapter and a new Chapter 2 was written on basic transducers, including some material drawn from the old Chapter 9. Chapter 9 was transformed into a new chapter on non-invasive techniques with the major emphasis on ultrasonics, a field that has developed greatly in recent years. However, some non-invasive techniques not covered in Chapter 9 are more appropriately included in other chapters.

Most of the material on physiology and basic principles has not been changed much, but the illustrative chapters contain many changes. Cardiovascular techniques have progressed considerably as reflected in the changes in Chapter 6. Because intensive care equipment and computers have also changed, Chapters 7 and 15 were virtually re-written. New topics such as echocardiography and computerized axial tomography have been added. Over two thirds of the illustrative photographs are new to reflect the many changes in the field.

This book now includes SI (Systeme Internationale) metric units, although other measurement units have been retained for comparison. Parentheses have been used where two sets of units are mentioned. However, it should be pointed out that the transition to SI metric units in the health care field is far from complete. Whereas some changes, such as linear measurements in centimeters, are now widely accepted others are not. Kilopascals is rarely used as a measurement for blood pressure, mmHg still being preferred. (1 mmHg is equal to 0.133 kilopascals.)

The authors again wish to thank the many manufacturers for their help and photographs, and the hospitals and physicians for their cooperation. These are individually acknowledged in the text. The authors also wish to thank Mrs. Irina Cromwell for typing and assembling the manuscript and Mrs. Elissa Schrader and Mrs. Erna Wellenstein for helping again in many ways in the preparation of this book. We are also indebted to California State University, Los Angeles, and the U.S. Veterans Administration for encouragement and use of facilities.

Los Angeles, California

LESLIE CROMWELL
FRED J. WEIBELL
ERICH A. PFEIFFER

Biomedical Instrumentation and Measurements

1

Introduction
to Biomedical
Instrumentation

Science has progressed through many gradual states. It is a long time since Archimedes and his Greek contemporaries started down the path of scientific discoveries, but a technological historian could easily trace the trends through the centuries. Engineering has emerged out of the roots of science, and since the Industrial Revolution the profession has grown rapidly. Again, there are definite stages that can be traced.

1.1. THE AGE OF BIOMEDICAL ENGINEERING

It is common practice to refer to developmental time eras as "ages." The age of the steam engine, of the automobile, and of radio communication each spanned a decade or so of rapid development. Since World War II there have been a number of overlapping technological ages. Nuclear engineering and aerospace engineering are good examples. Each of these fields reached a peak of activity and then settled down to a routine, orderly

1

progression. The age of computer engineering, with all its ramifications, has been developing rapidly and still has much momentum. The time for the age of biomedical engineering has now arrived.

The probability is great that the 1970s will be known as the decade in which the most rapid progress was made in this highly important field. There is one vital advantage that biomedical engineering has over many of the other fields that preceded it: the fact that it is aimed at keeping people healthy and helping to cure them when they are ill. Thus, it may escape many of the criticisms aimed at progress and technology. Many purists have stated that technology is an evil. Admittedly, although the industrial age introduced many new comforts, conveniences, and methods of transportation, it also generated many problems. These problems include air and water pollution, death by transportation accidents, and the production of such weapons of destruction as guided missiles and nuclear bombs. However, even though biomedical engineering is not apt to be criticized as much for producing evils, some new problems have been created, such as shock hazards in the use of electrical instruments in the hospital. Yet these side effects are minor compared to the benefits that mankind can derive from it.

One of the problems of "biomedical engineering" is defining it. The prefix *bio-*, of course, denotes something connected with life. Biophysics and biochemistry are relatively old "interdisciplines," in which basic sciences have been applied to living things. One school of thought subdivides bioengineering into different engineering areas—for example, biomechanics and bioelectronics. These categories usually indicate the use of that area of engineering applied to living rather than to physical components. *Bioinstrumentation* implies measurement of biological variables, and this field of measurement is often referred to as *biometrics,* although the latter term is also used for mathematical and statistical methods applied to biology.

[Naturally committees have been formed to define these terms; the professional societies have become involved.] The latter include the IEEE Engineering in Medicine and Biology Group, the ASME Biomechanical and Human Factors Division, the Instrument Society of America, and the American Institute of Aeronautics and Astronautics. Many new "cross-disciplinary" societies have also been formed.

A few years ago an engineering committee was formed to define bioengineering. This was Subcommittee B (Instrumentation) of the Engineers Joint Council Committee on Engineering Interactions with Biology and Medicine. Their recommendation was that *bioengineering* be defined as application of the knowledge gained by a cross fertilization of engineering and the biological sciences so that both will be more fully utilized for the benefit of man.

More recently, as new applications have emerged, the field has produced definitions describing the personnel who work in it. A tendency has arisen to define the *biomedical engineer* as a person working in research or development in the interface area of medicine and engineering, whereas the practitioner working with physicians and patients is called a *clinical engineer*.

One of the societies that has emerged in this interface area is the Association for the Advancement of Medical Instrumentation (AAMI). This association consists of both engineers and physicians. In late 1974, they developed a definition that is widely accepted:

> A *clinical engineer* is a professional who brings to health care facilities a level of education, experience, and accomplishment which will enable him to responsibly, effectively, and safely manage and interface with medical devices, instruments, and systems and the use thereof during patient care, and who can, because of this level of competence, responsibly and directly serve the patient and physician, nurse, and other health care professionals relative to their use of and other contact with medical instrumentation.

Most clinical engineers go into the profession through the engineering degree route, but many start out as physicists or physiologists. They must have at least a B.S. degree, and many of them have M.S. or Ph.D. degrees.

Another new term, also coined in recent years, the "biomedical equipment technician" (BMET), is defined as follows:

> A *biomedical equipment technician* (BMET) is an individual who is knowledgeable about the theory of operation, the underlying physiologic principles, and the practical, safe clinical application of biomedical equipment. His capabilities may include installation, calibration, inspection, preventive maintenance and repair of general biomedical and related technical equipment as well as operation or supervision of equipment control, safety and maintenance programs and systems.

This was also an AAMI definition. Typically, the BMET has two years of training at a community college. This person is not to be confused with the *medical technologist*. The latter is usually used in an operative sense, for example in blood chemistry and in the taking of electrocardiograms. The level of sophistication of the BMET is usually higher than that of the technologist in terms of equipment, but lower in terms of the life sciences.

In addition, other titles have been used, such as *hospital engineer* and *medical engineer*. In one hospital the title *biophysicist* is preferred for their biomedical engineers, for reasons best known to themselves.

It is now possible to become professionally registered as a clinical engineer, but unfortunately there are two different agencies who certify clinical engineers, and the requirements have not been standardized. Some states are also considering adding "biomedical" to their professional engineering registration.

These definitions are all noteworthy, but whatever the name, this age of the marriage of engineering to medicine and biology is destined to benefit all concerned. Improved communication among engineers, technicians, and doctors, better and more accurate instrumentation to measure vital physiological parameters, and the development of interdisciplinary tools to help fight the effects of body malfunctions and diseases are all a part of this new field. Remembering that Shakespeare once wrote "A rose by any other name . . .," it must be realized that the name is actually not too important; however, what the field can accomplish *is* important. With this point in mind, the authors of this book use the term *biomedical engineering* for the field in general and the term *biomedical instrumentation* for the methods of measurement within the field.

Another major problem of biomedical engineering involves communication between the engineer and the medical profession. The language and jargon of the physician are quite different from those of the engineer. In some cases, the same word is used by both disciplines, but with entirely different meanings. Although it is important for the physician to understand enough engineering terminology to allow him to discuss problems with the engineer, the burden of bridging the communication gap usually falls on the latter. The result is that the engineer, or technician, must learn the doctor's language, as well as some anatomy and physiology, in order that the two disciplines can work effectively together.

To help acquaint the reader with this special aspect of biomedical engineering, a basic introduction to medical terminology is presented in Appendix A. This appendix is in two parts: Appendix A.1 is a list of the more common roots, prefixes, and suffixes used in the language of medicine, and Appendix A.2 is a glossary of some of the medical terms frequently encountered in biomedical instrumentation.

In addition to the language problem, other differences may affect communication between the engineer or technician and the doctor. Since the physician is often self-employed, whereas the engineer is usually salaried, a different concept of the fiscal approach exists. Thus, some physicians are reluctant to consider engineers as professionals and would tend to place them in a subservient position rather than class them as equals. Also, engineers, who are accustomed to precise quantitative measurements based on theoretical principles, may find it difficult to accept the often imprecise, empirical, and qualitative methods employed by their counterparts.

Since the development and use of biomedical instrumentation must be a joint effort of the engineer or technician and the physician (or nurse), every effort must be exerted to avoid or overcome these "communication" problems. By being aware of their possible existence, the engineer or technician can take steps to avert these pitfalls by adequate preparation and care in establishing his relationship with the medical profession.

1.2. DEVELOPMENT OF BIOMEDICAL INSTRUMENTATION

The field of medical instrumentation is by no means new. Many instruments were developed as early as the nineteenth century—for example, the electrocardiograph, first used by Einthoven at the end of that century. Progress was rather slow until after World War II, when a surplus of electronic equipment, such as amplifiers and recorders, became available. At that time many technicians and engineers, both within industry and on their own, started to experiment with and modify existing equipment for medical use. This process occurred primarily during the 1950s and the results were often disappointing, for the experimenters soon learned that physiological parameters are not measured in the same way as physical parameters. They also encountered a severe communication problem with the medical profession.

During the next decade many instrument manufacturers entered the field of medical instrumentation, but development costs were high and the medical profession and hospital staffs were suspicious of the new equipment and often uncooperative. Many developments with excellent potential seemed to have become lost causes. It was during this period that some progressive companies decided that rather than modify existing hardware, they would design instrumentation specifically for medical use. Although it is true that many of the same components were used, the philosophy was changed; equipment analysis and design were applied directly to medical problems.

A large measure of help was provided by the U.S. government, in particular by NASA (National Aeronautics and Space Administration). The Mercury, Gemini, and Apollo programs needed accurate physiological monitoring for the astronauts; consequently, much research and development money went into this area. The aerospace medicine programs were expanded considerably, both within NASA facilities, and through grants to universities and hospital research units. Some of the concepts and features of patient-monitoring systems presently used in hospitals throughout the world evolved from the base of astronaut monitoring. The use of adjunct fields, such as biotelemetry, also finds some basis in the NASA programs.

Also, in the 1960s, an awareness of the need for engineers and technicians to work with the medical profession developed. All the major engineering technical societies recognized this need by forming "Engineering in
Medicine and Biology" subgroups, and new societies were organized.*
Along with the medical research programs at the universities, a need
developed for courses and curricula in biomedical engineering, and today
almost every major university or college has some type of biomedical engineering program. However, much of this effort is not concerned with
biomedical instrumentation per se.

1.3.   BIOMETRICS

The branch of science that includes the measurement of physiological
variables and parameters is known as *biometrics*. Biomedical instrumentation provides the tools by which these measurements can be achieved.

In later chapters each of the major forms of biomedical instrumentation is covered in detail, along with the physiological basis for the measurements involved. The physiological measurements themselves are summarized
in Appendix B, which also includes such information as amplitude and frequency range where applicable.

Some forms of biomedical instrumentation are unique to the field
of medicine but many are adaptations of widely used physical measurements. A thermistor, for example, changes its electrical resistance with
temperature, regardless of whether the temperature is that of an engine or
the human body. The principles are the same. Only the shape and size of
the device might be different. Another example is the strain gage, which is
commonly used to measure the stress in structural components. It operates
on the principle that electrical resistance is changed by the stretching of a
wire or a piece of semiconductor material. When suitably excited by a
source of constant voltage, an electrical output can be obtained that is proportional to the amount of the strain. Since pressure can be translated into
strain by various means, blood pressure can be measured by an adaptation
of this device. When the transducer is connected into a typical circuit, such
as a bridge configuration, and this circuit is excited from a source of constant input voltage, the changes in resistance are reflected in the output as
voltage changes. For a thermistor, the temperature is indicated on a
voltmeter calibrated in degrees Celsius or Fahrenheit.

In the design or specification of medical instrumentation systems,
each of the following factors should be considered.

*An example is the Biomedical Engineering Society.

1.3.1 Range

The *range* of an instrument is generally considered to include all the levels of input amplitude and frequency over which the device is expected to operate. The objective should be to provide an instrument that will give a usable reading from the smallest expected value of the variable or parameter being measured to the largest.

1.3.2. Sensitivity

The *sensitivity* of an instrument determines how small a variation of a variable or parameter can be reliably measured. This factor differs from the instrument's range in that sensitivity is not concerned with the absolute levels of the parameter but rather with the minute changes that can be detected. The sensitivity directly determines the *resolution* of the device, which is the minimum variation that can accurately be read. Too high a sensitivity often results in nonlinearities or instability.Thus, the optimum sensitivity must be determined for any given type of measurement. Indications of sensitivity are frequently expressed in terms of scale length per quantity to be measured—for example, inches per microampere in a galvanometer coil or inches per millimeter of mercury.* These units are sometimes expressed reciprocally. A sensitivity of 0.025 centimeter per millimeter of mercury (cm/mm Hg) could be expressed as 40 millimeters of mercury per centimeter.*

1.3.3. Linearity

The degree to which variations in the output of an instrument follow input variations is referred to as the *linearity* of the device. In a *linear system* the sensitivity would be the same for all absolute levels of input, whether in the high, middle, or low portion of the range. In some instruments a certain form of nonlinearity is purposely introduced to create a desired effect, whereas in others it is desirable to have linear scales as much as possible over the entire range of measurements. Linearity should be obtained over the most important segments, even if it is impossible to achieve it over the entire range.

1.3.4. Hysteresis

Hysteresis (from the Greek, *hysterein,* meaning "to be behind" or "to lag") is a characteristic of some instruments whereby a given value of the measured variable results in a different reading when reached in an ascend-

---

*1 mm Hg is 133.3 pascals in the SI metric system; 1 mm Hg is also equivalent to 1 torr.

ing direction from that obtained when it is reached in a descending direction. Mechanical friction in a meter, for example, can cause the movement of the indicating needle to lag behind corresponding changes in the measured variable, thus resulting in a hysteresis error in the reading.

1.3.5. Frequency Response

The *frequency response* of an instrument is its variation in sensitivity over the frequency range of the measurement. It is important to display a waveshape that is a faithful reproduction of the original physiological signal. An instrument system should be able to respond rapidly enough to reproduce all frequency components of the waveform with equal sensitivity. This condition is referred to as a "flat response" over a given range of frequencies.

1.3.6. Accuracy

Accuracy is a measure of systemic error. Errors can occur in a multitude of ways. Although not always present simultaneously, the following errors should be considered:

1. Errors due to tolerances of electronic components.
2. Mechanical errors in meter movements.
3. Component errors due to drift or temperature variation.
4. Errors due to poor frequency response.
5. In certain types of instruments, errors due to change in atmospheric pressure or temperature.
6. Reading errors due to parallax, inadequate illumination, or excessively wide ink traces on a pen recording.

Two additional sources of error should not be overlooked. The first concerns correct instrument zeroing. In most measurements, a zero, or a baseline, is necessary. It is often achieved by balancing the Wheatstone bridge or a similar device. It is very important that, where needed, balancing or zeroing is done prior to each set of measurements. Another source of error is the effect of the instrument on the parameter to be measured, and vice versa. This is especially true in measurements in living organisms and is further discussed later in this chapter.

1.3.7. Signal-to-Noise Ratio

It is important that the *signal-to-noise ratio* be as high as possible. In the hospital environment, power-line frequency noise or interference is common and is usually picked up in long leads. Also, interference due to electromagnetic, electrostatic, or diathermy equipment is possible. Poor grounding is often a cause of this kind of noise problem.

Such "interference noise," however, which is due to coupling from other energy sources, should be differentiated from thermal and shot noise, which originate within the elements of the circuit itself because of the discontinuous nature of matter and electrical current. Although thermal noise is often the limiting factor in the detection of signals in other fields of electronics, interference noise is usually more of a problem in biomedical systems.

It is also important to know and control the signal-to-noise ratio in the actual environment in which the measurements are to be made.

1.3.8. Stability

In control engineering, *stability* is the ability of a system to resume a steady-state condition following a disturbance at the input rather than be driven into uncontrollable oscillation. This is a factor that varies with the amount of amplification, feedback, and other features of the system. The overall system must be sufficiently stable over the useful range. *Baseline stability* is the maintenance of a constant baseline value without drift.

1.3.9. Isolation

Often measurements must be made on patients or experimental animals in such a way that the instrument does not produce a direct electrical connection between the subject and ground. This requirement is often necessary for reasons of electrical safety (see Chapter 16) or to avoid interference between different instruments used simultaneously. *Electrical isolation* can be achieved by using magnetic or optical coupling techniques, or radio telemetry. Telemetry is also used where movement of the person or animal to be measured is essential, and thus the encumbrance of connecting leads should be avoided (see Chapter 12).

1.3.10. Simplicity

All systems and instruments should be as simple as possible to eliminate the chance of component or human error.

Most instrumentation systems require calibration before they are actually used. Each component of a measurement system is usually calibrated individually at the factory against a standard. When a medical system is assembled, it should be calibrated as a whole. This step can be done external to the living organism or in situ (connected to or within the body). This point is discussed in later chapters. Calibration should always be done by using error-free devices of the simplest kind for references. An example would be that of a complicated, remote blood-pressure monitoring system, which is calibrated against a simple mercury manometer.

1.4. INTRODUCTION TO THE
MAN-INSTRUMENT SYSTEM

A classic exercise in engineering analysis involves the measurement of outputs from an unknown system as they are affected by various combinations of inputs. The object is to learn the nature and characteristics of the system. This unknown system, often referred to as a *black box,* may have a variety of configurations for a given combination of inputs and outputs. The end product of such an exercise is usually a set of input–output equations intended to define the internal functions of the box. These functions may be relatively simple or extremely complex.

One of the most complex black boxes conceivable is a living organism, especially the living human being. Within this box can be found electrical, mechanical, acoustical, thermal, chemical, optical, hydraulic, pneumatic, and many other types of systems, all interacting with each other. It also contains a powerful computer, several types of communication systems, and a great variety of control systems. To further complicate the situation, upon attempting to measure the inputs and outputs, an engineer would soon learn that none of the input–output relationships is deterministic. That is, repeated application of a given set of input values will not always produce the same output values. In fact, many of the outputs seem to show a wide range of responses to a given set of inputs, depending on some seemingly relevant conditions, whereas others appear to be completely random and totally unrelated to any of the inputs.

The living black box presents other problems, too. Many of the important variables to be measured are not readily accessible to measuring devices. The result is that some key relationships cannot be determined or that less accurate substitute measures must be used. Furthermore, there is a high degree of interaction among the variables in this box. Thus, it is often impossible to hold one variable constant while measuring the relationship between two others. In fact, it is sometimes difficult to determine which are the inputs and which are the outputs, for they are never labeled and almost inevitably include one or more feedback paths. The situation is made even worse by the application of the measuring device itself, which often affects the measurements to the extent that they may not represent normal conditions reliably.

At first glance an assignment to measure and analyze the variables in a living black box would probably be labeled "impossible" by most engineers; yet this is the very problem facing those in the medical field who attempt to measure and understand the internal relationships of the human body. The function of medical instrumentation is to aid the medical clinician and researcher in devising ways of obtaining reliable and meaningful measurements from a living human being.

Still other problems are associated with such measurements: the process of measuring must not in any way endanger the life of the person on whom the measurements are being made, and it should not require the subject to endure undue pain, discomfort, or any other undesirable conditions. This means that many of the measurement techniques normally employed in the instrumentation of nonliving systems cannot be applied in the instrumentation of humans.

Additional factors that add to the difficulty of obtaining valid measurements are (1) safety considerations, (2) the environment of the hospital in which these measurements are performed, (3) the medical personnel usually involved in the measurements, and (4) occasionally even ethical and legal considerations.

Because special problems are encountered in obtaining data from living organisms, especially human beings, and because of the large amount of interaction between the instrumentation system and the subject being measured, it is essential that the person on whom measurements are made be considered an integral part of the instrumentation system. In other words, in order to make sense out of the data to be obtained from the black box (the human organism), the internal characteristics of the black box must be considered in the design and application of any measuring instruments. Consequently, the overall system, which includes both the human organism and the intrumentation required for measurement of the human is called the *man–instrument system.*

An instrumentation system is defined as the set of instruments and equipment utilized in the measurement of one or more characteristics or phenomena, plus the presentation of information obtained from those measurements in a form that can be read and interpreted by man. In some cases. the instrumentation system includes components that provide a stimulus or drive to one or more of the inputs to the device being measured. There may also be some mechanism for automatic control of certain processes within the system, or of the entire system. As indicated earlier, the complete man–instrument system must also include the human subject on whom the measurements are being made.

The basic objectives of any instrumentation system generally fall into one of the following major categories:

1. *Information gathering:* In an information-gathering system, instrumentation is used to measure natural phenomena and other

variables to aid man in his quest for knowledge about himself and the universe in which he lives. In this setting, the characteristics of the measurements may not be known in advance.

2. *Diagnosis:* Measurements are made to help in the detection and, hopefully, the correction of some malfunction of the system being measured. In some applications, this type of instrumentation may be classed as "troubleshooting equipment."

3. *Evaluation:* Measurements are used to determine the ability of a system to meet its functional requirements. These could be classified as "proof-of-performance" or "quality control" tests.

4. *Monitoring:* Instrumentation is used to monitor some process or operation in order to obtain continuous or periodic information about the state of the system being measured.

5. *Control:* Instrumentation is sometimes used to automatically control the operation of a system based on changes in one or more of the internal parameters or in the output of the system.

The general field of biomedical instrumentation involves, to some extent, all the preceding objectives of the general instrumentation system. Instrumentation for biomedical research can generally be viewed as information-gathering instrumentation, although it sometimes includes some monitoring and control devices. Instrumentation to aid the physician in the diagnosis of disease and other disorders also has widespread use. Similar instrumentation is used in evaluation of the physical condition of patients in routine physical examinations. Also, special instrumentation systems are used for monitoring of patients undergoing surgery or under intensive care.

Biomedical instrumentation can generally be classified into two major types: clinical and research. *Clinical instrumentation* is basically devoted to the diagnosis, care, and treatment of patients, whereas *research instrumentation* is used primarily in the search for new knowledge pertaining to the various systems that compose the human organism. Although some instruments can be used in both areas, clinical instruments are generally designed to be more rugged and easier to use. Emphasis is placed on obtaining a limited set of reliable measurements from a large group of patients and on providing the physician with enough information to permit him to make clinical decisions. On the other hand, research instrumentation is normally more complex, more specialized, and often designed to provide a much higher degree of accuracy, resolution, and so on. Clinical instruments are used by the physician or nurse, whereas research instruments are generally operated by skilled technologists whose primary training is in the operation of such instruments. The concept of the man–instrument system applies to both clinical and research instrumentation.

Measurements in which biomedical instrumentation is employed can also be divided into two categories: in vivo and in vitro. An *in vivo* measurement is one that is made on or within the living organism itself. An example would be a device inserted into the bloodstream to measure the pH of the blood directly. An *in vitro* measurement is one performed outside the body, even though it relates to the functions of the body. An example of an in vitro measurement would be the measurement of the pH of a sample of blood that has been drawn from a patient. Literally, the term in vitro means "in glass," thus implying that in vitro measurements are usually performed in test tubes. Although the man–instrument system described here applies mainly to in vivo measurements, problems are often encountered in obtaining appropriate samples for in vitro measurements and in relating these measurements to the living human being.

1.5. COMPONENTS OF THE MAN–INSTRUMENT SYSTEM

A block diagram of the man–instrument system is shown in Figure 1.1. The basic components of this system are essentially the same as in any instrumentation system. The only real difference is in having a living human being as the subject. The system components are given below.

1.5.1. The Subject

The *subject* is the human being on whom the measurements are made. Since it is the subject who makes this system different from other instrumentation systems, the major physiological systems that constitute the human body are treated in much greater detail in Section 1.6.

1.5.2 Stimulus

In many measurements, the response to some form of external *stimulus* is required. The instrumentation used to generate and present this stimulus to the subject is a vital part of the man–instrument system whenever responses are measured. The stimulus may be visual (e.g., a flash of light), auditory (e.g., a tone), tactile (e.g., a blow to the Achilles tendon), or direct electrical stimulation of some part of the nervous system.

1.5.3. The Transducer

In general, a *transducer* is defined as a device capable of converting one form of energy or signal to another. In the man–instrument system, each

Figure 1.1. Block diagram—the man-instrument system.

transducer is used to produce an electric signal that is an analog of the phenomenon being measured. The transducer may measure temperature, pressure, flow, or any of the other variables that can be found in the body, but its output is always an electric signal. As indicated in Figure 1.1, two or more transducers may be used simultaneously to obtain relative variations between phenomena.

1.5.4. Signal-Conditioning Equipment

The part of the instrumentation system that amplifies, modifies, or in any other way changes the electric output of the transducer is called *signal-conditioning* (or sometimes *signal-processing*) equipment. Signal-conditioning equipment is also used to combine or relate the outputs of two or more transducers. Thus, for each item of signal-conditioning equipment, both the input and the output are electric signals, although the output signal is often greatly modified with respect to the input. In essence, then, the purpose of the signal-conditioning equipment is to process the signals from the transducers in order to satisfy the functions of the system and to prepare signals suitable for operating the display or recording equipment that follows.

1.5.5. Display Equipment

To be meaningful, the electrical output of the signal-conditioning equipment must be converted into a form that can be perceived by one of man's senses and that can convey the information obtained by the measurement in a meaningful way. The input to the *display* device is the modified electric signal from the signal-conditioning equipment. Its output is some form of visual, audible, or possibly tactile information. In the man–instrumentation system, the display equipment may include a graphic pen recorder that produces a permanent record of the data.

1.5.6. Recording, Data-Processing, and Transmission Equipment

It is often necessary, or at least desirable, to *record* the measured information for possible later use or to *transmit* it from one location to another, whether across the hall of the hospital or halfway around the world. Equipment for these functions is often a vital part of the man–instrument system. Also, where *automatic storage* or *processing* of data is required, or where computer control is employed, an on-line analog or digital computer may be part of the instrumentation system. It should be noted that the term *recorder* is used in two different contexts in biomedical instrumentation. A graphic pen recorder is actually a display device used to produce a paper record of analog waveforms, whereas the recording equipment referred to in this paragraph includes devices by which data can be recorded for future playback, as in a magnetic tape recorder.

1.5.7. Control Devices

Where it is necessary or desirable to have *automatic control* of the stimulus, transducers, or any other part of the man–instrument system, a control system is incorporated. This system usually consists of a feedback loop in which part of the output from the signal-conditioning or display equipment is used to control the operation of the system in some way.

1.6. PHYSIOLOGICAL SYSTEMS OF THE BODY

From the previous sections it should be evident that, to obtain valid measurements from a living human being, it is necessary to have some understanding of the subject on which the measurements are being made. Within the human body can be found electrical, mechanical, thermal, hydraulic, pneumatic, chemical, and various other types of systems, each of which communicates with an external environment, and internally with the other systems of the body. By means of a multilevel control system and communications network, these individual systems are organized to perform many complex functions. Through the integrated operation of all these systems, and their various subsystems, man is able to sustain life, learn to perform useful tasks, acquire personality and behavioral traits, and even reproduce himself.

Measurements can be made at various levels of man's hierarchy of organization. For example, the human being as a whole (the highest level of organization) communicates with his environment in many ways. These methods of communicating could be regarded as the inputs and outputs of the black box and are illustrated in Figure 1.2. In addition, these various inputs and outputs can be measured and analyzed in a variety of ways. Most are readily accessible for measurement, but some, such as speech, behavior, and appearance, are difficult to analyze and interpret.

Next to the whole being in the hierarchy of organization are the major functional systems of the body, including the nervous system, the cardiovascular system, the pulmonary system, and so on. Each major system is discussed later in this chapter, and most are covered in greater detail in later chapters. Just as the whole person communicates with his environment, these major systems communicate with each other as well as with the external environment.

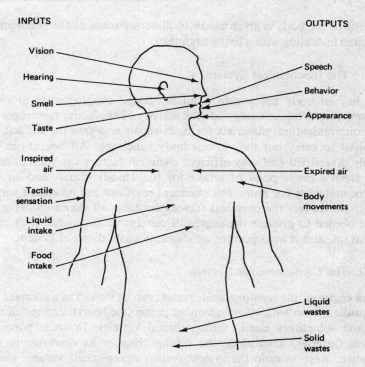

Figure 1.2. Communication of man with his environment.

These functional systems can be broken down into subsystems and organs, which can be further subdivided into smaller and smaller units. The process can continue down to the cellular level and perhaps even to the molecular level. The major goal of biomedical instrumentation is to make possible the measurement of information communicated by these various elements. If all the variables at all levels of the organization heirarchy could be measured, and all their interrelationships determined, the functions of the mind and body of man would be much more clearly understood and could probably be completely defined by presently known laws of physics, chemistry, and other sciences. The problem is, of course, that many of the inputs at the various organizational levels are not accessible for measurement. The interrelationships among elements are sometimes so complex and involve so many systems that the "laws" and relationships thus far derived are inadequate to define them completely. Thus, the models in use today contain so many assumptions and constraints that their application is often severely limited.

Although each of the systems is treated in much more detail in later chapters, a brief engineering-oriented description of the major physiological systems of the body is given below to illustrate some of the problems to be expected in dealing with a living organism.

1.6.1. The Biochemical System

The human body has within it an integrated conglomerate of *chemical systems* that produce energy for the activity of the body, messenger agents for communication, materials for body repair and growth, and substances required to carry out the various body functions. All operations of this highly diversified and very efficient chemical factory are self-contained in that from a single point of intake for fuel (food), water, and air, all the source materials for numerous chemical reactions are produced within the body. Moreover, the chemical factory contains all the monitoring equipment needed to provide the degree of control necessary for each chemical operation, and it incorporates an efficient waste disposal system.

1.6.2. The Cardiovascular System

To an engineer, the *cardiovascular system* can be viewed as a complex, closed hydraulic system with a four-chamber pump (the heart), connected to flexible and sometimes elastic tubing (blood vessels). In some parts of the system (arteries, arterioles), the tubing changes its diameter to control pressure. Reservoirs in the system (veins) change their volume and characteristics to satisfy certain control requirements, and a system of gates and variable hydraulic resistances (vasoconstrictors, vasodilators) continually alters the pattern of fluid flow. The four-chamber pump acts as two synchronized but functionally isolated two-stage pumps. The first stage of each pump (the atrium) collects fluid (blood) from the system and pumps it into the second stage (the ventricle). The action of the second stage is so timed that the fluid is pumped into the system immediately after it has been received from the first stage. One of the two-stage pumps (right side of the heart) collects fluid from the main hydraulic system (systemic circulation) and pumps it through an oxygenation system (the lungs). The other pump (left side of the heart) receives fluid (blood) from the oxygenation system and pumps it into the main hydraulic system. The speed of the pump (heart rate) and its efficiency (stroke volume) are constantly changed to meet the overall requirements of the system. The fluid (blood), which flows in a laminar fashion, acts as a communication and supply network for all parts of the system. Carriers (red blood cells) of fuel supplies and waste materials are transported to predetermined destinations by the fluid. The fluid also contains mechanisms for repairing small system punctures and for rejecting foreign elements from the system (platelets and white blood cells, respectively). Sensors provided to detect changes in the need for supplies, the buildup of waste materials, and out-of-tolerance pressures in the system are known as *chemoreceptors, P_{CO_2} sensors,* and *baroreceptors,* respectively. These and other mechanisms control the pump's speed and efficiency, the fluid flow pattern through the system, tubing diameters, and other factors. Because part of the system is required to work against gravity at times, special one-way valves are provided to prevent gravity from pulling fluid against the direction of flow between pump cycles. The variables of prime importance in this system are the pump (cardiac) output and the pressure, flow rate, and volume of the fluid (blood) at various locations throughout the system.

1.6.3. The Respiratory System

Whereas the cardiovascular system is the major hydraulic system in the body, the *respiratory system* is the pneumatic system. An air pump (diaphragm), which alternately creates negative and positive pressures in a sealed chamber (thoracic cavity), causes air to be sucked into and forced out of a pair of elastic bags (lungs) located within the compartment. The bags are connected to the outside environment through a passageway (nasal cavities, pharynx, larynx, trachea, bronchi, and bronchioles), which at one point is in common with the tubing that carries liquids and solids to the stomach. A special valving arrangement interrupts the pneumatic system whenever liquid or solid matter passes through the common region. The passageway divides to carry air into each of the bags, wherein it again subdivides many times to carry air into and out of each of many tiny air spaces (pulmonary alveoli) within the bags. The dual air input to the system (nasal cavities) has an alternate vent (the mouth) for use in the event of nasal blockage and for other special purposes. In the tiny air spaces of the bags is a membrane interface with the body's hydraulic system through which certain gases can diffuse. Oxygen is taken into the fluid (blood) from the incoming air, and carbon dioxide is transferred from the fluid to the air, which is exhausted by the force of the pneumatic pump. The pump operates with a two-way override. An automatic control center (respiratory center of the brain) maintains pump operation at a speed that is adequate to supply oxygen and carry off carbon dioxide as required by the system. Manual control can take over at any time either to accelerate or to inhibit the operation of the pump. Automatic control will return, however, if a condition is created that might endanger the system. System variables of primary importance are respiratory rate, respiratory airflow, respiratory volume, and concentration of CO_2 in the expired air. This system also has a number of relatively fixed volumes and capacities, such as tidal volume (the volume inspired or expired during each normal breath), inspiratory reserve volume (the additional volume that can be inspired after a normal inspiration), expiratory reserve volume (the additional amount of air that can be forced out of the lungs after normal expiration), residual volume (amount of air remaining in the lungs after all possible air has been forced out), and vital capacity (tidal volume, plus inspiratory reserve volume, plus expiratory reserve volume).

1.6.4. The Nervous System

The nervous system is the communication network for the body. Its center is a self-adapting central information processor or computer (the brain) with memory, computational power, decision-making capability, and a myriad of input–output channels. The computer is self adapting in that if a certain section is damaged, other sections can adapt and eventually take over (at least in part) the function of the damaged section. By use of this computer, a person is able to make decisions, solve complex problems, create art, poetry, and music, "feel" emotions, integrate input information from all parts of the body, and coordinate output signals to produce meaningful behavior. Almost as fascinating as the central computer are the millions of communication lines (afferent and efferent nerves) that bring sensory information into, and transmit control information out of the brain. In general, these lines are not single long lines but often complicated networks with many interconnections that are continually changing to meet the needs of the system. By means of the interconnection patterns, signals from a large number of sensory devices, which detect light, sound, pressure, heat, cold, and certain chemicals, are channeled to the appropriate parts of the computer, where they can be acted upon. Similarly, output control signals are channeled to specific motor devices (motor units of the muscles), which respond to the signals with some type of motion or force. Feedback regarding every action controlled by the system is provided to the computer through appropriate sensors. Information is usually coded in the system by means of electrochemical pulses (nerve action potentials) that travel along the signal lines (nerves). The pulses can be transferred from one element of a network to another in one direction only, and frequently the transfer takes place only when there is the proper combination of elements acting on the next element in the chain. Action by some elements tends to inhibit transfer by making the next element less sensitive to other elements that are attempting to actuate it. Both serial and parallel coding are used, sometimes together in the same system. In addition to the central computer, a large number of simple decision-making devices (spinal reflexes) are present to control directly certain motor devices from certain sensory inputs. A number of feedback loops are accomplished by this method. In many cases, only situations where important decision making is involved require that the central computer be utilized.

1.7. PROBLEMS ENCOUNTERED IN MEASURING A LIVING SYSTEM

The previous discussions of the man–instrument system and the physiological systems of the body imply measurements on a human subject. In some cases, however, animal subjects are substituted for humans in order to permit measurements or manipulations that cannot be performed without some risk. Although ethical restrictions sometimes are not as severe with animal subjects, the same basic problems can be expected in attempting measurements from any living system. Most of these problems were introduced in earlier sections of the chapter. However, they can be summarized as follows.

1.7.1. Inaccessibility of Variables to Measurement

One of the greatest problems in attempting measurements from a living system is the difficulty in gaining access to the variable being measured. In some cases, such as in the measurement of dynamic neurochemical activity in the brain, it is impossible to place a suitable transducer in a position to make the measurement. Sometimes the problem stems from the required physical size of the transducer as compared to the space available for the measurement. In other situations the medical operation required to place a transducer in a position from which the variable can be measured makes the measurement impractical on human subjects, and sometimes even on animals. Where a variable is inaccessible for measurement, an attempt is often made to perform an indirect measurement. This process involves the measurement of some other related variable that makes possible a usable estimate of the inaccessible variable under certain conditions. In using indirect measurements, however, one must be constantly aware of the limitations of the substitute variable and must be able to determine when the relationship is not valid.

1.7.2. Variability of the Data

Few of the variables that can be measured in the human body are truly deterministic variables. In fact, such variables should be considered as stochastic processes. A *stochastic process* is a time variable related to other variables in a nondeterministic way. Physiological variables can never be viewed as strictly deterministic values but must be represented by some kind of statistical or probabilistic distribution. In other words, measurements taken under a fixed set of conditions at one time will not necessarily be the same as similar measurements made under the same conditions at another time. The variability from one subject to another is even greater. Here, again, statistical methods must be employed in order to estimate relationships among variables.

1.7.3. Lack of Knowledge About Interrelationships

The foregoing variability in measured values could be better explained if more were known and understood about the interrelationships within the body. Physiological measurements with large tolerances are often accepted by the physician because of a lack of this knowledge and the resultant inability to control variations. Better understanding of physiological relationships would also permit more effective use of indirect measurements as substitutes for inaccessible measures and would aid engineers or technicians in their job of coupling the instrumentation to the physiological system.

1.7.4. Interaction Among Physiological Systems

Because of the large number of feedback loops involved in the major physiological systems, a severe degree of interaction exists both within a given system and among the major systems. The result is that stimulation of one part of a given system generally affects all other parts of that system in some way (sometimes in an unpredictable fashion) and often affects other systems as well. For this reason, "cause-and-effect" relationships become extremely unclear and difficult to define. Even when attempts are made to open feedback loops, collateral loops appear and some aspects of the original feedback loop are still present. Also, when one organ or element is rendered inactive, another organ or element sometimes takes over the function. This situation is especially true in the brain and other parts of the nervous system.

1.7.5. Effect of the Transducer on the Measurement

Almost any kind of measurement is affected in some way by the presence of the measuring transducer. The problem is greatly compounded in the measurement of living systems. In many situations the physical presence of the transducer changes the reading significantly. For example, a large flow transducer placed in a bloodstream partially blocks the vessel and changes the pressure-flow characteristics of the system. Similarly, an attempt to measure the electrochemical potentials generated within an individual cell requires penetration of the cell by a transducer. This penetration can easily kill the cell or damage it so that it can no longer function normally. Another problem arises from the interaction discussed earlier. Often the presence of a transducer in one system can affect responses in other systems. For example, local cooling of the skin, to estimate the circulation in the area, causes feedback that changes the circulation pattern as a reaction to the cooling. The psychological effect of the measurement can also affect the results. Long-term recording techniques for measuring blood pressure have shown that some individuals who would otherwise have normal pressures show an elevated pressure reading whenever they are in the physician's office. This is a fear response on the part of the patient, involving the autonomic nervous system. In designing a measurement system, the biomedical instrumentation engineer or technician must exert extreme care to ensure that the effect of the presence of the measuring device is minimal. Because of the limited amount of energy available in the body for many physiological variables, care must also be taken to prevent the measuring system from "loading" the source of the measured variable.

1.7.6. Artifacts

In medicine and biology, the term *artifact* refers to any component of a signal that is extraneous to the variable represented by the signal. Thus, random noise generated within the measuring instrument, electrical interference (including 60-Hz pickup), cross-talk, and all other unwanted variations in the signal are considered artifacts. A major source of artifacts in the measuring of a living system is the movement of the subject, which in turn results in movement of the measuring device. Since many transducers are sensitive to movement, the movement of the subject often produces variations in the output signal. Sometimes these variations are indistinguishable from the measured variable; at other times they may be sufficient to obscure the desired information completely. Application of anesthesia to reduce movement may itself cause unwanted changes in the system.

1.7.7. Energy Limitations

Many physiological measurement techniques require that a certain amount of energy be applied to the living system in order to obtain a measurement. For example, resistance measurements require the flow of electric current through the tissues or blood being measured. Some transducers generate a small amount of heat due to the current flow. In most cases, this energy level is so low that its effect is insignificant. However, in dealing with living cells, care must continually be taken to avoid the possibility of energy concentrations that might damage cells or affect the measurements.

1.7.8. Safety Considerations

As previously mentioned, the methods employed in measuring variables in a living human subject must in no way endanger the life or normal functioning of the subject. Recent emphasis on hospital safety requires that extra caution must be taken in the design of any measurement system to protect the patient. Similarly, the measurement should not cause undue pain, trauma, or discomfort, unless it becomes necessary to endure these conditions in order to save the patient's life.

1.8. SOME CONCLUSIONS

From the foregoing discussion is should be quite obvious that obtaining data from a living system greatly increases the complexity of instrumentation problems. Fortunately, however, new developments resulting in improved, smaller, and more effective measuring devices are continually being announced, thereby making possible measurements that had previously been considered impossible. In addition, greater knowledge of the physiology of the various systems of the body is emerging as man progresses in his monumental task of learning about himself. All of this will benefit the engineer, the technician, and the physician as time goes on by adding to the tools at their disposal in overcoming instrumentation problems.

When measurements are made on human beings, one further aspect must be considered. During its earlier days of development biomedical apparatus was designed, tested, and marketed with little specific governmental control. True, there were the controls governing hospitals and a host of codes and regulations such as those described in Chapter 16, but today a number of new controls exist, some of which are quite controversial. On the other hand, there is little control on the effectiveness of devices or their side effects. Food and drugs have long been subject to governmental control by a U.S. government agency, the Food and Drug Administration (FDA). In 1976 a new addition, the Medical Devices Amendments (Public Law 94-295), placed all medical devices from the simple to the complex under the jurisdiction of the FDA. Since then, panels and committees have been formed and symposia have been held by both physicians and engineers. Regulations have been issued which include "Good Laboratcry Practices" and "Good Manufacturing Practices." Although some control is essential, unfortunately many of the new regulations are tied up with so much red tape that producing new devices may be hazardous to one's economic health!

Engineers in this field should understand that they are subject to legal, moral, and ethical considerations in their practice since they deal with people's health. They should always be fully conversant with what is going on and be aware of issues and regulations that are brought about by technological, economic and political realities.

1.9. THE OBJECTIVES OF THIS BOOK

The purpose of this book is to relate specific engineering and instrumentation principles to the task of obtaining physiological data.

Each of the major body systems is discussed by presenting physiological background information. Then the variables to be measured are considered, followed by the principles of the instrumentation that could be used. Finally, applications to typical medical, behavioral, and biological use are given.

The subject matter is presented in such a way that it could be extended to classes of instruments that will be used in the future. Thus the material can be used as building blocks for the health-care instrumentation systems of tomorrow.

2

Basic Transducer Principles

A major function of medical instrumentation is the measurement of physiological variables. A *variable* is any quantity whose value changes with time. A variable associated with the physiological processes of the body is called a *physiological variable.* Examples of physiological variables used in clinical medicine are body temperature, the electrical activity of the heart (ECG), arterial blood pressure, and respiratory airflow. The physiological systems from which these variables originate were introduced in Chapter 1. The principal physiological variables and their methods of measurement are summarized in Appendix B and discussed in detail in various chapters of this book.

Physiological variables occur in many forms: as ionic potentials and currents, mechanical movements, hydraulic pressures and flows, temperature variations, chemical reactions, and many more. As stated in Chapter 1, a transducer is required to convert each variable into an electrical signal which can be amplified or otherwise processed and then converted into some form of display. Electrodes, which convert ionic potentials into electrical signals, are discussed in Chapter 4. Transducers for other types of variables are covered in this chapter. The fundamental principles involved in both active and passive transducers are presented, after which several basic types of transducers used in medical instrumentation are discussed.

2.1. THE TRANSDUCER AND TRANSDUCTION PRINCIPLES

The device that performs the conversion of one form of variable into another is called a *transducer*. In this book the primary concern is the conversion of all other forms of physiological variables into electrical signals. In this way a transducer is a component which has a nonelectrical variable as its input and an electrical signal as its output. To conduct its function properly, one (or more) parameters of the electrical output signal (say, its voltage, current, frequency, or pulse width) must be a nonambiguous function of the nonelectrical variable at the input. Ideally, the relationship between output and input should be linear with, for example, the voltage at the output of a pressure transducer being proportional to the applied pressure. A linear relationship is not always possible. For example, the relationship between input and output may follow a logarithmic function or a square law. As long as the transduction function is nonambiguous it is possible to determine the magnitude of the input variable from the electrical output signal, at least in principle. Certain other variables may interfere with the transduction process and can influence the accuracy of the measurement system, such as the hysteresis error, frequency response and baseline drift, which were discussed in Chapter 1.

Two quite different principles are involved in the process of converting nonelectrical variables into electrical signals. One of these is *energy conversion;* transducers based on this principle are called *active transducers*. The other principle involves control of an *excitation voltage* or *modulation of a carrier signal*. Transducers based on this principle are called *passive transducers*. In practical applications, the fact that a transducer is of the active or passive type is not usually significant. Occasionally, it is not even obvious to which group a transducer belongs. The two transducer types will nevertheless be described separately in the following sections.

2.2. ACTIVE TRANSDUCERS

In theory *active transducers* can utilize every known physical principle for converting nonelectrical energy. However, not all principles are of practical importance in the design of actual transducers, especially for biomedical applications. It is a characteristic of active transducers that frequently, but not always, the same transduction principle used to convert from a nonelectrical form of energy can also be used in the reverse direction to convert electrical energy into nonelectrical forms. For example, a magnetic loudspeaker can also be used in the opposite direction as a microphone. Sometimes different names are used to refer to essentially the same effect when used in opposite directions because the two applications were discovered by different people. Table 2.1 shows these conversion principles. These principles (with the exception of the Volta effect and electrical polarization, both of which are treated in Chapter 4) are described in later sections of this chapter.

TABLE 2.1.   SOME METHODS OF ENERGY CONVERSION
USED IN ACTIVE TRANSDUCERS

Energy Form	Transduced Form	Device or Effect	Reversible
Mechanical	Electrical	Magnetic induction	Yes
		Electric induction	
Pressure	Electrical	Piezoelectric	Yes
Thermal	Electrical	Thermoelectric	Yes
		Seebeck	No
Electrical	Thermal	Peltier	No
Light radiation	Electrical	Photoelectric	No
Electrical	Light	Light-emitting diodes	No
		Injection laser	
Chemical	Electrical	Volta	No
Electrical	Chemical	Electrical polarization	No
Sound	Electrical	Microphone	Yes
Electrical	Sound	Loudspeaker	Yes

2.2.1. Magnetic Induction

If an electrical conductor is moved in a magnetic field in such a way that the magnetic flux through the conductor is changed, a voltage is induced which is proportional to the rate of change of the magnetic flux. Conversely, if a current is sent through the same conductor, a mechanical force is exerted upon it proportional to the current and the magnetic field. The result, which depends on the polarities of voltage and current on the electrical side or the directions of force and motion on the mechanical side, is a conversion from electrical to mechanical energy, or vice versa. All electrical motors and generators and a host of other devices, such as solenoids and loudspeakers, utilize this principle.

Two basic configurations for transducers that use the principle of *magnetic induction* for the measurement of linear or rotary motion are shown in Figure 2.1(a) and (b). The output voltage in each case is propor-

Figure 2.1. Inductive transducers (a) for linear motion; (b) for rotary motion.

tional to the linear or angular velocity. The most important biomedical applications are heart sound microphones, pulse transducers, and electromagnetic blood-flow meters, all described in Chapter 6.

Magnetic induction also plays an important role at the output of many biomedical instrumentation systems. Analog meters using d'Arsonval movements, light-beam galvanometers in photographic recorders, and pen motors in ink or thermal recorders are all based on the principle of magnetic induction and closely resemble the basic transducer configuration shown in Figure 2.1(b).

It might be mentioned in passing that the principle of magnetic induction has an electrostatic equivalent called *electric induction*. Microphones based on this principle (condensor microphones) are now finding increasing use in audio applications because of their wide frequency response and high sensitivity. These microphones use an *electret* to create an electrostatic field between two capacitor plates. Electrets—which are the electrostatic equivalent of magnets—are normally in the form of foils of a special plastic material that have been heat-treated while being exposed to a strong electric field. It is conceivable that the principle of the electret microphone could also be applied advantageously to biomedical transducers.

2.2.2. The Piezoelectric Effect

When pressure is applied to certain nonconductive materials so that deformation takes place as shown in Figure 2.2(a) a charge separation occurs in the materials and an electrical voltage, V_P, can be measured across the material. The natural materials in which this *piezoelectric effect* can be observed are primarily slices from crystals of quartz (SiO_2) or Rochelle salt (sodium-potassium tartrate, $KNaC_4H_4O_6 \bullet 4H_2O$) which have been cut at a certain angle with respect to the crystal axis. Piezoelectric properties can be introduced into wafers of barium titanate (a ceramic material that is frequently used as a dielectric in disk-type capacitors) by heat-treating them in the presence of a strong electric field. The piezoelectric process is reversible. If an electric field is applied to a slab of material that has piezoelectric properties, it changes its dimensions.

By cutting the slab from the crystal at a different angle (or by a different application of the electrical field in the case of the barium titanate) the same effect can be obtained when a bending force is applied. Frequently, two slices, with proper orientation of the polarity of the piezoelectric voltages, are sandwiched between layers of conductive metal foil, thus forming the *bimorph* configuration shown in Figure 2.2(b). The electrically equivalent circuit of a piezoelectric transducer, shown in Figure 2.2(c), is that of a voltage source having a voltage, V_P, proportional to the applied mechanical force connected in series with a capacitor, which represents the conductive plates separated by the insulating piezoelectric material. The capacitive properties of the piezoelectric transducer interacting with the input impedance of the amplifier to which they are connected affect the response of the transducer. This effect is shown in Figure 2.3. The top trace shows the force applied to the transducer, which, after time T, is removed again. While the electrical field generated by the piezoelectric effect and the internal transducer voltage, V_P, of Figure 2.2(c) follow the applied force, the voltage, V_A, measured at the input of the amplifier depends on the values of the transducer capacitance, C, and the amplifier input impedance, R, with respect to the duration of the force (time T). If the product of R and C is much larger than T, the effect of the voltage division between these two components can be neglected and the measured voltage is proportional to the applied mechanical force as shown in trace 2. To meet this condition, even for large values of T, it may be necessary to make the amplifier input impedance very large. In some applications, electrometer amplifiers or charge amplifiers with extremely high input impedances have to be used. As an alternative, an external capacitor can be connected in parallel with the amplifier input. This effectively increases the capacity of the transducer but also reduces its sensitivity. Because the output voltages of piezoelectric transducers can be very high (they have occasionally even been used as high-voltage generators for ignition purposes),

Figure 2.2. Piezoelectric transducers; (a) principle; (b) transducer of biomorph type; (c) equivalent circuit of a piezoelectric transducer connected to an amplifier.

this approach may be permissible in certain applications. Changes of the input capacity, and thus the sensitivity, can also be caused by the mechanical movement of attached shielded or coaxial cables which can introduce motion artifacts. Special types of shielded cable that reduce this effect are available for piezoelectric transducers.

If the product of resistance and capacitance is made much smaller than T, the voltage at the amplifier input is proportional to the time derivative of the force at the transducer (or proportional to the rate at which the applied force changes) as shown in trace 3 of Figure 2.3. If the product of R and C *is of the same order of magnitude as* T, the resulting voltage is a compromise between the extremes in the two previous traces, as shown in trace 4. Because any mechanical input signal will contain various frequencies (corresponding to different times, T, in the time domain), a distortion of

Figure 2.3. Output signal of a piezoelectric transducer under different conditions. Trace 1: Force at the input of the transducer. Trace 2: Output signal when the product of R and C is much larger than T; the output voltage is proportional to the force. Trace 3: Output signal if the product of R and C is much smaller than T; the output voltage is proportional to the rate of change of the force. Trace 4: Output signal if the product of R and C is approximately equal to T; the output signal is a combination of the two other cases.

the waveform of the resulting signal can occur if these relationships are not taken into consideration.

The piezoelectric principle is occasionally used in microphones for heart sounds or other acoustical signals from within the body. A more important application of piezoelectric transducers in biomedical instrumentation is in ultrasonic instruments, where a piezoelectric transducer is used to both transmit and receive ultrasonic signals. Principles of ultrasound and biomedical applications are covered in Chapter 9.

2.2.3. The Thermoelectric Effect

If two wires of dissimilar metals (e.g., iron and copper) are connected so that they form a closed conductive loop as shown in Figure 2.4(a), a voltage can be observed at any point of interruption of the loop which is proportional to the difference in temperature between the two junctions between the metals. The polarity depends on which of the two junctions is warmer. The device formed in this fashion is called a *thermocouple,* shown in Figure 2.4(a). The sensitivity of a thermocouple is small and amounts to only 40 microvolts per degree Celsius (μV/°C) for a copper-constantan and 53 μV/°C for an iron-constantan pair (constantan is an alloy of nickel and copper).

The principle of active transducers requires that any electrical energy delivered at the output of the transducer be obtained from the nonelectrical variable at the input of the transducer. In the case of the thermocouple it might not be quite obvious how the thermal energy is converted. Actually, the delivery of electrical energy causes the transfer of heat from the hotter to the colder junction; the hotter junction gets cooler while the colder junction gets warmer. In most practical applications of thermocouples this effect can be neglected. Because the thermocouple measures a temperature difference rather than an absolute temperature, one of the junctions must be kept at a known reference temperature, usually at the freezing point of water (0°C or 32°F). Frequently, instead of an icebath for the reference

Figure 2.4. Thermocouple (a) principle; (b) thermocouple with double reference junction to connect to measurement circuit using copper wire.

Thermo-voltage

Metal A

Metal B

Junction 1   Junction 2

(a)

Metal A   Copper

Reference junction

Metal B

Measurement junction   (b)

junction, an electronic compensating circuit is used. The inconvenience of having to make the whole circuit from the two metals used in the thermocouple can be overcome by using a double reference junction that connects to copper conductors as shown in Figure 2.4(b).

Because of their low sensitivity, thermocouples are seldom used for the measurement of physiological temperatures, where the temperature range is so limited. Instead, one of the passive transducers described later is usually preferred. Thermocouples have an advantage at very high temperatures where passive transducers might not be usable or sometimes where transducers of minute size are required.

The use of the thermoelectric effect to convert from thermal to electrical energy is called the *Seebeck effect.* In the reverse direction it is called the *Peltier effect,* where the flow of current causes one junction to heat and the other to cool. The Peltier effect is occasionally used to cool parts of instruments (e.g., a microscopic stage).

(a)

Figure 2.5. Photoelectric cells (a) selenium cell (left) and silicon (solar) cell (right). (b) Spectral sensitivity of the two cell types.

(b)

2.2.4. The Photoelectric Effect

The *selenium cell,* shown in Figure 2.5(a), has long been used to measure the intensity of light in photographic exposure meters or the light absorption of chemical solutions. The silicon photoelectric cell, better known as the *solar cell,* has a much higher efficiency than the selenium cell. Its spectral sensitivity peaks in the infrared, however, while that of the selenium cell is maximum in the visible light range. When operated into a small load resistance the current delivered by either cell is proportional to the intensity of the incident light. The voltage of these cells cannot exceed a certain value (about 0.6 V for the silicon cell); if the light intensity or the load resistance is such that the output voltage approaches this value, it becomes nonlinear.

2.3. PASSIVE TRANSDUCERS

Passive transducers utilize the principle of controlling a dc excitation voltage or an ac carrier signal. The actual transducer consists of a usually passive circuit element which changes its value as a function of the physical variable to be measured. The transducer is part of a circuit, normally an arrangement similar to a Wheatstone bridge, which is powered by an ac or dc excitation signal. The voltage at the output of the circuit reflects the physical variable. There are only three passive circuit elements that can be utilized as passive transducers: resistors, capacitors, and inductors. It should be noted that active circuit elements, vacuum tubes and transistors, are also occasionally used. This terminology might seem confusing since the terms "active" and "passive" have different meanings when they are applied to transducers than when they are applied to circuit elements. Unlike active transducers, passive transducers cannot be operated in the reverse direction (i.e., to convert an electrical signal into a physical variable) since a different basic principle is involved.

2.3.1. Passive Transducers Using Resistive Elements

Any resistive element that changes its resistance as a function of a physical variable can, in principle, be used as a transducer for that variable. An ordinary potentiometer, for example, can be used to convert rotary motion or displacement into a change of resistance. Similarly, the special linear potentiometers shown in Figure 2.6 can be used to convert linear displacement into a resistance change.

The resistivity of conductive materials is a function of temperature. In resistors this characteristic is a disadvantage; however, in resistive temperature transducers it serves a useful purpose. Temperature transducers are described in more detail in Chapter 9.

A   B

Linear input

C

LINEAR DISPLACEMENT

Rotary input

A   C   B

ROTATIONAL DISPLACEMENT

(a)

Figure 2.6. Linear potentiometer (a) principle; (b) view of the device. (Courtesy of Bourns, Inc., Riverside, CA.)

Body

Contact bar

Shaft retainer

Wiper post

Shaft

Transduction element (potentiometer)

Wiper post

Wiper(s) (one piece)

Transduction element

(b)

In certain semiconductor materials the conductivity is increased by light striking the material. This effect which occurs as a surface effect in certain polycrystalline materials such as cadmium sulfide, is used in *photoresistive cells,* a form of photoelectric transducer. This type of transducer is very sensitive, but has a somewhat limited frequency response. A different type of photoelectric transducer is the *photo diode,* which utilizes charge carriers generated by incident radiation in a reverse-biased diode junction. Although less sensitive than the photoresistive cell, the photodiode has improved frequency response. A photo diode can also be used as a photoelectric transducer without a bias voltage. In this case it operates as an active transducer. The *photoemissive cell* (either vacuum or gas-filled) is only of historical interest because it has generally been replaced by photoelectric transducers of the semiconductor type.

Most transducers used for mechanical variables utilize a resistive element called the *strain gage.* The principle of a strain gage can easily be understood with the help of Figure 2.7. Figure 2.7(a) shows a cylindrical resistor element which has length, L, and cross-sectional area, A. If it is made of a material having a resistivity of r ohm-cm, its resistance is

$$R = r \cdot L/A \text{ ohms } (\Omega).$$

If an axial force is applied to the element to cause it to stretch, its length increases by an amount, ΔL, as shown (exaggerated) in Figure 2.7(b). This stretching, on the other hand, causes the cross-sectional area of the cylinder to decrease by an amount ΔA. Either an increase in L or a decrease in A results in an increase in resistance. The ratio of the resulting resistance change $\Delta R/R$ to the change in length $\Delta L/L$ is called the *gage factor, G.* Thus;

$$G = \frac{\Delta R/R}{\Delta L/L}$$

The gage factor for metals is about 2, whereas the gage factor for silicon (a crystalline semiconductor material) is about 120.

Figure 2.7. Principle of strain gage; (a) cylindrical conductor with length, L, and cross sectional area, A. (b) Application of an axial force has increased the length by L while the cross sectional area has been reduced by A.

Figure 2.8. Unbonded strain gage transducer. (From D. Bartholomew, *Electrical Measurement and Instruments.* Allyn & Bacon, Inc., Boston, MA., by permission.)

The basic principle of the strain gage can be utilized for transducers in a number of different ways. In the *mercury strain gage* the resistive material consists of a column of mercury enclosed in a piece of silicone rubber tubing. The use of this type of strain gage for the measurement of physiological variables (the diameter of blood vessels) was first described by Whitney. Mercury strain gages are, therefore, sometimes called *Whitney gages*. An application of this type of transducer, the *mercury strain gage plethysmograph,* is described in Chapter 6. Because the silicone rubber yields easily to stretching forces, mercury strain gages are frequently used to measure changes in the diameter of body sections or organs. A disadvantage is that for practical dimensions the resistance of the mercury columns is inconveniently low (usually only a few ohms). This problem can be overcome by substituting an electrolyte solution for the mercury. However, silicone rubber is permeable to water vapor, so elastomers other than silicone rubber have to be used as the enclosures for gages containing electrolytes.

When metallic strain gages are used rather than mercury, the possible amount of stretching and the corresponding resistance changes are much more limited. Metal strain gages can be of two different types: unbonded and bonded. In the *unbonded strain gage,* thin wire is stretched between insulating posts as shown in Figure 2.8(a). In order to obtain a convenient resistance (120 Ω is a common value), several turns of wire must be used. Here the moving part of the transducer is connected to the stationary frame by four unbonded strain gages, R_1 through R_4. If the moving member is forced to the right, R_2 and R_3 are stretched and their resistance increases while the stress in R_1 and R_4 is reduced, thus decreasing the resistance of these strain gage wires. By connecting the four strain gages into a bridge circuit as shown in Figure 2.8(b), all resistance changes influence the output voltage in the same direction, increasing the sensitivity of the transducer by a factor of 4. At the same time, resistance changes of the strain gage due to changing temperatures tend to compensate each other. In the form shown, the unbonded strain gage is basically a force transducer. The same principle is also utilized in transducers for other variables. For example, the blood pressure transducers shown in Chapter 6 employ unbonded strain gages as the transducer elements.

The principle of the *bonded strain gage* is shown in Figure 2.9. A thin wire shaped in a zigzag pattern is cemented between two paper covers or is cemented to the surface of a paper carrier. This strain gage is then cemented to the surface of a structure. Any changes in surface dimensions of the structure due to mechanical strain are transmitted to the resistance wire, causing an increase or decrease of its length and a corresponding resistance change. The bonded strain gage, therefore, is basically a transducer for surface strain.

Related to the bonded wire strain gage is the *foil gage*. In this gage the conductor consists of a foil pattern on a substrate of plastic which is manufactured by the same photoetching techniques as those used in printed circuit boards. This process permits the manufacture of smaller gages with more complicated gage patterns (rosettes), which allow the measurement of different strain components.

In *semiconductor strain gages* a small slice of silicon replaces the wire or foil pattern as a conductor. Because of the crystalline nature of the silicon, these strain gages have a much larger gage factor than metal strain gages. Typical values are as high as 120. By varying the amount of im-

Figure 2.9. Typical bonded strain gage configuration.

purities in the silicon its conductivity can be controlled. With modern manufacturing techniques developed for semiconductor components, silicon strain gages can be made even smaller than the smallest foil gages. If the structure whose surface strain is to be measured is also made of silicon (e.g, in the shape of a beam or diaphragm), the size of the strain gage can be reduced even further by manufacturing it as a resistive pattern on the silicon surface. Such patterns can be obtained using the photolithographic and diffusion techniques developed for the manufacture of integrated circuits. The gages are isolated from the silicon substrate by reverse-biased diode junctions.

As with the unbonded gage, the resistance of a bonded strain gage is influenced by a change in temperature. In semiconductor strain gages, these changes are even more pronounced. Therefore, at least two strain-gage elements are usually used, with the second element either employed strictly for temperature compensation, or as part of a bridge in an arrangement similar to that shown in Figure 2.8(b) to increase the transducer sensitivity at the same time.

2.3.2. Passive Transducers Using Inductive Elements

In principle, the inductance of a coil can be changed either by varying its physical dimensions or by changing the effective permeability of its magnetic core. The latter can be achieved by moving a core having a permeability higher than air through the coil as shown in Figure 2.10. This arrangement appears to be very similar to that of an inductive transducer. However, in the inductive transducer the core is a permanent magnet which, when moved induces a voltage in the coil. In this passive transducer the core is made of a soft magnetic material which changes the inductance of the coil when it is moved inside. The inductance can then be measured using an ac signal.

Displacement

Figure 2.10. Example of variable inductance displacement transducer.

Another passive transducer involving inductance is the *variable reluctance transducer,* in which the core remains stationary but the air gap in the magnetic path of the core is varied to change the effective permeability. This principle is also used in active transducers in which the magnetic path includes a permanent magnet.

The inductance of the coil in these types of transducers is usually not related linearly to the displacement of the core or the size of the air gap, especially if large displacements are encountered. The *linear variable differential transformer* (LVDT), shown in Figure 2.11, overcomes this limita-

Figure 2.11. Differential transformer schematic.

tion. It consists of a transformer with one primary and two secondary windings. The secondary windings are connected so that their induced voltages oppose each other. If the core is in the center position, as shown in the figure, the voltages in the two secondary windings are equal in magnitude and the resulting output voltage is zero. If the core is moved upward as indicated by the arrow, the voltage in secondary 1 increases while that in secondary 2 decreases. The magnitude of the output voltage changes with the amount of displacement of the core from its central or neutral position. Its phase with respect to the voltage at the primary winding depends on the direction of the displacement. Because nonlinearities in the magnitudes of the voltages induced in the two output coils tend to compensate each other, the output voltage of the differential transducer is proportional to core movement even with fairly large displacements.

2.3.3. Passive Transducers Using Capacitive Elements

The capacitance of a plate capacitor can be changed by varying the physical dimensions of the plate structure or by varying the dielectric constant of the medium between the capacitor plates. Both effects have occasionally been used in the design of transducers for biomedical applications. The capacitance plethysmograph shown in Chapter 6 is an example. As with the transducers using an inductive element, it is sometimes not apparent whether a capacitive transducer is of the passive type or is actually an active transducer utilizing the principle of electric induction. If there is doubt, an examination of the carrier signal can help in the classification. Passive transducers utilize ac carriers, whereas a dc bias voltage is used in transducers based on the principle of electric induction.

2.3.4. Passive Transducers Using Active Circuit Elements

The distinction between "active" and "passive" when used for circuit elements is based on a different principle than that which is used for transducers. Active circuit elements are those which provide power gain for

41

a signal (i.e., vacuum tubes and transistors). Such circuit elements have occasionally been used as transducers. Because, as transducers they employ the principle of carrier modulation (the carrier being the plate or collector voltage), these active circuit elements are nevertheless passive transducers, by definition. A variable-transconductance vacuum tube in which the distance between the control grid and cathode of a vacuum tube was changed by the displacement of a mechanical connection is an early example of this type of transducer. More recently, transistors have been manufactured in which a mechanical force applied to the base region of the planar transistor causes a change in the current gain.

The most important application of active circuit elements in passive transducers is in the area of photoelectric transducers. The *photomultiplier* consists of a photoemissive cathode of the type used in photoemissive cells. When struck by photons, the electrons emitted by the cathode are amplified by several stages of secondary emission electrodes called dynodes. The photomultiplier is still the most sensitive light detector. One of its applications for biomedical purposes is in the scintillation detector for nuclear radiation described in Chapter 14.

The sensitivity of a photo diode can be increased if the reverse-biased diode is incorporated into a transistor as the collector–base junction to form a *photo transistor*. In this device, the photo-diode current is essentially amplified by the transistor and appears at the collector, multiplied by the current gain. In the *photo Darlington,* a photo transistor is connected to a second transistor on the same substrate, with the two transistors forming a Darlington circuit. This effectively multiplies the photo current of the collector-base junction of the first transistor by the product of the current gains of both transistors. This arrangement makes the photo Darlington a very sensitive transducer.

Another semiconductor transducer element is the *Hall generator,* which provides an output voltage that is proportional to both the applied current and any magnetic field in which it is placed.

2.4. TRANSDUCERS FOR BIOMEDICAL APPLICATIONS

Several basic physical variables and the transducers (active or passive) used to measure them are listed in Table 2.2. It should be noted that many variables of great interest in biomedical applications, such as pressure and fluid or gas flow, are not included. These and many other variables of interest can be measured, however, by first converting each of them into one of the variables for which basic transducers are available. Some very ingenious methods have been developed to convert some of the more elusive quantities for measurement by one of the transducers described.

Table 2.2. BASIC TRANSDUCERS

Physical Variable	Type of Transducer
Force (or pressure)	Piezoelectric
	Unbonded strain gage
Displacement	Variable resistance
	Variable capacitance
	Variable inductance
	Linear variable differential transducer
	Mercury strain gage
Surface strain	Strain gage
Velocity	Magnetic induction
Temperature	Thermocouple
	Thermistor
Light	Photovoltaic
	Photoresistive
Magnetic field	Hall effect

[a]In medical applications the basic physiological variables is first transformed into one of the physical variables listed. Examples would be measurement of blood pressure using strain gages and blood flow by magnetic induction.

2.4.1. Force Transducers

A design element frequently used for the conversion of physical variables is the *force-summing member*. One possible configuration of this device is shown in Figure 2.12(a). In this case, the force-summing member is a leaf spring. When the spring is bent downward, it exerts an upward-directed force that is proportional to the displacement of the end of the spring. If a force is applied to the end of the spring in a downward direction, the spring bends until its upward-directed force equals the downward-directed applied force, or, expressed differently, until the vector sum of both forces equals zero. From this it derives its name "force-summing member." In the configuration shown, the force-summing member can be used to convert a force into a variable for which transducers are more readily available. The bending of the spring, for example, results in a surface strain that can be measured by means of bonded strain gages as shown in Figure 2.12(b).

The transducers shown in Figure 2.13 utilize this principle. The photographs illustrate that force and displacement transducers are closely related. Sometimes, the terms *isotonic* and *isometric* are used to describe the characteristics of these transducers. Ideally a force transducer would be isometric; that is, it would not yield (change its dimensions) when a force is applied. On the other hand, a displacement transducer would be isotonic and offer zero or a constant resistance to an applied displacement. In reality, almost all transducers combine the characteristics of both ideal transducer

(a)

(b)

(c)

(d)

Figure 2.12. Force transducers using various transduction principles. (a) The force summing member, here in the form of a leaf spring. (b) Force transducer with bonded strain gages. (c) Force transducer using a differential transformer. (d) Force transducer using a lamp and photo resistor to measure the displacement of the force summing member.

Figure 2.13. Force-displacement transducer with bonded strain gage. (Courtesy of Biocom, Inc., Culver City, CA.)

Figure 2.14. Photoelectric displacement transducer: (a) block diagram; (b) photograph. (Courtesy of Narco BioSystems, Houston, TX.)

types. Figure 2.13, for example, shows the same basic transducer type equipped with two different springs. With the long, soft spring shown in the upper photograph, the transducer assumes the characteristics of an *isotonic displacement transducer*. With the short, stiff spring shown in the lower photograph, it becomes an *isometric force transducer*.

Figure 2.12(c) shows measurement of displacement using a differential transformer transducer. A less frequently used type of displacement transducer is shown in Figure 2.12(d). Here the displacement of a spring is used to modulate the intensity of a light beam via a mechanical shutter. The resulting light intensity is measured by a photoresistive cell. In this example, a multiple conversion of variables takes place: force to displacement, displacement to light intensity, and light intensity to resistance. This principle is actually employed in the commercial transducer shown in Figure 2.14.

2.4.2. Transducers for Displacement, Velocity, and Acceleration

Displacement, D, velocity, V, and acceleration, A, are linked by the following relationships:

$$V = \frac{dD}{dt} \qquad A = \frac{dV}{dt} = \frac{d^2D}{dt^2}$$

and the inverse:

$$V = \int A \, dt \qquad D = \int V \, dt = \iint A \, (dt)^2$$

If any one of the three variables can be measured, it is possible—at least in principle—to obtain the other two variables by integration or differentiation. Both operations can readily be performed by electronic methods operating on either analog or digital signals. Expressed in the frequency domain, the integration of a signal corresponds to a lowpass filter with a slope of 6 dB/octave, whereas differentiation corresponds to a highpass filter with the same slope. Because the performance of analog circuits is limited by bandwidth and noise considerations, integration and differentiation of analog signals is possible only within a limited frequency range. Usually, integration poses fewer problems than differentiation. It should also be noted that discontinuities in the transducer characteristic (c.g., the finite resolution of a potentiometric transducer in which the resistive element is of the wire-wound type) are greatly enhanced by the differentiation process.

Table 2.2 shows that transducers for displacement and velocity are readily available. However, the principles listed for these measurements require that part of the transducer be attached to the body structure whose displacement, velocity, or acceleration is to be measured, and that a reference point be available. Since these two conditions cannot always be met in biomedical applications, indirect methods sometimes have to be used. Contactless methods for measuring displacement and velocity, based on optical or magnetic principles, are occasionally used. Magnetic methods usually require that a small magnet or piece of metal be attached to the body structure. Ultrasonic methods, described in Chapter 9, are used more frequently.

2.4.3. Pressure Transducers

Pressure transducers are closely related to force transducers. Some of the force-summing members used in pressure transducers are shown in Figure 2.15. Pressure transducers utilizing flat diaphragms normally have bonded or semiconductor strain gages attached directly to the diaphragms. The small implantable pressure transducer shown in Chapter 6 is of this design. Even smaller dimensions are possible if the diaphragm is made directly from a thin silicon wafer with the strain gages diffused into its surface. The corrugated diaphragm lends itself to the design of pressure transducers using unbonded strain gages or a differential transformer as the transducer element. The LVDT blood pressure transducer shown in Chapter 6 uses these principles. Flat or corrugated diaphragms have also occasionally been used in transducers which employ the variable reluctance or variable capacitance principles. Although diaphragm-type pressure transducers can be designed for a wide range of operating pressures, depending on the diameter and stiffness of the diaphragm, *Bourdon tube* transducers are usually used for high pressure ranges.

It should be noted that the amount of deformation of the force-summing member in a pressure transducer actually depends on the difference in the pressure between the two sides of the diaphragm. If absolute pressure is to be measured, there must be a vacuum on one side of the diaphragm. It is much more common to measure the pressure relative to atmospheric pressure by exposing one side of the diaphragm to the atmosphere. In *differential pressure transducers* the two pressures are applied to opposite sides of the diaphragm.

Figure 2.15. Force-summing members used in pressure transducers; (a) flat diaphragm; (b) corrugated diaphragm; (c) Bourdon tube. (Dashed line shows new position by motion.)

(a)　　　　　　　　　　(b)　　　　　　　　　　(c)

2.4.4. Flow Transducers

The flow rate of fluids or gases is a very elusive variable and many different methods have been developed to measure it. These methods are described in detail in Chapter 6 for blood flow and cardiac output, and in Chapter 8 for the measurement of gas flow as used in measurements in the respiratory system.

2.4.5. Transducers with Digital Output

Increasingly, biomedical instrumentation systems are utilizing digital methods for the processing of data, which require that any data entered into the system be in digital rather than in analog form. Analog-to-digital converters, described in Chapter 15, can be used to convert an analog transducer output into digital form. It is often desirable to have a transducer whose output signal originates in digital form. Although such transducers are very limited in their application, they are available for measurement of linear or rotary displacement. These transducers contain encoding disks or rulers with digital patterns (see Figure 2.16) photographically etched on glass plates. A light source and an array of photodetectors, usually made up of photos diodes or photo transistors, are used to obtain a digital signal in parallel format that indicates the position of the encoding plate, and thereby represents the displacement being measured.

Figure 2.16. Digital shaft encoder patterns. (Courtesy of Itek, Wayne George Division, Newborn, MA.)

3

Sources of Bioelectric Potentials

In carrying out their various functions, certain systems of the body generate their own monitoring signals, which convey useful information about the functions they represent. These signals are the bioelectric potentials associated with nerve conduction, brain activity, heartbeat, muscle activity, and so on. Bioelectric potentials are actually ionic voltages produced as a result of the electrochemical activity of certain special types of cells. Through the use of transducers capable of converting ionic potentials into electrical voltages, these natural monitoring signals can be measured and results displayed in a meaningful way to aid the physician in his diagnosis and treatment of various diseases.

The idea of electricity being generated in the body goes back as far as 1786, when an Italian anatomy professor, Luigi Galvani, claimed to have found electricity in the muscle of a frog's leg. In the century that followed several other scientists discovered electrical activity in various animals and in man. But it was not until 1903, when the Dutch physician Willem

Einthoven introduced the string galvanometer, that any practical application could be made of these potentials. The advent of the vacuum tube and amplification and, more recently, of solid-state technology has made possible better representation of the bioelectric potentials. These developments, combined with a large amount of physiological research activity, have opened many new avenues of knowledge in the application and interpretation of these important signals.

3.1. RESTING AND ACTION POTENTIALS

Certain types of cells within the body, such as nerve and muscle cells, are encased in a semipermeable membrane that permits some substances to pass through the membrane while others are kept out. Neither the exact structure of the membrane nor the mechanism by which its permeability is controlled is known, but the substances involved have been identified by experimentation.

Surrounding the cells of the body are the body fluids. These fluids are conductive solutions containing charged atoms known as *ions*. The principal ions are sodium (Na^+), potassium (K^+), and chloride (C^-). The membrane of excitable cells readily permits entry of potassium and chloride ions but effectively blocks the entry of sodium ions. Since the various ions seek a balance between the inside of the cell and the outside, both according to concentration and electric charge, the inability of the sodium to penetrate the membrane results in two conditions. First, the concentration of sodium ions inside the cell becomes much lower than in the intercellular fluid outside. Since the sodium ions are positive, this would tend to make the outside of the cell more positive than the inside. Second, in an attempt to balance the electric charge, additional potassium ions, which are also positive, enter the cell, causing a higher concentration of potassium on the inside than on the outside. This charge balance cannot be achieved, however, because of the concentration imbalance of potassium ions. Equilibrium is reached with a potential difference across the membrane, negative on the inside and positive on the outside.

This membrane potential is called the *resting potential* of the cell and is maintained until some kind of disturbance upsets the equilibrium. Since measurement of the membrane potential is generally made from inside the cell with respect to the body fluids, the resting potential of a cell is given as negative. Research investigators have reported measuring membrane potentials in various cells ranging from -60 to -100 mV. Figure 3.1 illustrates in simplified form the cross section of a cell with its resting potential. A cell in the resting state is said to be *polarized*.

Figure 3.1. Polarized cell with its resting potential.

When a section of the cell membrane is excited by the flow of ionic current or by some form of externally applied energy, the membrane changes its characteristics and begins to allow some of the sodium ions to enter. This movement of sodium ions into the cell constitutes an ionic current flow that further reduces the barrier of the membrane to sodium ions. The net result is an avalanche effect in which sodium ions literally rush into the cell to try to reach a balance with the ions outside. At the same time potassium ions, which were in higher concentration inside the cell during the resting state, try to leave the cell but are unable to move as rapidly as the sodium ions. As a result, the cell has a slightly positive potential on the inside due to the imbalance of potassium ions. This potential is known as the *action potential* and is approximately + 20 mV. A cell that has been excited and that displays an action potential is said to be *depolarized;* the process of changing from the resting state to the action potential is called *depolarization.* Figure 3.2 shows the ionic movements associated with depolarization, and Figure 3.3 illustrates the cross section of a depolarized cell.

Figure 3.2. Depolarization of a cell. Na^+ ions rush into the cell while K^+ ions attempt to leave.

51

Figure 3.3. Depolarized cell during an action potential.

Once the rush of sodium ions through the cell membrane has stopped (a new state of equilibrium is reached), the ionic currents that lowered the barrier to sodium ions are no longer present and the membrane reverts back to its original, selectively permeable condition, wherein the passage of sodium ions from the outside to the inside of the cell is again blocked. Were this the only effect, however, it would take a long time for a resting potential to develop again. But such is not the case. By an active process, called a *sodium pump,* the sodium ions are quickly transported to the outside of the cell, and the cell again becomes polarized and assumes its resting potential. This process is called *repolarization.* Although little is known of the exact chemical steps involved in the sodium pump, it is quite generally believed that sodium is withdrawn against both charge and concentration gradients supported by some form of high-energy phosphate compound. The rate of pumping is directly proportional to the sodium concentration in the cell. It

Figure 3.4. Waveform of the action potential. (Time scale varies with type of cell.)

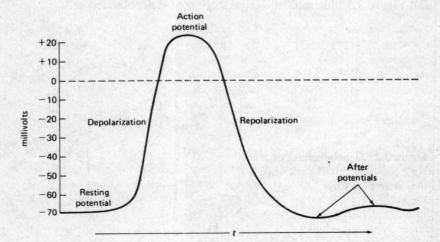

is also believed that the operation of this pump is linked with the influx of potassium into the cell, as if a cyclic process involving an exchange of sodium for potassium existed.

Figure 3.4 shows a typical action-potential waveform, beginning at the resting potential, depolarizing, and returning to the resting potential after repolarization. The time scale for the action potential depends on the type of cell producing the potential. In nerve and muscle cells, repolarization occurs so rapidly following depolarization that the action potential appears as a spike of as little as 1 msec total duration. Heart muscle, on the other hand, repolarizes much more slowly, with the action potential for heart muscle usually lasting from 150 to 300 msec.

Regardless of the method by which a cell is excited or the intensity of the stimulus (provided it is sufficient to activate the cell), the action potential is always the same for any given cell. This is known as the *all-or-nothing law.* The *net height* of the action potential is defined as the difference between the potential of the depolarized membrane at the peak of the action potential and the resting potential.

Following the generation of an action potential, there is a brief period of time during which the cell cannot respond to any new stimulus. This period, called the *absolute refractory period,* lasts about 1 msec in nerve cells. Following the absolute refractory period, there occurs a *relative refractory period,* during which another action potential can be triggered, but a much stronger stimulation is required. In nerve cells, the relative refractory period lasts several milliseconds. These refractory periods are believed to be the result of after-potentials that follow an action potential.

3.2. PROPAGATION OF ACTION POTENTIALS

When a cell is excited and generates an action potential ionic currents begin to flow. This process can, in turn, excite neighboring cells or adjacent areas of the same cell. In the case of a nerve cell with a long fiber, the action potential is generated over a very small segment of the fiber's length but is propagated in both directions from the original point of excitation. In nature, nerve cells are excited only near their "input end" (see Chapter 10 for details). As the action potential travels down the fiber, it cannot reexcite the portion of the fiber immediately upstream, because of the refractory period that follows the action potential.

The rate at which an action potential moves down a fiber or is propagated from cell to cell is called the *propagation rate.* In nerve fibers the propagation rate is also called the *nerve conduction rate,* or *conduction velocity.* This velocity varies widely, depending on the type and diameter of the nerve fiber. The usual velocity range in nerves is from 20 to 140 meters per second (m/sec). Propagation through heart muscle is slower, with an average rate from 0.2 to 0.4 m/sec. Special time-delay fibers between the atria and ventricles of the heart cause action potentials to propagate at an even slower rate, 0.03 to 0.05 m/sec.

3.3. THE BIOELECTRIC POTENTIALS

To measure bioelectric potentials, a transducer capable of converting ionic potentials and currents into electric potentials and currents is required. Such a transducer consists of two *electrodes,* which measure the ionic potential difference between their respective points of application. Electrodes are discussed in detail in Chapter 4.

Although measurement of individual action potentials can be made in some types of cells, such measurements are difficult because they require precise placement of an electrode inside a cell. The more common form of measured biopotentials is the combined effect of a large number of action potentials as they appear at the surface of the body, or at one or more electrodes inserted into a muscle, nerve, or some part of the brain.

The exact method by which these potentials reach the surface of the body is not known. A number of theories have been advanced that seem to explain most of the observed phenomena fairly well, but none exactly fits the situation. Many attempts have been made, for example, to explain the biopotentials from the heart as they appear at the surface of the body. According to one theory, the surface pattern is a summation of the potentials developed by the electric fields set up by the ionic currents that generate the individual action potentials. This theory, although plausible, fails to explain a number of the characteristics indicated by the observed surface patterns. A closer approximation can be obtained if it is assumed that the surface pattern is a function of the summation of the first derivatives (rates of change) of all the individual action potentials, instead of the potentials themselves. Part of the difficulty arises from the numerous assumptions that must be made concerning the ionic current and electric field patterns throughout the body. The validity of some of these assumptions is considered somewhat questionable. Regardless of the method by which these patterns of potentials reach the surface of the body or implanted measuring electrodes, they can be measured as specific bioelectric signal patterns that have been studied extensively and can be defined quite well.

The remainder of this chapter is devoted to a description of each of the more significant bioelectric potential waveforms. The designation of the waveform itself generally ends in the suffix *gram,* whereas the name of the instrument used to measure the potentials and graphically reproduce the waveform ends in the suffix *graph*. For example, the *electrocardiogram* (the name of the waveform resulting from the heart's electrical activity) is measured on an *electrocardiograph* (the instrument). Ranges of amplitudes and frequency spectra for each of the biopotential waveforms described below are included in Appendix B.

3.3.1. The Electrocardiogram (ECG)

The biopotentials generated by the muscles of the heart result in the *electrocardiogram,* abbreviated *ECG (sometimes EKG, from the German electrokardiogram).* To understand the origin of the ECG, it is necessary to have some familiarity with the anatomy of the heart. Figure 3.5 shows a cross section of the interior of the heart. The heart is divided into four chambers. The two upper chambers, the left and right *atria,* are synchronized to act together. Similarly, the two lower chambers, the *ventricles,* operate together. The right atrium receives blood from the veins of the body and pumps it into the right ventricle. The right ventricle pumps the blood through the lungs, where it is oxygenated. The oxygen-enriched blood then enters the left atrium, from which it is pumped into the left ventricle. The left ventricle pumps the blood into the arteries to circulate throughout the body. Because the ventricles actually pump the blood through the vessels (and therefore do most of the work), the ventricular muscles are much larger and more important than the muscles of the atria. For the cardiovascular system to function properly, both the atria and the ventricles must operate in a proper time relationship.

Each action potential in the heart originates near the top of the right atrium at a point called the *pacemaker* or *sinoatrial* (SA) *node.* The pacemaker is a group of specialized cells that spontaneously generate action potentials at a regular rate, although the rate is controlled by innervation. To initiate the heartbeat, the action potentials generated by the pacemaker propagate in all directions along the surface of both atria. The wavefront of activation travels parallel to the surface of the atria toward the junction of the atria and the ventricles. The wave terminates at a point near the center of the heart, called the *atrioventricular* (AV) *node.* At this point, some special fibers act as a "delay line" to provide proper timing between the action of the atria and the ventricles. Once the electrical excitation has passed through the delay line, it is rapidly spread to all parts of both ventricles by the *bundle of His* (pronounced "hiss"). The fibers in this bundle, called *Purkinje fibers,* divide into two branches to initiate action potentials simultaneously in the powerful musculature of the two ventricles. The wavefront in the ventricles does not follow along the surface but is perpendicular to it and moves from the inside to the outside of the ventricular wall, terminating at the tip or *apex* of the heart. As indicated earlier, a wave of repolarization follows the depolarization wave by about 0.2 to 0.4 second. This repolarization, however, is not initiated from neighboring muscle cells but occurs as each cell returns to its resting potential independently.

(a)

Figure 3.5. The heart: (a) internal structure; (b) conducting system. (From W.F. Evans, *Anatomy and Physiology, The Basic Principles,* Englewood Cliffs, N.J., Prentice-Hall, Inc., 1971, by permission.)

(b)

Figure 3.6. The electrocardiogram waveform.

Figure 3.6 shows a typical ECG as it appears when recorded from the surface of the body. Alphabetic designations have been given to each of the prominent features. These can be identified with events related to the action potential propagation pattern. To facilitate analysis, the horizontal segment of this waveform preceding the P wave is designated as the *baseline* or the *isopotential line*. The *P wave* represents depolarization of the atrial musculature. The *QRS complex* is the combined result of the repolarization of the atria and the depolarization of the ventricles, which occur almost simultaneously. The *T wave* is the wave of ventricular repolarization, whereas the *U wave,* if present, is generally believed to be the result of after-potentials in the ventricular muscle. The *P-Q interval* represents the time during which the excitation wave is delayed in the fibers near the AV node.

The shape and polarity of each of these features vary with the location of the measuring electrodes with respect to the heart, and a cardiologist normally bases his diagnosis on readings taken from several electrode locations. Measurement of the electrocardiogram is covered in more detail in Chapter 6.

3.3.2. The Electroencephalogram (EEG)

The recorded representation of bioelectric potentials generated by the neuronal activity of the brain is called the *electroencephalogram,* abbreviated EEG. The EEG has a very complex pattern, which is much more difficult to recognize than the ECG. A typical sample of the EEG is shown in Figure 3.7. As can be seen, the waveform varies greatly with the location of the measuring electrodes on the surface of the scalp. EEG potentials, measured at the surface of the scalp, actually represent the combined effect of potentials from a fairly wide region of the cerebral cortex and from various points beneath.

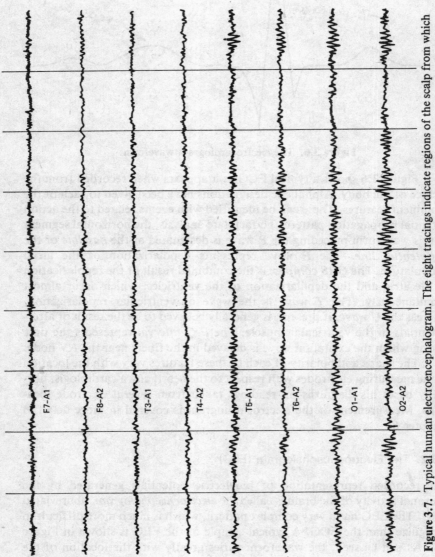

Figure 3.7. Typical human electroencephalogram. The eight tracings indicate regions of the scalp from which each channel of EEG was measured with respect to one of two reference ear electrodes (A1 and A2). Figure 10.12 shows the layout of the electrodes.) (Courtesy Veterans Administration Hospital, Sepulveda, CA.)

Experiments have shown that the frequency of the EEG seems to be affected by the mental activity of a person. The wide variation among individuals and the lack of repeatability in a given person from one occasion to another make the establishment of specific relationships difficult. There are, however, certain characteristic EEG waveforms that can be related to epileptic seizures and sleep. The waveforms associated with the different stages of sleep are shown in Figure 3.8. An alert, wide-awake person usually displays an unsynchronized high-frequency EEG. A drowsy person, particularly one whose eyes are closed, often produces a large amount of rhythmic activity in the range 8 to 13 Hz. As the person begins to fall asleep, the amplitude and frequency of the waveform decrease; and in light sleep, a large-amplitude, low-frequency waveform emerges. Deeper sleep generally results in even slower and higher-amplitude waves. At certain times, however, a person, still sound asleep, breaks into an unsynchronized high-frequency EEG pattern for a time and then returns to the low-frequency sleep pattern. The period of high-frequency EEG that occurs during sleep is called *paradoxical sleep,* because the EEG is more like that of an awake, alert person than of one who is asleep. Another name is *rapid eye movement* (REM) sleep, because associated with the high-frequency EEG is a large amount of rapid eye movement beneath the closed eyelids. This phenomenon is often associated with dreaming, although it has not been shown conclusively that dreaming is related to REM sleep.

The various frequency ranges of the EEG have arbitrarily been given Greek letter designations because frequency seems to be the most prominent feature of an EEG pattern. Electroencephalographers do not agree on the exact ranges, but most classify the EEG frequency bands or rhythms approximately as follows:

Below 3½ Hz	delta
From 3½ Hz to about 8 Hz	theta
From about 8 Hz to about 13 Hz	alpha
Above 13 Hz	beta

Portions of some of these ranges have been given special designations, as have certain subbands that fall on or near the stated boundaries. Most humans seem to develop EEG patterns in the alpha range when they are relaxed with their eyes closed. This condition seems to represent a form of synchronization, almost like a "natural" or "idling" frequency of the brain. As soon as the person becomes alert or begins "thinking," the alpha rhythm disappears and is replaced with a "desynchronized" pattern, generally in the beta range. Much research is presently devoted to attempts to learn the physiological sources in the brain responsible for these phenomena, but so far nothing conclusive has resulted.

Voltage Scale: 50 microvolts   100 microvolts

Figure 3.8. Typical human EEG patterns for different stages of sleep. In each case the upper record is from the left frontal region of the brain and the lower tracing is from the right occipital region. (a) Awake and alert—mixed EEG frequencies; (b) Stage 1—subject is drowsy and produces large amount of alpha waves; (c) Stage 2—light sleep; (e) Stage 4—deeper slow wave sleep; (f) Paradoxical or rapid eye movement (REM) sleep. (Courtesy Veterans Administration Hospital, Sepulveda, CA.)

Experiments in biofeedback have shown that under certain conditions, people can learn to control their EEG patterns to some extent when information concerning their EEG is fed back to them either visibly or audibly. The reader is referred to the section on biofeedback in Chapter 11.

As indicated, the frequency content of the EEG pattern seems to be extremely important. In addition, phase relationships between similar EEG patterns from different parts of the brain are also of great interest. Information of this type may lead to discoveries of EEG sources and will, hopefully, provide additional knowledge regarding the functioning of the brain.

Another form of EEG measurement is the *evoked response*. This is a measure of the "disturbance" in the EEG pattern that results from external stimuli, such as a flash of light or a click of sound. Since these "disturbance" responses are quite repeatable from one flash or click to the next, the evoked response can be distinguished from the remainder of EEG activity, and from the noise, by averaging techniques. These techniques, as well as other methods of measuring EEG, are covered in Chapter 10.

3.3.3. Electromyogram (EMG)

The bioelectric potentials associated with muscle activity constitute the *electromyogram*, abbreviated EMG. These potentials may be measured at the surface of the body near a muscle of interest or directly from the muscle by penetrating the skin with needle electrodes. Since most EMG measurements are intended to obtain an indication of the amount of activity of a given muscle, or group of muscles, rather than of an individual muscle fiber, the pattern is usually a summation of the individual action potentials from the fibers constituting the muscle or muscles being measured. As with the EEG, EMG electrodes pick up potentials from all muscles within the range of the electrodes. This means that potentials from nearby large muscles may interfere with attempts to measure the EMG from smaller muscles, even though the electrodes are placed directly over the small muscles. Where this is a problem, needle electrodes inserted directly into the muscle are required.

As stated in Section 3.1, the action potential of a given muscle (or nerve fiber) has a fixed magnitude, regardless of the intensity of the stimulus that generates the response. Thus, in a muscle, the intensity with which the muscle acts does not increase the net height of the action potential pulse but does increase the rate with which each muscle fiber fires and the number of fibers that are activated at any given time. The amplitude of the measured EMG waveform is the instantaneous sum of all the action potentials generated at any given time. Because these action potentials occur in both positive and negative polarities at a given pair of electrodes, they sometimes add and sometimes cancel. Thus, the EMG waveform appears very much like a random-noise waveform, with the energy of the signal a function of the amount of muscle activity and electrode placement. Typical EMG waveforms are shown in Figure 3.9. Methods and instrumentation for measuring EMG are described in Chapter 10.

Figure 3.9. Typical electromyogram waveform. EMG of normal "interference pattern" with full strength muscle contraction producing obliteration of the baseline. Sweep speed is 10 milliseconds per cm; amplitude is 1 millivolt per cm. (Courtesy of the Veterans Administration Hospital, Portland, OR.)

3.3.4. Other Bioelectric Potentials

In addition to the three most significant bioelectric potentials (ECG, EEG, and EMG), several other electric signals can be obtained from the body, although most of them are special variations of EEG, EMG, or nerve-firing patterns. Some of the more prominent ones are the following:

1. *Electroretinogram (ERG):* A record of the complex pattern of bioelectric potentials obtained from the retina of the eye. This is usually a response to a visual stimulus.
2. *Electro-oculogram (EOG):* A measure of the variations in the corneal-retinal potential as affected by the position and movement of the eye.
3. *Electrogastrogram (EGG):* The EMG patterns associated with the peristaltic movements of the gastrointestinal tract.

4

Electrodes

In observing the measurement of the electrocardiogram (ECG) or the result of some other form of bioelectric potentials as discussed in Chapter 3, a conclusion could easily be reached that the measurement electrodes are simply electrical terminals or contact points from which voltages can be obtained at the surface of the body. Also, the purpose of the electrolyte paste or jelly often used in such measurements might be assumed to be only the reduction of skin impedance in order to lower the overall input impedance of the system. These conclusions, however, are incorrect and do not satisfy the theory that explains the origin of bioelectric potentials. It must be realized that the bioelectric potentials generated in the body are ionic potentials, produced by ionic current flow. Efficient measurement of these ionic potentials requires that they be converted into electronic potentials before they can be measured by conventional methods. It was the realization of this fact that led to the development of the modern noise-free, stable measuring devices now available.

Devices that convert *ionic* potentials into electronic potentials are called *electrodes*. The theory of electrodes and the principles that govern their design are inherent in an understanding of the measurement of bioelectric potentials. This same theory also applies to electrodes used in chemical transducers, such as those used to measure pH, P_{O_2}, and P_{CO_2} of the blood. This chapter deals first with the basic theory of electrodes and then with the various types used in biomedical instrumentation.

4.1. ELECTRODE THEORY

The interface of metallic ions in solution with their associated metals results in an electrical potential that is called the *electrode potential*. This potential is a result of the difference in diffusion rates of ions into and out of the metal. Equilibrium is produced by the formation of a layer of charge at the interface. This charge is really a double layer, with the layer nearest the metal being of one polarity and the layer next to the solution being of opposite polarity. Nonmetallic materials, such as hydrogen, also have electrode potentials when interfaced with their associated ions in solution. The electrode potentials of a wide variety of metals and alloys are listed in Table 4.1.

It is impossible to determine the absolute electrode potential of a single electrode, for measurement of the potential across the electrode and its ionic solution would require placing another metallic interface in the solution. Therefore all electrode potentials are given as relative values and must be stated in terms of some reference. By international agreement, the normal hydrogen electrode was chosen as the reference standard and arbitrarily assigned an electrode potential of zero volts. All the electrode potentials listed in Table 4.1 are given with respect to the hydrogen electrode. They represent the potentials that would be obtained across the stated electrode and a hydrogen electrode if both were placed in a suitable ionic solution.

Another source of an electrode potential is the unequal exchange of ions across a membrane that is semipermeable to a given ion when the membrane separates liquid solutions with different concentrations of that ion. An equation relating the potential across the membrane and the two concentrations of the ion is called the *Nernst equation* and can be stated as follows:

$$E = -\frac{RT}{nF} \ln \frac{C_1 f_1}{C_2 f_2}$$

where R = gas constant (8.315×10^7 ergs/mole/degree Kelvin)
              T = absolute temperature, degrees Kelvin

n = valence of the ion (the number of electrons added or removed to ionize the atom)

F = Faraday constant (96,500 coulombs)

C_1, C_2 = two concentrations of the ion on the two sides of the membrane

f_1, f_2 = respective activity coefficients of the ion on the two sides of the membrane

Unfortunately, the gas constant, $R = 8.315 \times 10^7$, is in electromagnetic cgs units, whereas the Faraday constant, $F = 96,500$, is in absolute coulombs. These units are not compatible. To solve the Nernst equation in electromagnetic cgs units, F must be divided by 10 (there are 10 absolute coulombs in each electromagnetic cgs unit). This calculation gives

Table 4.1. ELECTRODE POTENTIALS[a]

Electrode Reaction	E_0 (volts)	Electrode Reaction	E_0 (volts)
Li $\rightleftarrows$ Li+	−3.045	V $\rightleftarrows$ V^3+	−0.876
Rb $\rightleftarrows$ Rb+	−2.925	Zn $\rightleftarrows$ Zn^2+	−0.762
K $\rightleftarrows$ K+	−2.925	Cr $\rightleftarrows$ Cr^2+	−0.74
Cs $\rightleftarrows$ Cs+	−2.923	Ga $\rightleftarrows$ Ga^2+	−0.53
Ra $\rightleftarrows$ Ra^2+	−2.92	Fe $\rightleftarrows$ Fe^2+	−0.440
Ba $\rightleftarrows$ Ba^2+	−2.90	Cd $\rightleftarrows$ Cd^2+	−0.402
Sr $\rightleftarrows$ Sr^2+	−2.89	In $\rightleftarrows$ In^2+	−0.342
Ca $\rightleftarrows$ Ca^2+	−2.87	Tl $\rightleftarrows$ Tl+	−0.336
Na $\rightleftarrows$ Na+	−2.714	Mn $\rightleftarrows$ Mn^3+	−0.283
La $\rightleftarrows$ La^3+	−2.52	Co $\rightleftarrows$ Co^2+	−0.277
Mg $\rightleftarrows$ Mg^2+	−2.37	Ni $\rightleftarrows$ Ni^2+	−0.250
Am $\rightleftarrows$ Am^3+	−2.32	Mo $\rightleftarrows$ Mo^3+	−0.2
Pu $\rightleftarrows$ Pu^3+	−2.07	Ge $\rightleftarrows$ Ge^4+	−0.15
Th $\rightleftarrows$ Th^4+	−1.90	Sn $\rightleftarrows$ Sn^2+	−0.136
Np $\rightleftarrows$ Np^3+	−1.86	Pb $\rightleftarrows$ Pb^2+	−0.126
Bc $\rightleftarrows$ Bc^2+	−1.85	Fe $\rightleftarrows$ Fe^3+	−0.036
U $\rightleftarrows$ U^3+	−1.80	D$_2$ $\rightleftarrows$ D+	−0.0034
Hf $\rightleftarrows$ Hf^4+	−1.70	H$_2$ $\rightleftarrows$ H+	0.000
Al $\rightleftarrows$ Al^3+	−1.66	Cu $\rightleftarrows$ Cu^2+	+0.337
Ti $\rightleftarrows$ Ti^2+	−1.63	Cu $\rightleftarrows$ Cu+	+0.521
Zr $\rightleftarrows$ Zr^4+	−1.53	Hg $\rightleftarrows$ Hg$_2^2$+	+0.789
U $\rightleftarrows$ U^4+	−1.50	Ag $\rightleftarrows$ Ag+	+0.799
Np $\rightleftarrows$ Np^4+	−1.354	Rh $\rightleftarrows$ Rh^3+	+0.80
Pu $\rightleftarrows$ Pu^4+	−1.28	Hg $\rightleftarrows$ Hg^2+	+0.857
Ti $\rightleftarrows$ Ti^3+	−1.21	Pd $\rightleftarrows$ Pd^2+	+0.987
V $\rightleftarrows$ V^2+	−1.18	Ir $\rightleftarrows$ Ir^3+	+1.000
Mn $\rightleftarrows$ Mn^2+	−1.18	Pt $\rightleftarrows$ Pt^2+	+1.19
Nb $\rightleftarrows$ Nb^3+	−1.1	Au $\rightleftarrows$ Au^3+	+1.50
Cr $\rightleftarrows$ Cr^2+	−0.913	Au $\rightleftarrows$ Au+	+1.68

[a]Reproduced by permission from Brown, J. H. V., J. E. Jacobs, and L. Stark, *Biomedical Engineering*, F. A. Davis Company, Philadelphia, 1971.

the membrane potential in abvolts, the electromagnetic cgs unit for potential. However, 1 standard volt equals 10^8 abvolts; therefore, to convert the membrane potential into standard volts, the entire equation must be multiplied by a constant 10^{-8}.

The activity coefficients, f_1 and f_2, depend on such factors as the charges of all ions in the solution and the distance between ions. The product, $C_1 f_1$, of a concentration and its associated activity coefficient is called the *activity* of the ion responsible for the electrode potential. From the Nernst equation it can be seen that the electrode potential across the membrane is proportional to the logarithm of the ratio of the activities of the subject ion on the two sides of the membrane. In a very dilute solution the activity coefficient f approaches unity, and the electrode potential becomes a function of the logarithm of the ratio of the two concentrations.

In electrodes used for the measurement of bioelectric potentials, the electrode potential occurs at the interface of a metal and an electrolyte, whereas in biochemical transducers both membrane barriers and metal-electrolyte interfaces are used. The sections that follow describe electrodes of both types.

4.2. BIOPOTENTIAL ELECTRODES

A wide variety of electrodes can be used to measure bioelectric events, but nearly all can be classified as belonging to one of three basic types:

1. *Microelectrodes:* Electrodes used to measure bioelectric potentials near or within a single cell.
2. *Skin surface electrodes:* Electrodes used to measure ECG, EEG, and EMG potentials from the surface of the skin.
3. *Needle electrodes:* Electrodes used to penetrate the skin to record EEG potentials from a local region of the brain or EMG potentials from a specific group of muscles.

All three types of biopotential electrodes have the metal–electrolyte interface described in the previous section. In each case, an electrode potential is developed across the interface, proportional to the exchange of ions between the metal and the electrolytes of the body. The double layer of charge at the interface acts as a capacitor. Thus, the equivalent circuit of biopotential electrode in contact with the body consists of a voltage in series with a resistance–capacitance network of the type shown in Figure 4-1.

Since measurement of bioelectric potentials requires two electrodes, the voltage measured is really the difference between the instantaneous potentials of the two electrodes, as shown in Figure 4-2. If the two electrodes are of the same type, the difference is usually small and depends

Figure 4.1. Equivalent circuit of biopotential electrode interface.

Figure 4.2. Measurement of biopotentials with two electrodes—equivalent circuit.

essentially on the actual difference of ionic potential between the two points of the body from which measurements are being taken. If the two electrodes are different, however, they may produce a significant dc voltage that can cause current to flow through both electrodes as well as through the input circuit of the amplifier to which they are connected. The dc voltage due to the difference in electrode potentials is called the *electrode offset voltage*. The resulting current is often mistaken for a true physiological event. Even two electrodes of the same material may produce a small electrode offset voltage.

In addition to the electrode offset voltage, experiments have shown that the chemical activity that takes place within an electrode can cause voltage fluctuations to appear without any physiological input. Such variations may appear as noise on a bioelectric signal. This noise can be reduced by proper choice of materials or, in most cases, by special treatment, such as coating the electrodes by some electrolytic method to improve stability. It has been found that, electrochemically, the *silver–silver chloride electrode* is very stable. This type of electrode is prepared by electrolytically coating a piece of pure silver with silver chloride. The coating is normally done by placing a cleaned piece of silver into a bromide-free sodium chloride solution. A second piece of silver is also placed in the solution, and the two are connected to a voltage source such that the electrode to be chlorided is made positive with respect to the other. The silver ions combine with the chloride ions from the salt to produce neutral silver chloride molecules that coat the silver electrode. Some variations in the process are used to produce electrodes with specific characteristics.

The resistance-capacitance networks shown in Figures 4.1 and 4.2 represent the impedance of the electrodes (one of their most important characteristics) as fixed values of resistance and capacitance. Unfortunately, the impedance is not constant. The impedance is frequency-dependent because of the effect of the capacitance. Furthermore, both the electrode potential and the impedance are varied by an effect called *polarization*.

Polarization is the result of direct current passing through the metal–electrolyte interface. The effect is much like that of charging a battery with the polarity of the charge opposing the flow of current that generates the charge. Some electrodes are designed to avoid or reduce polarization. If the amplifier to which the electrodes are connected has an extremely high input impedance, the effect of polarization or any other change in electrode impedance is minimized.

Size and type of electrode are also important in determining the electrode impedance. Larger electrodes tend to have lower impedances. Surface electrodes generally have impedances of 2 to 10 kΩ, whereas small needle electrodes and microelectrodes have much higher impedances. For best results in reading or recording the potentials measured by the electrodes, the input impedance of the amplifier must be several times that of the electrodes.

4.2.1. Microelectrodes

Microelectrodes are electrodes with tips sufficiently small to penetrate a single cell in order to obtain readings from within the cell. The tip must be small enough to permit penetration without damaging the cell. This action is usually complicated by the difficulty of accurately positioning an electrode with respect to a cell.

Microelectrodes are generally of two types: metal and micropipet. Metal microelectrodes are formed by electrolytically etching the tip of a fine tungsten or stainless-steel wire to the desired size. Then the wire is coated almost to the tip with an insulating material. Some electrolytic processing can also be performed on the tip to lower the impedance. The metal–ion interface takes place where the metal tip contacts the electrolytes either inside or outside the cell.

The micropipet type of microelectrode is a glass micropipet with the tip drawn out to the desired size [usually about 1 micron (now more commonly called micrometer, μm) in diameter]. The micropipet is filled with an electrolyte compatible with the cellular fluids. This type of microelectrode has a dual interface. One interface consists of a metal wire in contact with the electrolyte solution inside the micropipet, while the other is the interface between the electrolyte inside the pipet and the fluids inside or immediately outside the cell.

A commercial type of microelectrode is shown in Figure 4.3. In this electrode a thin film of precious metal is bonded to the outside of a drawn glass microelectrode. The manufacturer claims such advantages as lower impedance than the micropipet electrode, infinite shelf life, repeatable and reproducible performance, and easy cleaning and maintenance. The metal-electrolyte interface is between the metal film and the electrolyte of the cell.

Figure 4.3. Commercial microelectrode with metal film on glass. (Courtesy of Transidyne General Corporation, Ann Arbor, MI.)

Microelectrodes, because of their small surface areas, have impedances well up into the megohms. For this reason, amplifiers with extremely high impedances are required to avoid loading the circuit and to minimize the effects of small changes in interface impedance.

4.2.2. Body Surface Electrodes

Electrodes used to obtain bioelectric potentials from the surface of the body are found in many sizes and forms. Although any type of surface electrode can be used to sense ECG, EEG, or EMG potentials, the larger electrodes are usually associated with ECG, since localization of the measurement is not important, whereas smaller electrodes are used in EEG and EMG measurements.

The earliest bioelectric potential measurements used *immersion electrodes,* which were simply buckets of saline solution into which the subject placed his hands and feet, one bucket for each extremity. As might be expected, this type of electrode (Figure 4.4) presented many difficulties, such as restricted position of the subject and danger of electrolyte spillage.

Figure 4.4. ECG measurement using immersion electrodes. Original Cambridge electrocardiograph (1912) built for Sir Thomas Lewis. Produced under agreement with Prof. Willem Einthoven, the father of electrocardiography. (Courtesy of Cambridge Instruments, Inc., Cambridge, MA.)

A great improvement over the immersion electrodes were the plate electrodes, first introduced about 1917. Originally, these electrodes were separated from the subject's skin by cotton or felt pads soaked in a strong saline solution. Later a conductive jelly or paste (an electrolyte) replaced the soaked pads and metal was allowed to contact the skin through a thin coat of jelly. Plate electrodes of this type are still in use today. An example is shown in Figure 4.5.

Figure 4.5. Metal plate electrode. These plates are usually made of, or plated with, silver, nickel, or some similar alloy.

Figure 4.6. Suction cup electrode.

Another fairly old type of electrode still in use is the suction-cup electrode shown in Figure 4.6. In this type, only the rim actually contacts the skin.

One of the difficulties in using plate electrodes is the possibility of electrode slippage or movement. This also occurs with the suction-cup electrode after a sufficient length of time. A number of attempts were made to overcome this problem, including the use of adhesive backing and a surface resembling a nutmeg grater that penetrates the skin to lower the contact impedance and reduce the likelihood of slippage.

All the preceding electrodes suffer from a common problem. They are all sensitive to movement, some to a greater degree than others. Even the slightest movement changes the thickness of the thin film of electrolyte between metal and skin and thus causes changes in the electrode potential and impedance. In many cases, the potential changes are so severe that they completely block the bioelectric potentials the electrodes attempt to measure. The adhesive tape and "nutmeg grater" electrodes reduce this movement artifact by limiting electrode movement and reducing interface impedance, but neither is satisfactorily insensitive to movement.

Later, a new type of electrode, the *floating electrode,* was introduced in varying forms by several manufacturers. The principle of this electrode is to practically eliminate movement artifact by avoiding any direct contact of the metal with the skin. The only conductive path between metal and skin is the electrolyte paste or jelly, which forms an electrolyte bridge. Even with the electrode surface held at a right angle with the skin surface, performance is not impaired as long as the electrolyte bridge maintains contact with both the skin and the metal. Figure 4.7 shows a cross section of a floating electrode, and Figure 4.8 shows a commercially available configuration of the floating electrode.

71

Silver–silver chloride disk

Plastic or rubber support and spacer

Lead wire

Skin surface

Space for electrode jelly

Figure 4.7. Diagram of floating type skin surface electrode.

Figure 4.8. Floating skin surface electrode. (Courtesy of Beckman Instruments, Inc., Fullerton, CA.)

Figure 4.9. Application of floating type skin surface electrode. (Courtesy of Beckman Instruments, Inc., Fullerton, CA.)

Figure 4.10. Disposable electrodes.

Floating electrodes are generally attached to the skin by means of two-sided adhesive collars (or rings), which adhere to both the plastic surface of the electrode and the skin. Figure 4.9 shows an electrode in position for biopotential measurement.

Special problems encountered in the monitoring of the ECG of astronauts during long periods of time, and under conditions of perspiration and considerable movement, led to the development of *spray-on electrodes,* in which a small spot of conductive adhesive is sprayed or painted over the skin, which had previously been treated with an electrolyte coating.

Various types of *disposable electrodes* have been introduced in recent years to eliminate the requirement for cleaning and care after each use. An example is shown in Figure 4.10. Primarily intended for ECG monitoring, these electrodes can also be used for EEG and EMG as well. In general, disposable electrodes are of the floating type with simple snap connectors by which the leads, which are reusable, are attached. Although some disposable electrodes can be reused several times, their cost is usually low enough that cleaning for reuse is not warranted. They come pregelled, ready for immediate use.

Special types of surface electrodes have been developed for other applications. For example, a special *ear-clip electrode* (Figure 4.11) was developed for use as a reference electrode for EEG measurements. Scalp *surface electrodes* for EEG are usually small disks about 7 mm in diameter or small solder pellets that are placed on the cleaned scalp, using an electrolyte paste. This type of electrode is shown in Figure 4.12.

Figure 4.11. Ear-clip electrode. (Courtesy of Sepulveda Veterans Administration Hospital.)

Figure 4.12. EEG scalp surface electrode. (Courtesy of Sepulveda Veterans Administration Hospital.)

4.2.3. Needle Electrodes

To reduce interface impedance and, consequently, movement artifacts, some electroencephalographers use small subdermal needles to penetrate the scalp for EEG measurements. These needle electrodes, shown in Figure 4.13, are not inserted into the brain; they merely penetrate the skin. Generally, they are simply inserted through a small section of the skin just beneath the surface and parallel to it.

Figure 4.13. Subdermal needle electrode for EEG. (Courtesy of Sepulveda Veterans Administration Hospital.)

74

In animal research (and occasionally in man) longer needles are actually inserted into the brain to obtain localized measurement of potentials from a specific part of the brain. This process requires longer needles precisely located by means of a map or atlas of the brain. Sometimes a special instrument, called a *stereotaxic instrument,* is used to hold the animal's head and guide the placement of electrodes. Often these electrodes are implanted to permit repeated measurements over an extended period of time. In this case, a connector is cemented to the animal's skull and the incision through which the electrodes were implanted is allowed to heal.

In some research applications, simultaneous measurement from various depths in the brain along a certain axis is required. Special multiple-depth electrodes have been developed for this purpose. This type of electrode usually consists of a bundle of fine wires, each terminating at a different depth or each having an exposed conductive surface at a specific, but different, depth. These wires are generally brought out to a connector at the surface of the scalp and are often cemented to the skull.

Needle electrodes for EMG consist merely of fine insulated wires, placed so that their tips, which are bare, are in contact with the nerve, muscle, or other tissue from which the measurement is made. The remainder of the wire is covered with some form of insulation to prevent shorting. Wire electrodes of copper or platinum are often used for EMG pickup from specific muscles. The wires are either surgically implanted or introduced by means of a hypodermic needle that is later withdrawn, leaving the wire electrode in place. With this type of electrode, the metal–electrolyte interface takes place between the uninsulated tip of the wire and the electrolytes of the body, although the wire is dipped into an electrolyte paste before insertion in some cases. The hypodermic needle is sometimes a part of the electrode configuration and is not withdrawn. Instead, the wires forming the electrodes are carried inside the needle, which creates the hole necessary for insertion, protects the wires, and acts as a grounded shield. A single wire inside the needle serves as a *unipolar electrode,* which measures the potentials at the point of contact with respect to some indifferent reference. If two wires are placed inside the needle, the measurement is called *bipolar* and provides a very localized measurement between the two wire tips.

Electrodes for measurement from beneath the skin need not actually take the form of needles, however. Surgical clips penetrating the skin of a mouse or rat in the spinal region provide an excellent method of measuring the ECG of an essentially unrestrained, unanesthetized animal. Conductive catheters permit the recording of the ECG from within the esophagus or even from within the chambers of the heart itself.

Needle electrodes and other types of electrodes that create an interface beneath the surface of the skin seem to be less susceptible to movement artifacts than surface electrodes, particularly those of the older types. By making direct contact with the subdermal tissue or the intercellular fluids, these electrodes also seem to have lower impedances than surface electrodes of comparable interface area.

4.3.   BIOCHEMICAL TRANSDUCERS

At the beginning of this chapter it was stated that an electrode potential is generated either at a metal–electrolyte interface or across a semipermeable membrane separating two different concentrations of an ion that can diffuse through the membrane. Both methods are used in transducers designed to measure the concentration of an ion or of a certain gas dissolved in blood or some other liquid. Also, as stated earlier, since it is impossible to have a single electrode interface to a solution, a second electrode is required to act as a reference. If both electrodes were to exhibit the same response to a given change in concentration of the measured solution, the potential measured between them would not be related to concentration and would, therefore, be useless as a measurement parameter. The usual method of measuring concentrations of ions or gases is to use one electrode (sometimes called the *indicator* or *active electrode*) that is sensitive to the substance or ion being measured and to choose the second, or *reference electrode,* of a type that is insensitive to that substance.

4.3.1. Reference Electrodes

As stated in Section 4.1, the hydrogen gas/hydrogen ion interface has been designated as the reference interface and was arbitrarily assigned an electrode potential of zero volts. For this reason, it would seem logical that the hydrogen electrode should actually be used as the reference in biochemical measurements. Hydrogen electrodes can be built and are available commercially. These electrodes make use of the principle that an inert metal, such as platinum, readily absorbs hydrogen gas. If a properly treated piece of platinum is partially immersed in the solution containing hydrogen ions and is also exposed to hydrogen gas, which is passed through the electrode, an electrode potential is formed. The electrode lead is attached to the platinum.

Unfortunately, the hydrogen electrode is not sufficiently stable to serve as a good reference electrode. Furthermore, the problem of maintaining the supply of hydrogen to pass through the electrode during a measurement limits its usefulness to a few special applications. However, since measurement of electrochemical concentrations simply requires a change of potential proportional to a change in concentration, the electrode potential

Figure 4.14. Reference electrode—basic configuration. (Courtesy Beckman Instruments, Inc., Fullerton, CA.)

Internal (Ag/Ag Cl or calomel)

Filling solution

Liquid junction

of the reference electrode can be any amount, as long as it is stable and does not respond to any possible changes in the composition of the solution being measured. Thus, the search for a good reference electrode is essentially a search for the most stable electrode available. Two types of electrodes have interfaces sufficiently stable to serve as reference electrodes—the silver–silver chloride electrode and the calomel electrode. Their basic configurations are shown in Figure 4.14.

The *silver–silver chloride electrode* used as a reference in electrochemical measurements utilizes the same type of interface described in Section 4.2 for bioelectric potential electrodes. In the chemical transducer, the ionic (silver chloride) side of the interface is connected to the solution by an electrolyte bridge, usually a dilute potassium chloride (KC1) filling solution which forms a liquid junction with the sample solution. The electrode can be successfully employed as a reference electrode if the KC1 solution is also saturated with precipitated silver chloride. The electrode potential for the silver–silver chloride reference electrode depends on the concentration of the KC1. For example, with a 0.01-mole*-solution, the potential is 0.343 V, whereas for a 1.0-mole solution the potential is only 0.236 V.

An equally popular reference electrode is the *calomel electrode.* Calomel is another name for mercurous chloride, a chemical combination of mercury and chloride ions. The interface between mercury and mercurous chloride generates the electrode potential. By placing the calomel side of the interface in a potassium chloride (KC1) filling solution, an elec-

---

*A 0.01-mole solution of a substance is defined as 0.01 mole of the substance dissolved in 1 liter of solution. A mole is the quantity of the substance that has a weight equal to its molecular weight, usually in grams.

trolytic bridge is formed to the sample solution from which the measurement is to be made. Like the silver–silver chloride electrode, the calomel electrode is very stable over long periods of time and serves well as a reference electrode in many electrochemical measurements. Also, like the silver–silver chloride electrode, the electrode potential of the calomel electrode depends on the concentration of KCl. An electrode with a 0.01-mole solution of KCl has an electrode potential of 0.388 V, whereas a saturated KCl solution (about 3.5 moles) has a potential of only 0.247 V.

4.3.2. The pH Electrode

Perhaps the most important indicator of chemical balance in the body is the pH of the blood and other body fluids. The pH is directly related to the hydrogen ion concentration in a fluid. Specifically, it is the logarithm of the reciprocal of the H^+ ion concentration. In equation form,

$$pH = -\log_{10}[H^+] = \log_{10} \frac{1}{[H^+]}$$

The pH is a measure of the acid–base balance of a fluid. A neutral solution (neither acid nor base) has a pH of 7. Lower pH numbers indicate acidity, whereas higher pH values define a basic solution. Most human body fluids are slightly basic. The pH of normal arterial blood ranges between 7.38 and 7.42. The pH of venous blood is 7.35, because of the extra CO_2.

Because a thin glass membrane allows passage of only hydrogen ions in the form of H_3O^+, a glass electrode provides a "membrane" interface for hydrogen. The principle is illustrated in Figure 4.15. Inside the glass bulb is a highly acidic buffer solution. Measurement of the potential across the glass interface is achieved by placing a silver–silver chloride electrode in the solution inside the glass bulb and a calomel or silver–silver chloride reference electrode in the solution in which the pH is being measured. In the measurement of pH and, in fact, any electrochemical measurement, each of the two electrodes required to obtain the measurement is called a *half-cell*. The electrode potential for a half-cell is sometimes called the *half-cell potential*. For pH measurement, the glass electrode with the silver–silver chloride electrode inside the bulb is considered one half-cell, while the calomel reference electrode constitutes the other half-cell.

To facilitate the measurement of the pH of a solution, combination electrodes of the type shown in Figure 4.16 are available, with both the pH glass electrode and reference electrode in the same enclosure.

The glass electrode is quite adequate for pH measurements in the physiological range (around pH 7), but may produce considerable error at the extremes of the range (near pH of zero or 13 to 14). Special types of pH

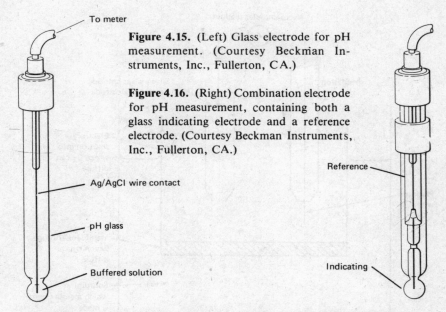

Figure 4.15. (Left) Glass electrode for pH measurement. (Courtesy Beckman Instruments, Inc., Fullerton, CA.)

Figure 4.16. (Right) Combination electrode for pH measurement, containing both a glass indicating electrode and a reference electrode. (Courtesy Beckman Instruments, Inc., Fullerton, CA.)

electrodes are available for the extreme ranges. Glass electrodes are also subject to some deterioration after prolonged use but can be restored repeatedly by etching the glass in a 20 percent ammonium bifluoride solution.

The type of glass used for the membrane has much to do with the pH response of the electrode. Special hydroscopic glass that readily absorbs water provides the best pH response.

Modern pH electrodes have impedances ranging from 50 to 500 megohms ($M\Omega$). Thus, the input of the meter that measures the potential difference between the glass electrode and the reference electrode must have an extremely high input impedance. Most pH meters employ electrometer inputs.

4.3.3. Blood Gas Electrodes

Among the more important physiological chemical measurements are the partial pressures of oxygen and carbon dioxide in the blood. The partial pressure of a dissolved gas is the contribution of that gas to the total pressure of all dissolved gases in the blood. The partial pressure of a gas is proportional to the quantity of that gas in the blood. The effectiveness of both the respiratory and cardiovascular systems is reflected in these important parameters.

The partial pressure of oxygen, P_{O_2}, often called *oxygen tension,* can be measured both in vitro and in vivo. The basic principle is shown in Figure

Figure 4.17. Diagram of P_{O_2} electrode with platinum cathode showing principle of operation.

4.17. A fine piece of platinum or some other noble metal wire, embedded in glass for insulation purposes, with only the tip exposed, is placed in an electrolyte into which oxygen is allowed to diffuse. If a voltage of about 0.7 V is applied between the platinum wire and a reference electrode (also placed into the electrolyte), with the platinum wire negative, reduction of the oxygen takes place at the platinum cathode. As a result, an oxidation–reduction current proportional to the partial pressure of the diffused oxygen can be measured. The electrolyte is generally sealed into the chamber that holds the platinum wire and the reference electrode by means of a membrane across which the dissolved oxygen can diffuse from the blood.

The platinum cathode and the reference electrode can be integrated into a single unit (the *Clark electrode*). This electrode can be placed in a cuvette of blood for in vitro measurements, or a micro version can be placed at the tip of a catheter for insertion into various parts of the heart or vascular system for direct in vivo measurements.

One of the problems inherent in this method of measuring P_{O_2} is the fact that the reduction process actually removes a finite amount of the oxygen from the immediate vicinity of the cathode. By careful design and use of proper procedures, modern P_{O_2} electrodes have been able to reduce this potential source of error to a minimum. Another apparent error in P_{O_2} measurement is a gradual reduction of current with time, almost like the polarization effect described for skin surface electrodes in Section 4.2.2. This effect, generally called *aging,* has also been minimized in modern P_{O_2} electrodes.

The measurement of the partial pressure of carbon dioxide, P_{CO_2}, makes use of the fact that there is a linear relationship between the logarithm of the P_{CO_2} and the pH of a solution. Since other factors also influence the pH, measurement of P_{CO_2} is essentially accomplished by surrounding a pH electrode with a membrane selectively permeable to CO_2. A modern, improved type of P_{CO_2} electrode is called the *Severinghaus electrode.* In this type of electrode, the membrane permeable to the CO_2 is made of Teflon, which is not permeable to other ions that might affect the pH. The space between the Teflon and the glass contains a matrix consisting of thin cellophane, glass wool, or sheer nylon. This matrix serves as the support for an aqueous bicarbonate layer into which the CO_2 gas molecules can diffuse. One of the difficulties with older types of CO_2 electrodes is the length of time required for the CO_2 molecules to diffuse and thus obtain a reading. The principal advantage of the Severinghaus-type electrode is the more rapid reading that can be obtained because of the improved membrane and bicarbonate layer.

In some applications, measurements of P_{O_2} and P_{CO_2} are combined into a single electrode that also includes a common reference half-cell. Such a combination electrode is shown in diagram form in Figure 4.18.

Figure 4.18. Combination of P_{CO_2} and P_{O_2} electrode. (Courtesy of J.W. Severinghaus, M.D.)

4.3.4. Specific Ion Electrodes

Just as the glass electrode provides a semipermeable membrane for the hydrogren ion in the pH electrode (see Section 4.3.2), other materials can be used to form membranes that are semipermeable to other specific ions. In each case, measurement of the ion concentration is accomplished by measurement of potentials across a membrane that has the correct degree of permeability to the specific ion to be measured. The permeability should be sufficient to permit rapid establishment of the electrode potential. Both liquid and solid membranes are used for specific ions. As in the case of the pH electrode, a silver–silver chloride interface is usually provided on the electrode side of the membrane, and a standard reference electrode serves as the other half-cell in the solution.

Figure 4.19 shows a solid-state electrode of the type used for measurement of fluoride ions. Figure 4.20 shows three specific ion electrodes along with a pH glass electrode. The sodium electrode in Figure 4.20(a) is commonly used to determine sodium ion activity in blood and other physiological solutions. The cationic electrode (b) is used when studying alkaline metal ions or enzymes. The ammonia electrode (d) is designed for determinations of ammonia dissolved in aqueous solutions. Its most popular application is in determining nitrogen as free ammonia or total Kjeldahl nitrogen.

Figure 4.21 is a diagram showing the construction of a flow-through type of electrode. This is a liquid-membrane, specific-ion electrode. One of the difficulties encountered in the measurement of specific ions is the effect of other ions in the solution. In cases where more than one type of membrane could be selected for measurement of a certain ion, the choice of membrane actually used might well depend on other ions that may be expected. In fact, some specific-ion electrodes can be used in measurement of a given ion only in the absence of certain other ions.

For measurement of divalent ions, a liquid membrane is often used for ion exchange. In this case, the exchanger is usually a salt of an organophosphoric acid, which shows a high degree of specificity to the ion being measured. A calcium chloride solution bridges the membrane to the silver–silver chloride electrode. Electrodes with membranes of solid materials are also used for measurement of divalent ions.

Figure 4.19. Electrode for measurement of fluoride ions. (Courtesy Beckman Instruments, Inc., Fullerton, CA.)

Figure 4.20. Specific ion electrodes with pH glass electrode. (a) Sodium ion electrode; (b) cationic electrode; (c) pH glass electrode; (d) ammonia electrode. (Courtesy Beckman Instruments, Inc., Fullerton, CA.)

Figure 4.21. Diagram showing construction of flow-through liquid membrane specific ion electrode. (Courtesy of Orion Research, Inc., Cambridge, MA.)

5

The
Cardiovascular
System

The heart attack, in its various forms, is the cause of many deaths in the world today. The use of engineering methods and the development of instrumentation have contributed substantially to progress made in recent years in reducing death from heart diseases. Blood pressure, flow, and volume are measured by using engineering techniques. The electrocardiogram, the echocardiogram, and the phonocardiogram are measured and recorded with electronic instruments. Intensive and coronary care units now installed in many hospitals rely on bioinstrumentation for their function. There are also cardiac assist devices, such as the electronic pacemaker and defibrillator, which, although not measuring instruments per se, are electronic devices often used in conjunction with measurement systems.

In this chapter the cardiovascular system is discussed, not only from the point of view of basic physiology but also with the idea that it is an engineering system. In this way the important parameters can be illustrated in correct perspective. Included are the pump and flow characteristics, as well as the ancillary ideas of electrical activity and heart sounds.

The electrocardiogram has already been introduced in Chapter 3. The actual measurements and devices are discussed in Chapters 6, 7, and 9.

5.1. THE HEART AND CARDIOVASCULAR SYSTEM

The heart may be considered as a two-stage pump, physically arranged in parallel but with the circulating blood passing through the pumps in a series sequence. The right half of the heart, known as the *right heart,* is the pump that supplies blood to the rest of the system. The circulatory path for blood flow-through the lungs is called the *pulmonary circulation,* and the circulatory system that supplies oxygen and nutrients to the cells of the body is called the *systemic circulation.*

From an engineering standpoint, the systemic circulation is a high-resistance circuit with a large pressure gradient between the arteries and veins. Thus, the pump constituting the left heart may be considered as a pressure pump. However, in the pulmonary circulation system, the pressure difference between the arteries and the veins is small, as is the resistance to flow, so the right heart may be considered as a volume pump. The muscle contraction of the left heart is larger and stronger than that of the right heart because of the greater pressures required for the systemic circulation. The volume of blood delivered per unit of time by the two sides is the same when measured over a sufficiently long interval. The left heart develops a pressure head sufficient to cause blood to flow to all the extremities of the body.

The pumping action itself is performed by contraction of the heart muscles surrounding each chamber of the heart. These muscles receive their own blood supply from the *coronary arteries,* which surround the heart like a crown (corona). The *coronary arterial system* is a special branch of the systemic circulation.

The analogy to a pump and hydraulic piping system should not be used too indiscriminately. The pipes, the arteries and the veins, are not rigid but flexible. They are capable of helping and controlling blood circulation by their own muscular action and their own valve and receptor system. Blood is not a pure Newtonian fluid; rather, it possesses properties that do not always comply with the laws governing hydraulic motion. In addition, the blood needs the help of the lungs for the supply of oxygen, and it interacts with the lymphatic system. Furthermore, many chemicals and hormones affect the operation of the system. Thus, oversimplication could lead to error if carried too far.

The actual physiological system for the heart and circulation is illustrated in Figure 5.1, with the equivalent engineering type of piping diagram shown in Figure 5.2. Referring to these figures, the operation of the circulatory system can be described as follows. Blood enters the heart on the right side through two main veins: the *superior vena cava,* which leads from the body's upper extremities, and the *inferior vena cava* leading from the body's organs and extremities below the heart. The incoming blood fills

Figure 5.1. The cardiovascular system. (From K. Schmidt-Nielsen, *Animal Physiology,* 3rd ed., Prentice-Hall, Inc., 1979, by permission.)

the storage chamber, the *right atrium.* In addition to the two veins mentioned, the *coronary sinus* also empties into the right atrium. The coronary sinus contains the bood that has been circulating through the heart itself via the coronary loop.

When the right atrium is full, it contracts and forces blood through the *tricuspid valve* into the *right ventricle,* which then contracts to pump the blood into the pulmonary circulation system. When ventricular pressure exceeds atrial pressure, the tricuspid valve closes and the pressure in the ventricle forces the semilunar *pulmonary valve* to open, thereby causing blood to flow into the pulmonary artery, which divides into the two lungs.

In the *alveoli* of the lungs, an exchange takes place. The red blood cells are recharged with oxygen and give up their carbon dioxide. Not shown on the diagram are the details of this exchange. The pulmonary artery *bifurcates* (divides) many times into smaller and smaller arteries, which become arterioles with extremely small cross sections. These arterioles supply blood to the alveolar capillaries, in which the exchange of oxygen and carbon dioxide takes place. On the other side of the lung mass is a similar construction in which the capillaries feed into tiny veins, or *venules.* The latter combine to form larger veins, which in turn combine until ultimately all the oxygenated blood is returned to the heart via the pulmonary vein.

Figure 5.2. Cardiovascular circulation.

The blood enters the *left atrium* from the pulmonary vein, and from there it is pumped through the *mitral,* or *bicuspid valve,* into the left ventricle by contraction of the atrial muscles. When the left ventricular muscles contract, the pressure produced by the contraction mechanically closes the mitral valve, and the buildup of pressure in the ventricle forces the *aortic valve* to open, causing the blood to rush from the ventricle into the *aorta.* It should be noted that this action takes place synchronously with the right ventricle as it pumps blood into the pulmonary artery.

The heart's pumping cycle is divided into two major parts: systole and diastole. *Systole* (sĭs´tō•lē) is defined as the period of contraction of the heart muscles, specifically the ventricular muscle, at which time blood is pumped into the pulmonary artery and the aorta. *Diastole* (dī•ăs´tō•lē) is the period of dilation of the heart cavities as they fill with blood.

Once the blood has been pumped into the arterial system, the heart relaxes, the pressure in the chambers decreases, the outlet valves close, and in a short time the inlet valves open again to restart the diastole and initiate a new cycle in the heart. The mechanism of this cycle and its control will be discussed later.

After passing through many bifurcations of the arteries, the blood reaches the vital organs, the brain, and the extremities. The last stage of the arterial system is the gradual decrease in cross section and the increase in the number of arteries until the smallest type (arterioles) is reached. These feed into the capillaries, where oxygen is supplied to the cells and carbon dioxide is received from the cells. In turn, the capillaries join into venules, which become small veins, then larger veins, and ultimately form the superior and inferior vena cavae. The blood supply to the heart itself is from the aorta through the coronary arteries into a similar capillary system to the cardiac veins. This blood returns to the heart chambers by way of the coronary sinus, as stated above.

Since continued reference has been made to the cardiovascular system in engineering terms, some numbers of interest should be mentioned. The heart beats at an average rate of about 75 beats per minute in a normal adult, although this figure can vary considerably. The heart rate increases when a person stands up and decreases when he sits down, the range being from about 60 to 85. On the average, it is higher in women and generally decreases with age. In an infant, the heart rate may be as high as 140 beats per minute under normal conditions. The heart rate also increases with heat exposure and other physiological and psychological factors, which will be discussed later.

The heart pumps about 5 liters of blood per minute, and since the volume of blood in the average adult is about 5 to 6 liters, this corresponds to a complete turnover every minute during rest. With heavy exercise, the circulation rate is increased considerably. At any given time, about 75 to 80 percent of the blood volume is in the veins, about 20 percent in the arteries, and the remainder in the capillaries.

Systolic (maximum) blood pressure in the normal adult is in the range of 95 to 140 mm Hg, with 120 mm Hg being average.* These figures are subject to much variation with age, climate, eating habits, and other factors. Normal diastolic blood pressure (lowest pressure between beats) ranges from 60 to 90 mm Hg, 80 mm Hg being about average. This pressure is usually measured in the brachial artery in the arm. For comparison purposes with pressures of 130/75 in the aorta, 130/5 can be expected in the left ventricle, 9/5 in the left atrium, 25/0 in the right ventricle, 3/0 in the right atrium, and 25/12 in the pulmonary artery. These values are given as:

systolic pressure/diastolic pressure

5.2 THE HEART

The general behavior of the heart as the pump used to force the blood through the cardiovascular system has been discussed. A more detailed analysis of the anatomy of the heart, plus a discussion of the electrical excitation system necessary to produce and control the muscular contractions, should help to round out the background material needed for an understanding of cardiac dynamics. The electrocardiogram, as a record of biopotential events, has already been discussed in Chapter 3, but some repetition is necessary in order to consider the system as a whole and the relationships that exist between the electrical and mechanical events of the heart. Figure 5.3 is an illustration of the heart.

The heart is contained in the *pericardium,* a membranous sac consisting of an external layer of dense fibrous tissue and an inner serous layer that surrounds the heart directly. The base of the pericardium is attached to the central tendon of the diaphragm, and its cavity contains a thin serous liquid. The two sides of the heart are separated by the *septum,* or dividing wall of tissue. The septum also includes the *atrioventricular node* (AV node), which, as will be explained later, plays a role in the electrical conduction through the cardiac muscles.

Each of the four chambers of the heart is different from the others because of its functions. The *right atrium* is elongated and lies between the inferior (lower) and superior (upper) vena cava. Its interior is complex, the anterior (front) wall being very rough, whereas the posterior (rear) wall

---

*Clinically, the *mm Hg* is still the unit used for blood pressure measurements. To convert to SI metric unit *kilopascals* (kPa), multiply the mm Hg figure by 0.133. Figure 5.5 has both scales, for comparison purposes. The *torr* is also a measure of pressure and is equivalent to the mm Hg.

Left common carotid artery

Brachiocephalic trunk

Left subclavian artery

Pulmonary trunk

Aorta

Superior vena cava

Left pulmonary artery

Right pulmonary artery

Left pulmonary veins

Right pulmonary veins

Left atrium

Aortic semilunar valve

Pulmonary semilunar valve

Bicuspid (left atrioventricular) valve

Right atrium

Tricuspid (right atrioventricular) valve

Left ventricle

Chordae tendinae

Papillary muscle

Inferior vena cava

Descending aorta

Right ventricle

(a)

Cardiac (cardioaccelerator nerves)

Vagus nerve (cardioinhibitor nerve)

Sinoatrial node (pacemaker)

Atrioventricular node

Bundle of His

Purkinje fibers

Right bundle branch

Left bundle branch

(b)

Figure 5.3. The heart: (a) internal structure; (b) conduction system. (From W.F. Evans, *Anatomy and Physiology, The Basic Principles,* Englewood Cliffs, N.J., Prentice-Hall, Inc., 1971, by permission.)

(which forms a part of the septum) and the remaining walls are smooth. At the junction of the right atrium and the superior vena cava is situated the *sinoatrial node* (SA node), which is the *pacemaker* or initiator of the electrical impulses that excite the heart. The *right ventricle* is situated below and to the left of the right atrium. They are separated by a fatty structure in which is contained the right branch of the coronary artery. This fatty separation is incapable of conducting electrical impulses; communication between the atria and the ventricles is accomplished only via the AV node and delay line.

Since the ventricle has to perform a more powerful pumping action, its walls are thicker than those of the atrium and its surfaces are ridged. Between the anterior wall of the ventricle and the septum is a muscular ridge that is part of the heart's electrical conduction system, known as the *bundle of His,* described in Section 3.3.1. At the junction of the right and left atrium and the right ventricle on the septum is another node, the atrioventricular node. The bundle of His is attached to this node.

The right atrium and right ventricle are joined by a fibrous tissue known as the *atrioventricular ring,* to which are attached the three cusps of the tricuspid valve, which is the connecting valve between the two chambers.

The *left atrium* is smaller than the right atrium. Entry to it is through four pulmonary veins. The walls of the chamber are fairly smooth. It is joined to the left ventricle through the *mitral valve,* sometimes called the *bicuspid* valve since it consists of two cusps.

The *left ventricle* is considered the most important chamber, for this is the power pump for all the systemic circulation. Its walls are approximately three times as thick as the walls of the right ventricle because of this function. Conduction to the left ventricle is through the left bundle branch, which is in the ventricular muscle on the septum side.

As mentioned earlier, the outputs from the ventricles are through the aortic and pulmonary valves, respectively, for left and right ventricles.

Some aspects of the electrical activity of the heart have already been discussed in Section 3.3, but certain details will be elaborated on in the present context.

Unlike most other muscle innervations, excitation of the heart does not proceed directly from the central nervous system but is initiated in the sinoatrial (SA) node, or pacemaker, a special group of excitable cells. The electrical events that occur within the heart are reflected in the electrocardiogram.

The SA node creates an impulse of electrical excitation that spreads across the right and left atria; the right atrium receives the earlier excitation because of its proximity to the SA node. This excitation causes the atria to contract and, a short time later, stimulates the atrioventricular (AV) node.

The activated AV node, after a brief delay, initiates an impulse into the ventricles, through the bundle of His, and into the bundle branches that connect to the *Purkinje fibers* in the myocardium. The contraction resulting in the myocardium supplies the force to pump the blood into the circulatory systems.

The heart rate is controlled by the frequency at which the SA node generates impulses. However, nerves of the sympathetic nervous system and the vagus nerve of the parasympathetic nervous system (see Chapter 10) cause the heart rate to quicken or slow down, respectively. Anatomically, the fibers of the sympathetic and vagus nerves enter the heart at the cardiac plexus under the arch of the aorta and are distributed quite profusely at and near both the SA and AV nodes. Vagal fibers are mostly found distributed in the atria, the bundle of His and branches, whereas the sympathetic fibers are found within the muscular walls of the atria and ventricles.

Although the effects of the sympathetic and vagus nerves are in opposition to each other, if they both occur together in opposite directions, the result is additive. That is, heart rate will increase from a combination of increased sympathetic activity concurrent with decreased vagal activity. The action of these nerves is called their *tone;* and by the various activities of each type of nerve, the rate of the heart, its coronary blood supply, and its contractability may be affected. The nerves affecting the rate of the heart in this way originate from the medullary centers in the brain and are controlled both by cardiac acceleration and by inhibition centers, each being sensitive to stimulation from higher centers of the brain. It is in this sequence that the heart rate is affected when a person is anxious, frightened, or excited. Heart attacks may be caused by this type of stimulation. The heart rate can also be affected, but in a more indirect way, by overeating, respiration problems, extremes of body temperature, and blood changes.

One other effect that should be mentioned is that of the *pressoreceptors* or *baroreceptors* situated in the arch of the aorta and in the carotid sinus. Their function is to alter the vagal tone whenever the blood pressure within the aorta or carotid sinus changes. When blood pressure rises, vagal tone is increased and the heart rate slows; when blood pressure falls, vagal tone is decreased and the heart rate increases.

A good engineering analog is illustrated in Figure 5.4, which shows the physiological system as a pump model. The pump is initially set to operate under predetermined conditions, as are the valves representing the resistance in the various organs. The pressure transducers sense the pressure continuously. With the pressure head set at some normal level, if one of the valves opens farther to obtain greater flow in that branch, the pressure head will decrease. This is picked up as a lower pressure by the sensors, which feed a signal to the controller, which, in turn, closes other valves, speeds up the pump, or does both in order to try to maintain a constant pressure head.

CONTROL OF ARTERIAL BLOOD PRESSURE

Figure 5.4 Control of arterial blood pressure. (From
R.F. Rushmer, *Cardiovascular Dynamics,* 3rd ed.,
W.B. Saunders Co., 1970, by permission.)

5.3. BLOOD PRESSURE

In the arterial system of the body, the large pressure variations from
systole to diastole are smoothed into a relatively steady flow through the
peripheral vessels into the capillaries. This system, with some modifications, obeys the simple physical laws of hydrodynamics. As an analog, the
potential (blood pressure) acting through the resistance of the arterial
vascular pathways causes flow throughout the system. The resistance must
not be so great as to impede flow, so that even the most remote capillaries
receive sufficent blocd and are able to return it into the venous system. On
the other hand, the vessels of the system must be capable of damping out
any large pressure fluctuations.

Since the system must be capable of maintaining an adequate pressure
head while controlling flow, monitoring and feedback control loops are required. Demand on the system comes from various sources, such as from
the gastrointestinal tract after a large meal or from the skeletal muscles during exercise. The result is vascular dilation at these particular points. If sufficient demands were to occur simultaneously so that increased blood flow

were needed in many parts of the body, the blood pressure would drop. In this way, flow to the vital regions of heart and brain might be affected. Fortunately, however, the body is equipped with a monitoring system that can sense systemic arterial blood pressure and can compensate in the cardiovascular operations. Pressure is therefore maintained within a relatively narrow range, and the flow is kept within the normal range of the heart.

With regard to measurements, the events in the heart that relate to the blood pressure as a function of time should be understood. Figure 5.5 illustrates this point. The two basic stages of diastole and systole are shown with a more detailed time scale of phases of operation below. The blood pressure waves for the aorta, the left atrium, and the left ventricle are drawn to show time and magnitude relationships. Also, the correlated electrical events are shown at the bottom in the form of the electrocardiogram, and the basic relationship of the heart sounds, which are discussed in Section 5.5, are shown in Figure 5.8.

Examining the aortic wave, it can be seen that during systole, the ejection of blood from the left ventricle is rapid at first. As the rate of pressure change decreases, the rounded maximum of the curve is obtained. The peak aortic pressure during systole is a function of left ventricular stroke volume, the peak rate of ejection, and the distensibility of the walls of the aorta. In a diseased heart, ventricular contractability and rigid atherosclerotic arteries produce unwanted rises in blood pressure.

When the systolic period is completed, the aortic valve is closed by the back pressure of blood (against the valve). This effect can be seen on the pressure pulse waveform as the *dicrotic notch*. When the valve is closed completely, the arterial pressure gradually decreases as blood pours into the countless peripheral vascular networks. The rate at which the pressure falls is determined by the pressure achieved during the systolic interval, the rate of outflow through the peripheral resistances, and the diastolic interval.

The form of the arterial pressure pulse changes as it passes through the arteries. The walls of the arteries cause damping and reflections; and as the arteries branch out into smaller arteries with smaller cross-sectional areas, the pressures and volumes change, hence the rate of flow also changes. The peak systolic pressure gets a little higher and the diastolic pressure flatter. The mean pressure in some arteries (e.g., the brachial artery) can be as much as 20 mm Hg higher than that in the aorta.

As the blood flows into the smaller arteries and arterioles, the pressure decreases and loses its oscillatory character. Pressure in the arterioles can vary from about 60 mm Hg down to 30 mm Hg. As the blood enters the venous system after flowing through the capillaries, the pressure is down to about 15 mm Hg.

In the venous system, the pressure in the venules decreases to approximately 8 mm Hg, and in the veins to about 5 mm Hg. In the vena cava, the

Figure 5.5. Blood pressure variations as a function of time. (Note: S.I. metric scale on right ordinate.)

pressure is only about 2 mm Hg. Because of these differences in pressure, measurement of arterial blood pressure is quite different from that of venous pressure. For example, a 2-mm Hg error in systolic pressure is only of the order of 1.5 percent. In a vein, however, this would be a 100 percent error. Also because of these pressure differences, the arteries have thick walls, while the veins have thin walls. Moreover, the veins have larger internal diameters. Since about 75 to 80 percent of the blood volume is contained in the venous system, the veins tend to serve as a reservoir for the body's blood supply.

Occipital

External carotid

Internal carotid

Right common carotid

Brachiocephalic

Arch of aorta

Right coronary

Aorta

Celiac

Superior mesenteric

Common iliac

Internal iliac

External iliac

Deep femoral

Popliteal

Posterior tibial

Left common carotid

Left subclavion

Pulmonary

Axillary

Brachial

Left coronary

Splenic

Renal

Inferior mesenteric

Radial

Ulnar

Palmar arch deep superficial

Digital

Femoral

Anterior tibial

Peroneal

Dorsal metatarsal

Dorsal pedis

Arcuate

(a)

Labels on figure (left side, top to bottom):
External jugular
Internal jugular
Right brachiocephalic
Superior vena cava
Azygos
Inferior vena cava
Hepatic
Renal
Common iliac
Middle sacral
External iliac
Internal iliac
Femoral
Great saphenous
Small saphenous
Popliteal
Posterior tibial
Anterior tibial

Labels on figure (right side, top to bottom):
Superficial temporal
Facial vein
Subclavian
Left internal mammary
Axillary
Brachial
Basilic
Intercostal
Phrenic
Suprarenal
Spermatic
Lumbar
Radial
Cephalic
Ulnar
Basilic

(b)

Figure 5.6. (a) Major arteries of the body; (b) major veins of the body. (From W.F. Evans, *Anatomy and Physiology, The Basic Principles,* Englewood Cliffs, N.J., Prentice-Hall, Inc., 1971, by permission.)

A summary of the dimensions, blood flow velocities, and blood pressures at major points in the cardiovascular system is shown in Table 5.1. The figures are typical or average for comparative reference. The complete arterial and venous systems are shown in Figure 5.6.

Table 5.1. CARDIOVASCULAR SYSTEM-TYPICAL VALUES

Vessel	Number (thousands)	Diameter (mm)	Length (mm)	Mean Velocity (cm/sec)	Pressure (mm Hg)
Aorta	—	10.50	400	40.0	100
Terminal arteries	1.8	0.60	10	<10.0	40
Arterioles	40,000	0.02	2	0.5	40–25
Capillaries	> million	0.008	1	<0.1	25–12
Venules	80,000	0.03	2	<0.3	12–8
Terminal veins	1.8	1.50	100	1.0	<8
Vena cava	—	12.50	400	20.0	3–2

5.4. CHARACTERISTICS OF BLOOD FLOW

The blood flow at any point in the circulatory system is the volume of blood that passes that point during a unit of time. It is normally measured in milliliters per minute or liters per minute. Blood flow is highest in the pulmonary artery and the aorta, where these blood vessels leave the heart. The flow at these points, called *cardiac output,* is between 3.5 and 5 liters/min in a normal adult at rest. In the capillaries, on the other hand, the blood flow can be so slow that the travel of individual blood cells can be observed under a microscope.

From the cardiac output or the blood flow in a given vessel, a number of other characteristic variables can be calculated. The cardiac output divided by the number of heartbeats per minute gives the amount of blood that is ejected during each heartbeat, or the *stroke volume.* If the total amount of blood in circulation is known, and this volume is divided by the cardiac output, the *mean circulation time* is obtained. From the blood flow through a vessel, divided by the cross-sectional area of the vessel, the *mean velocity* of the blood at the point of measurement can be calculated.

In the arteries, blood flow is pulsatile. In fact, in some blood vessels a reversal of the flow can occur during certain parts of the heartbeat cycle. Because of the elasticity of their walls, the blood vessels tend to smooth out the pulsations of blood flow and blood pressure. Both pressure and flow are greatest in the aorta, where the blood leaves the heart.

Blood flow is a function of the blood pressure and flow resistance of the blood vessels in the same way as electrical current flow depends on voltage and resistance. The flow resistance of the capillary bed, however, can vary over a wide range. For instance, when exposed to low temperatures or under the influence of certain drugs (e.g., nicotine), the body reduces the blood flow through the skin by *vasoconstriction* (narrowing) of the capillaries. Heat, excitement, or local inflammation, among other things, can cause *vasodilation* (widening) of the capillaries, which increases the blood flow, at least locally. Because of the wide variations that are possible in the flow resistance, the determination of blood pressure alone is not sufficient to assess the status of the circulatory system.

The velocity of blood flowing through a vessel is not constant throughout the cross section of the vessel but is a function of the distance from the wall surfaces. A thin layer of blood actually adheres to the wall, resulting in zero velocity at this place, whereas the highest velocity occurs at the center of the vessel. The resulting "velocity profile" is shown in Figure 5.7. Some blood flow meters do not actually measure the blood flow but measure the mean velocity of the blood. If, however, the cross-sectional area of the blood vessel is known, these devices can be calibrated directly in terms of blood flow.

If the local blood velocity exceeds a certain limit (as may happen when a blood vessel is constricted), small eddies can occur, and the *laminar flow* of Figure 5.7 changes to a *turbulent flow* pattern, for which the flow rate is more difficult to determine.

The proper functioning of all body organs depends on an adequate blood supply. If the blood supply to an organ is reduced by a narrowing of the blood vessels, the function of that organ can be severely limited. When the blood flow in a certain vessel is completely obstructed (e.g., by a blood clot or *thrombus*), the tissue in the area supplied by this vessel may die. Such an obstruction in a blood vessel of the brain is one of the causes of a *cerebrovascular accident* (CVA) or *stroke*. An obstruction of part of the

Figure 5.7. Laminar flow in a blood vessel.

coronary arteries that supply blood for the heart muscle is called a *myocar-dial* (or *coronary*) *infarct* or *heart attack,* whereas merely a reduced flow in the coronary vessels can cause a severe chest pain called *angina pectoris.* A blood clot in a vessel in the lung is called an *embolism.* Blood clots can also afflict the circulation in the lower extremities (*thrombosis*). Although the foregoing events afflict only a limited, although often vital, area of the body, the total circulatory system can also be affected. Such is the case if the cardiac output, the amount of blood pumped by the heart, is greatly reduced. This situation can be due to a mechanical malfunction such as a leaking or torn heart valve. It can also occur as *shock* — for example, after a severe injury when the body reacts with vasoconstriction of the capillaries, which reduces the blood loss but also prevents the blood from returning to the heart.

Most of these events have severe, and often fatal, results. Therefore, it is of great interest to be able to determine the blood flow in such cases to provide an early diagnosis and begin treatment before irreparable tissue damage has occurred.

5.5. HEART SOUNDS

For centuries the medical profession has been aided in its diagnosis of certain types of heart disorders by the sounds and vibrations associated with the beating of the heart and the pumping of blood. The technique of listening to sounds produced by the organs and vessels of the body is called *auscultation,* and it is still in common use today. During his training the physician learns to recognize sounds or changes in sounds that he can associate with various types of disorders.

In spite of its widespread use, however, auscultation is rather subjective, and the amount of information that can be obtained by listening to the sounds of the heart depends largely on the skill, experience, and hearing ability of the physician. Different physicians may hear the same sounds differently, and perhaps interpret them differently.

The heart sounds heard by the physician through his stethoscope actually occur at the time of closure of major valves in the heart. This timing could easily lead to the false assumption that the sounds which are heard are primarily caused by the snapping together of the vanes of these valves. In reality, this snapping action produces almost no sound, because of the cushioning effect of the blood. The principal cause of heart sounds seems to be vibrations set up in the blood inside the heart by the sudden closure of the valves. These vibrations, together with eddy currents induced in the blood as it is forced through the closing valves, produce vibrations in the walls of the heart chambers and in the adjoining blood vessels.

With each heartbeat, the normal heart produces two distinct sounds that are audible in the stethoscope—often described as "lub-dub." The "lub" is caused by the closure of the *atrioventricular valves,* which permit flow of blood from the atria into the ventricles but prevent flow in the reverse direction. Normally, this is called the *first heart sound,* and it occurs approximately at the time of the QRS complex of the electrocardiogram and just before ventricular systole. The "dub" part of the heart sounds is called the *second heart sound* and is caused by the closing of the *semilunar valves,* which release blood into the pulmonary and systemic circulation systems. These valves close at the end of systole, just before the atrioventricular valves reopen. This second heart sound occurs about the time of the end of the T wave of the electrocardiogram.

A *third heart sound* is sometimes heard, especially in young adults. This sound, which occurs from 0.1 to 0.2 sec. after the second heart sound, is attributed to the rush of blood from the atria into the ventricles, which causes turbulence and some vibration of the ventricular walls. This sound actually precedes atrial contraction, which means that the inrush of blood to the ventricles causing this sound is passive, pushed only by the venous pressure at the inlets to the atria. Actually, about 70 percent of blood flow into the ventricles occurs before atrial contraction.

An *atrial heart sound,* which is not audible but may be visible on a graphic recording, occurs when the atria actually do conract, squeezing the remainder of the blood into the ventricles. The inaudibility of this heart sound is a result of the low amplitude and low frequency of the vibrations.

Figure 5.8 shows the time relationships between the first, second, and third heart sounds with respect to the electrocardiogram, and the various pressure waveforms. Opening and closing times of valves are also shown. This figure should also be compared with Figure 5.5.

In abnormal hearts additional sounds, called *murmurs,* are heard between the normal heart sounds. Murmurs are generally caused either by improper opening of the valves (which requires the blood to be forced through a small aperture) or by regurgitation, which results when the valves do not close completely and allow some backward flow of blood. In either case, the sound is due to high-velocity blood flow through a small opening. Another cause of murmurs can be a small opening in the septum, which separates the left and right sides of the heart. In this case, pressure differences between the two sides of the heart force blood through the opening, usually from the left ventricle into the right ventricle, bypassing the systemic circulation.

Normal heart sounds are quite short in duration, approximately one-tenth of a second for each, while murmurs usually extend between the normal sounds. Figure 5.9 shows a record of normal heart sounds and several types of murmurs.

There is also a difference in frequency range between normal and ab-

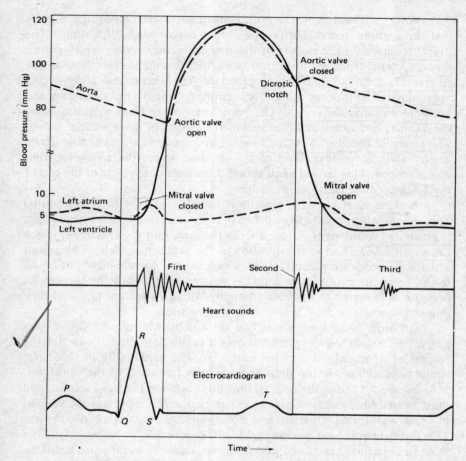

Figure 5.8. Relationship of heart sounds to function of the cardiovascular system.

normal heart sounds. The first heart sound is composed primarily of energy in the 30- to 45-Hz range, with much of the sound below the threshold of audibility. The second heart sound is usually higher in pitch than the first, with maximum energy in the 50- to 70-Hz range. The third heart sound is an extremely weak vibration, with most of its energy at or below 30 Hz. Murmurs, on the other hand, often produce much higher pitched sounds. One particular type of regurgitation, for example, causes a murmur in the 100-to 600-Hz range.

Although auscultation is still the principal method of detecting and analyzing heart sounds, other techniques are also often employed. For example, a graphic recording of heart sounds, such as shown in Figure 5.8, is called a *phonocardiogram*. Even though the phonocardiogram is a graphic record like the electrocardiogram, it extends to a much higher frequency range. ~~diff.~~

An entirely different waveform is produced by the vibrations of the heart against the thoracic cavity. The vibrations of the side of the heart as it thumps against the chest wall form the *vibrocardiogram,* whereas the tip or apex of the heart hitting the rib cage produces the *apex cardiogram.*

Sounds and pulsations can also be detected and measured at various locations in the systemic arterial circulation system where major arteries approach the surface of the body. The most common one is the *pulse,* which can be felt with the fingertips at certain points on major arteries. The waveform of this pulse can also be measured and recorded. In addition, when an artery is partially occluded so that the blood velocity through the constriction is increased sufficiently, identifiable sounds can be heard downstream through a stethoscope. These sounds, called *Korotkoff sounds,* are used in the common method of blood pressure measurements and are discussed in detail in Chapter 6.

Another cardiovascular measurement worthy of note is the *ballistocardiogram.* Although not a heart sound or vibration measurement

Figure 5.9. Normal and abnormal heart sounds. (From A.C. Guyton, *Textbook of Medical Physiology,* 4th ed., W.B. Saunders Co., 1971, by permission.)

of the type described earlier, the ballistocardiogram is related to these measures in that it is a direct result of the dynamic forces of the heart as it beats and pumps blood into the major arteries. The beating heart exerts certain forces on the body as it goes through its sequence of motions. As in any situation involving forces, the body responds, but because of the greater mass of the body, these responses are generally not noticeable. However, when a person is placed on a platform that is free to move with these small dynamic responses, the motions of the body due to the beating of the heart and the corresponding blood ejection can be measured and recorded to produce the ballistocardiogram. Like the vibrocardiogram and the apex cardiogram, the ballistocardiogram provides information about the heart that cannot be obtained by any other measurement.

6

Cardiovascular Measurements

To this point the reader has been exposed to the overall concepts of the biomedical instrumentation system, some basic descriptions of component parts, and a description of the cardiovascular physiology. The next step is to combine this information and study measurement of a major body system.

It is not by accident that the cardiovascular system has been chosen as the first of the major physiological measurement groupings to be studied. Instrumentation for obtaining measurements from this system has contributed greatly to advances in medical diagnosis.

Since such instrumentation includes devices to measure various types of physiological variables, such as electrical, mechanical, thermal, fluid, and auditory, this chapter is intended to provide a basis for studying all types of biomedical instrumentation. Each type of measurement is considered separately, beginning with the measurement of biopotentials that result in the electrocardiogram. Then the various methods, both direct and indirect, of measuring blood pressure, blood flow, cardiac output, and blood volume (plethysmography) are discussed. The final section is concerned with the measurement of heart sounds and vibrations.

It should be noted that some of the methods discussed in this chapter involve *noninvasive techniques,* measurements that can be made without "invading" the body. Some of these techniques are included in this chapter under cardiovascular methods to keep them in that perspective. Others are covered in Chapter 9.

6.1. ELECTROCARDIOGRAPHY

The *electrocardiogram* (ECG or EKG) is a graphic recording or display of the time-variant voltages produced by the myocardium during the cardiac cycle. Figure 6.1 shows the basic waveform of the normal electrocardiogram. The P, QRS, and T waves reflect the rhythmic electrical depolarization and repolarization of the myocardium associated with the contractions of the atria and ventricles. The electrocardiogram is used clinically in diagnosing various diseases and conditions associated with the heart. It also serves as a timing reference for other measurements.

A discussion of the ECG waveform has already been presented in Section 3.2 and will not be repeated here, except in the concept of measurement details. To the clinician, the shape and duration of each feature of the ECG are significant. The waveform, however, depends greatly upon the lead configuration used, as discussed below. In general, the cardiologist looks critically at the various time intervals, polarities, and amplitudes to arrive at his diagnosis.

Some normal values for amplitudes and durations of important ECG parameters are as follows:

Amplitude:	P	wave	0.25 mV
	R	wave	1.60 mV
	Q	wave	25% of R wave
	T	wave	0.1 to 0.5 mV

Duration:	P-R	interval	0.12 to 0.20 sec
	Q-T	interval	0.35 to 0.44 sec
	S-T	segment	0.05 to 0.15 sec
	P	wave interval	0.11 sec
	QRS	interval	0.09 sec

For his diagnosis, a cardiologist would typically look first at the heart rate. The normal value lies in the range of 60 to 100 beats per minute. A slower rate than this is called *bradycardia* (slow heart) and a higher rate, *tachycardia* (fast heart). He would then see if the cycles are evenly spaced. If

Figure 6.1. The electrocardiogram in detail.

not, an *arrhythmia* may be indicated. If the P-R interval is greater than 0.2 second, it can suggest blockage of the AV node. If one or more of the basic features of the ECG should be missing, a heart block of some sort might be indicated.

In healthy individuals the electrocardiogram remains reasonably constant, even though the heart rate changes with the demands of the body. It should be noted that the position of the heart within the thoracic region of the body, as well as the position of the body itself (whether erect or recumbent), influences the "electrical axis" of the heart. The *electrical axis* (which parallels the anatomical axis) is defined as the line along which the greatest electromotive force is developed at a given instant during the cardiac cycle. The electrical axis shifts continually through a repeatable pattern during every cardiac cycle.

Under pathological conditions, several changes may occur in the ECG. These include (1) altered paths of excitation in the heart, (2) changed origin of waves (ectopic beats), (3) altered relationships (sequences) of features, (4) changed magnitudes of one or more features, and (5) differing durations of waves or intervals.

As mentioned earlier, an instrument used to obtain and record the electrocardiogram is called an *electrocardiograph*. The electrocardiograph was the first electrical device to find widespread use in medical diagnostics, and it still remains the most important tool for the diagnosis of cardiac disorders. Although it provides invaluable diagnostic information, especially in the case of arrhythmias and myocardial infarction, certain disorders—for instance, those involving the heart valves—cannot be diagnosed from the electrocardiogram. Other diagnostic techniques, however, such as angiography (Chapter 14) and echocardiography (Chapter 9), can provide the information not available in the electrocardiogram. The first electrocardiographs appeared in hospitals around 1910, and while ECG machines have benefited from technological innovations over the years, little has actually changed in the basic technique. Most of the terminology and several of the methods still employed date back to the early days of electrocardiography and can be understood best in an historical context.

6.1.1 History

The discovery that muscle contractions involve electrical processes dates to the eighteenth century. At that time, however, the technology was not advanced enough to allow a quantitative study of the electrical voltages generated by the contracting heart muscle. It was not until 1887 that the first electrocardiogram was recorded by Waller, who used the *capillary electrometer* introduced by Lippman in 1875. This device consisted of a mercury-filled glass capillary immersed in dilute sulfuric acid. The position of the meniscus, which formed the dividing line between the two fluids, changed when an electrical voltage was applied between the mercury and acid. This movement was very small, but it could be recorded on a moving piece of light-sensitive paper or film with the help of a magnifying optical projection system. The capillary electrometer, however, was cumbersome to operate and the inertia of the mercury column limited its frequency range.

The string galvanometer, which was introduced to electrocardiography by Einthoven in 1903, was a considerable improvement. It consisted of an extremely thin platinum wire or a gold-plated quartz fiber, about 5 μm thick, suspended in the air gap of a strong electromagnet. An electrical current flowing through the string caused movement of the string perpendicular to the direction of the magnetic field. The magnitude of the movement was small but could be magnified several hundred times by an optical projection system for recording on a moving film or paper. The small mass of the moving fiber resulted in a frequency response sufficiently high for the faithful recording of the electrocardiogram. The sensitivity of the galvanometer could be adjusted by changing the mechanical tension on the string. To measure the sensitivity of the galvanometer, a standardization switch allowed a calibration voltage of 1 mV to be connected to the galvanometer terminals. Modern electrocardiographs, although they have a calibrated sensitivity, still retain this feature. The string galvanometer had dc response, and a difference in the contact potentials of the electrodes could easily drive the string off scale. A compensation voltage, adjustable in magnitude and polarity, was provided to center the shadow of the string on a ground-glass screen prior to recording the electrocardiogram. To facilitate measurement of the time differences between the characteristic parts of the ECG waveform, time marks were provided on the film by a wheel with five spokes driven by a constant-speed motor.

String galvanometer electrocardiographs like the one shown in Figure 4.4 were used until about 1920, when they were replaced by devices incorporating electronic amplification. This allowed the use of less sensitive and more rugged recording devices. Early ECG machines incorporating amplification used the Dudell oscillograph as a recorder. This oscillograph was similar in design to the string galvanometer but had the single string replaced by a hairpin-shaped wire stretched between two fixed terminals and a spring-loaded support pulley. A small mirror cemented across the two legs of the hairpin wire was rotated when a current (the amplified ECG signal) flowed through the wire. The mirror was used to deflect a narrow light beam, throwing a small light spot on a moving film. While recording systems of this type are mechanically more rugged than the fragile string galvanometers, they still require photosensitive film or paper which has to be processed before the electrocardiogram can be read.

This disadvantage was overcome with the introduction of direct-writing recorders (about 1946), which used ink or the transfer of pigment from a ribbon to record the ECG trace on a moving paper strip, where it was immediately visible without processing. Later, a special heat-sensitive paper was developed. This type of paper is now used almost exclusively as a recording medium for electrocardiograms. Basically, the pen motor of such a recorder has a meter movement with a writing tip at the end of the indicator. Because this type of indicator naturally moves in a circular path, special measures are required to convert this motion to a straight line when a *rectilinear* rather than a *curvilinear* recording is desired.

The higher mass of moving parts used in direct-writing pen motors makes their frequency response inherently inferior to that of optical recording systems. Despite this handicap, modern direct-writing electrocardiographs have a frequency range extending to over 100 Hz, which is completely adequate for clinical ECG recordings. An improvement in performance over that of older direct-writing recorders can be partially attributed to the use of servo techniques in which the actual position of the pen is electrically sensed and the pen motor is included as part of a servo loop. For these reasons optical recording methods are seldom used in modern electrocardiographs.

6.1.2. ECG Amplifiers

The early string galvanometer had the advantage that it could easily be isolated from ground. Thus, the potential difference between two electrodes on the patient could be measured with less electrical interference than can be done with a grounded system. Electronic amplifiers, however, are normally referenced to ground through their power supplies. This creates an interference problem (unless special measures are taken) when such amplifiers are used to measure small bioelectric potentials. The technique usually employed, not only in electrocardiography but also in the measurement of other bioelectric signals, is the use of a *differential amplifier*. The principle of the differential amplifier can be explained with the help of Figure 6.2.

A differential amplifier can be considered as two amplifiers with separate inputs [Figure 6.2 (a)], but with a common output terminal, which

Figure 6.2. The differential amplifier: (a) represented as two amplifiers with separate inputs and common output; (b) as used for amplification of bioelectric signals (see text for explanation.)

delivers the sum of the two amplifier output voltages. Both amplifiers have the same voltage gain, but one amplifier is inverting (output voltage is 180° out of phase with respect to the input) while the other is noninverting (input and output voltages are in phase). If the two amplifier inputs are connected to the same input source, the resulting *common-mode gain* should be zero, because the signals from the inverting and the noninverting amplifiers cancel each other at the common output. However, because the gain of the two amplifiers is not exactly equal, this cancellation is not complete. Rather, a small residual common-mode output remains. When one of the amplifier inputs is grounded and a voltage is applied only to the other amplifier input, the input voltage appears at the output amplified by the gain of the amplifier. This gain is called the *differential gain* of the differential amplifier. The ratio of the differential gain to the common-mode gain is called the ***common-mode rejection ratio*** of the differential amplifier, which in modern amplifiers can be as high as 1,000,000:1.

When a differential amplifier is used to measure bioelectric signals that occur as a potential difference between two electrodes, as shown in Figure 6.2(b), the bioelectric signals are applied between the inverting and noninverting inputs of the amplifier. The signal is therefore amplified by the differential gain of the amplifier. For the interference signal, however, both inputs appear as though they were connected together to a common input source. Thus, the common-mode interference signal is amplified only by the much smaller common-mode gain.

Figure 6.2(b) also illustrates another interesting point. The electrode impedances, R_{e+} and R_{e-}, each form a voltage divider with the input impedance of the differential amplifier. If the electrode impedances are not identical, the interference signals at the inverting and noninverting inputs of the differential amplifier may be different, and the desired degree of cancellation does not take place. Because the electrode impedances can never be made exactly equal, the high common-mode rejection ratio of a differential amplifier can only be realized if the amplifier has an input impedance much higher than the impedance of the electrodes to which it is connected. As indicated in the figure, this input impedance may not be the same for the differential signal as it is for the common-mode signal. The use of a differential amplifier also requires a third connection for the reference or grouped input.

6.1.3. Electrodes and Leads

To record an electrocardiogram, a number of electrodes, usually five, are affixed to the body of the patient. The electrodes are connected to the ECG machine by the same number of electrical wires. These wires and, in a more general sense, the electrodes to which they are connected are usually called *leads*. The electrode applied to the right leg of the patient, for example, is called the RL lead. For the recording of the electrocardiogram, two electrodes or one electrode and an interconnected group of electrodes are selected and connected to the input of the recording amplifier. It is somewhat confusing that the particular electrodes selected and the way in which they are connected are also referred to as a lead. To avoid this ambiguity, in this book the term *lead* will be used only to indicate a particular group of electrodes and the way in which they are connected to the amplifier. For the individual lead wire, as well as the physical connection to the body of the patient, the term *electrode* will be used. The reader, however, should be aware of the double meaning that the term "lead" can have in normal usage.

The voltage generated by the pumping action of the heart is actually a vector whose magnitude, as well as spatial orientation, changes with time. Because the ECG signal is measured from electrodes applied to the surface of the body, the waveform of this signal is very dependent on the placement of the electrodes. Figure 6.1 shows a typical ECG waveform. Some of the segments of this trace may, however, almost disappear for certain electrode placements, whereas others may show up clearly on the recording. For this reason, in a normal electrocardiographic examination, the electrocardiogram is recorded from a number of different leads, usually 12, to ensure that no important detail of the waveform is missed. Placement of electrodes and names and configurations of the leads have become standardized and are used the same way throughout the world.

6.1.3.1. Electrodes. The placement of the electrodes, as well as the color code used to identify each electrode, is shown in Figure 6.3. In his experiments Einthoven had found it advantageous to record the electrocardiogram from electrodes placed vertically as well as horizontally on the body. As shown in Figure 4.4, he had his patients place not only both arms but also one leg into the earthenware crocks used as immersion electrodes.

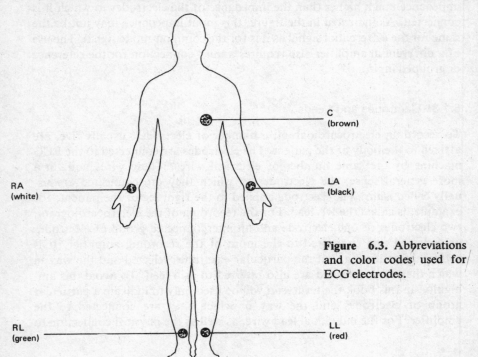

Figure 6.3. Abbreviations and color codes used for ECG electrodes.

The leg selected was the left one, probably because it terminates vertically below the heart. The early electrocardiograph machines thus employed three electrodes, of which only two were used at one time. With the introduction of the electronic amplifier, an additional connection to the body was needed as a ground reference. Although an electrode could have been positioned almost anywhere on the body for this purpose, it became a convention to use the "free" right leg.

Chest or *precordial electrodes* were introduced later. Although plate electrodes are normally used for the electrodes at the extremities, the chest electrode is often the suction type shown in Figure 4.6. It should be noted that abbreviations referring to the extremities are used to identify the electrodes even when they are actually placed on the chest, as in the case of the patient-monitoring applications described in Chapter 7.

6.1.3.2. Leads. In the normal electrode placement shown in Figure 6.3, four electrodes are used to record the electrocardiogram; the electrode on the right leg is only for ground reference. Because the input of the ECG recorder has only two terminals, a selection must be made among the available active electrodes. The 12 standard leads used most frequently are shown in Figure 6.4. The three *bipolar limb lead* selections first introduced by Einthoven, shown in the top row of the figure, are as follows:

Lead I: Left Arm (LA) and Right Arm (RA)
Lead II: Left Leg (LL) and Right Arm (RA)
Lead III: Left Leg (LL) and Left Arm (LA)

These three leads are called *bipolar* because for each lead the electrocardiogram is recorded from two electrodes and the third electrode is not connected.

In each of these lead positions, the QRS of a normal heart is such that the R wave is positive.

In working with electrocardiograms from these three basic limb leads, Einthoven postulated that at any given instant of the cardiac cycle, the frontal plane representation of the electrical axis of the heart is a two-dimensional vector. Further, the ECG measured from any one of the three basic limb leads is a time-variant single-dimensional component of that vector. Einthoven also made the assumption that the heart (the origin of the vector) is near the center of an equilateral triangle, the apexes of which are the right and left shoulder and the crotch. By assuming that the ECG potentials at the shoulders are essentially the same as the wrists and that the potentials at the crotch differ little from those at either ankle, he let the points of this triangle represent the electrode positions for the three limb leads. This triangle, known as the *Einthoven triangle,* is shown in Figure 6.5.

Bipolar limb leads

Lead I   Lead II   Lead III

(Augmented) Unipolar limb leads

Lead aVR   Lead aVL   Lead aVF

V_1 Fourth intercostal space, at right sternal margin.

V_2 Fourth intercostal space, at left sternal margin.

V_3 Midway between V_2 and V_4.

V_4 Fifth intercostal space, at mid-clavicular line.

V_5 Same level as V_4, on anterior axillary line.

V_6 Same level as V_4, on mid-axillary line.

Unipolar chest leads

$V_1 - V_6$

Figure 6.4. ECG lead configurations.

The sides of the triangle represent the lines along which the three projections of the ECG vector are measured. Based on this, Einthoven showed that the instantaneous voltage measured from any one of the three limb lead positions is approximately equal to the algebraic sum of the other two, or

Figure 6.5. The Einthoven Triangle.

that the vector sum of the projections on all three lines is equal to zero. For these statements to actually hold true, the polarity of the lead II measurement must be reversed.

Of the three limb leads, lead II produces the greatest R-wave potential. Thus, when the amplitudes of the three limb leads are measured, the R-wave amplitude of lead II is equal to the sum of the R-wave amplitudes of leads I and III.

The other leads shown in Figure 6.4 are of the *unipolar* type, which was introduced by Wilson in 1944. For unipolar leads, the electrocardiogram is recorded between a single *exploratory electrode* and the *central terminal,* which has a potential corresponding to the center of the body. This central terminal is obtained by connecting the three active limb electrodes together through resistors of equal size. The potential at the connection point of the resistors corresponds to the mean or average of the potentials at the three electrodes. In the *unipolar limb leads,* one of the limb electrodes is used as an exploratory electrode as well as contributing to the central terminal. This double use results in an ECG signal that has a very small amplitude. In *augmented unipolar limb leads,* the limb electrode used as an exploratory electrode is not used for the central terminal, thereby increasing the amplitude of the ECG signal without changing its waveform appreciably. These leads are designated aVR, aVL, and aVF (F as in foot).

For the *unipolar chest leads,* a single chest electrode (exploring electrode) is sequentially placed on each of the six predesignated points on the chest. These chest positions are called the *precordial unipolar* leads and are designated V_1 through V_6. These leads are diagrammed in the lower part of Figure 6.4. All three active limb electrodes are used to obtain the central terminal, while a separate chest electrode is used as an exploratory electrode.

The electrocardiograms recorded from these 12 lead selections are shown in Figure 6.6. It can be seen that the trace from lead selection I or II resembles most closely the idealized waveform of Figure 6.1; some of the other traces are quite different in appearance.

Figure 6.6. Typical patient ECG.

Figure 6.6. Continued

In addition to the lead systems already discussed, there are certain additional lead modifications that are of considerable use in the coronary care unit. The most widely used modification for ongoing ECG monitoring is the *modified chest lead I* (MCL₁) also called the *Marriott lead,* named after its inventor. This lead system simulates the V₁ position with electrode placement as follows: positive electrode, fourth intercostal space, right sternal border; negative electrode just below the outer portion of the left clavicle, with ground just about anywhere, but usually below the right clavicle. The monitor is set on lead I for this bipolar tracing. Recordings obtained in this way are very useful in differentiating left ventricular ectopic rhythms from aberrant right ventricular or supraventricular rhythms. The former situation usually necessitates prompt therapeutic action; the latter is of less clinical significance.

6.1.4. ECG Recorder Principles

The principal parts or building blocks of an ECG recorder are shown in Figure 6.7. Also shown are the controls usually found on ECG recorders; the dashed lines indicate the building block with which each control interacts.

The connecting wires for the patient electrodes originate at the end of a *patient cable,* the other end of which plugs into the ECG recorder. The wires from the electrodes connect to the *lead selector switch,* which also incorporates the resistors necessary for the unipolar leads. A pushbutton

Figure 6.7. Electrocardiograph building blocks.

118

allows the insertion of a *standardization* voltage of 1 mV to standardize or calibrate the recorder. Although modern recorders are stable and their sensitivity does not change with time, the ritual of inserting the standardization pulse before or after each recording when recording a 12-lead ECG is still followed. Changing the setting of the lead selector switch introduces an artifact on the recorded trace. A special contact on the lead selector switch turns off the amplifier momentarily whenever this switch is moved and turns it on again after the artifact has passed. From the lead selector switch the ECG signal goes to a *preamplifier,* a differential amplifier with high common-mode rejection. It is ac-coupled to avoid problems with small dc voltages that may originate from polarization of the electrodes. The preamplifier also provides a switch to set the *sensitivity* or *gain.* Older ECG machines also have a continuously variable sensitivity adjustment, sometimes marked *standardization adjustment.* By means of this adjustment, the sensitivity of the ECG recorder can be set so that the standardization voltage of 1 mV causes a pen deflection of 10 mm. In modern amplifiers the gain usually remains stable once adjusted, so the continuously variable gain control is now frequently a screwdriver adjustment at the side or rear of the ECG recorder.

The preamplifier is followed by a dc amplifier called the *pen amplifier,* which provides the power to drive the *pen motor* that records the actual ECG trace. The input of the pen amplifier is usually accessible separately, with a special *auxiliary input* jack at the rear or side of the ECG recorder. Thus, the ECG recorder can be used to record the output of other devices, such as the *electromotograph,* which records the Achilles reflex. A *position* control on the pen amplifier makes it possible to center the pen on the recording paper. All modern ECG recorders use heat-sensitive paper, and the pen is actually an electrically heated *stylus,* the temperature of which can be adjusted with a *stylus heat control* for optimal recording trace. Beside the recording stylus, there is a *marker* stylus that can be actuated by a pushbutton and allows the operator to mark a coded indication of the lead being recorded at the margin of the electrocardiogram. Normally, electrocardiograms are recorded at a paper speed of 25 mm/s, but a faster speed of 50 mm/s is provided to allow better resolution of the QRS complex at very high heart rates or when a particular waveform detail is desired.

The *power switch* of an ECG recorder has three positions. In the *ON* position the power to the amplifier is turned on, but the paper drive is not running. In order to start the paper drive, the switch must be placed in the *RUN* position. In some ECG machines the lead selector switch has auxiliary positions (between the lead positions) in which the paper drive is stopped. In older ECG machines a pushbutton or metal "finger contact" allows the operator to check whether the recorder is connected to the power line with the right polarity. Because the improper connection of older machines can create a shock hazard for the patient, this test must be performed prior to

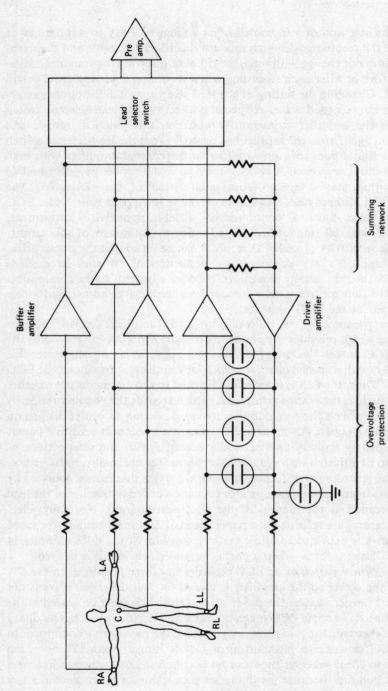

Figure 6.8. Input circuit of modern ECG machine with buffer amplifier; driven right-leg lead andover-voltage protection.

connecting the electrodes to the patient. Modern ECG machines, which have line plugs with grounding pins, do not require such a polarity test.

Although Figure 6.7 shows the principal building blocks of an electrocardiograph, it does not show the circuit details that are found in modern devices of this type. Some of these features are shown in Figure 6.8. To increase the input impedance and thus reduce the effect of variations in electrode impedance, these instruments usually include a *buffer amplifier* for each patient lead. The transistors in these amplifiers are often protected by a network of resistors and neon lamps from overvoltages that may occur when the electrocardiograph is used during surgery in conjunction with high-frequency devices for cutting and coagulation.

A more severe problem is the protection of the electrocardiograph from damage during defibrillation. The voltages that may be encountered in this case can reach several thousand volts. Thus, special measures must be incorporated into the electrocardiograph to prevent burnout of components and provide fast recovery of the trace so as to permit the success of the countershock to be judged.

Some modern devices do not connect the right leg of the patient to the chassis, but utilize a "driven right leg lead." This involves a summing network to obtain the sum of the voltages from all other electrodes and a driving amplifier, the output of which is connected to the right leg of the patient. The effect of this arrangement is to force the reference connection at the right leg of the patient to assume a voltage equal to the sum of the voltages at the other leads. This arrangement increases the common-mode rejection ratio of the overall system and reduces interference. It also has the effect of reducing the current flow in the right leg electrode. Increased concern for the safety aspect of electrical connections to the patient have caused modern ECG designs to abandon the principle of a ground reference altogether and use isolated or floating-input amplifiers, as described in Chapter 16.

6.1.5. Types of ECG Recorders

There are numerous types of ECG recorders. Many of these are portable units, while others are part of permanent installations. In this section the most commonly used types are discussed. The reader will find further examples in Chapter 7 in the context of the coronary-care unit and in Chapter 12 in the discussion of emergency care. The use of the computer in connection with electrocardiography is covered in Chapter 15.

6.1.5.1. Single-channel recorders. The most frequently used type of EGG recorder is the portable single-channel unit illustrated in Figure 6.9. For hospital use this recorder is usually mounted on a cart so that it can be wheeled to the bedside of a patient with relative ease.

If the electrocardiogram of a patient is recorded in the 12 standard lead configurations, the resulting paper strip is from 3 to 6 ft long. Even if folded in accordion fashion, the strip is still inconvenient to read and store. Therefore, it is usually cut up, and sections of the recordings from the 12 leads are mounted as shown in Figure 6.6. Because it is easy to mix up the cut sections, the lead for each trace is encoded at the margin of the paper, using the marker pen, during the recording process. The code markers consist of short marks (dots) and long marks (dashes) and look similar to Morse code. No standard code has been established for this purpose, however.

The cut sections of the electrocardiogram can be mounted by inserting them in pockets of a special folder with cutouts to make the trace visible.

Figure 6.9. Single-channel portable ECG machine. (Courtesy of Hewlett-Packard Co., Andover, MA.)

This is the way in which the electrocardiogram in Figure 6.6 was mounted. It should be noted that the recordings from the three limb leads are longer than those from the other lead selections in order to show several QRS complexes; they are called *rhythm strips.* Commercial systems are available to simplify the mounting by die-cutting the paper strip and using mounting cards with adhesive pads. With the automatic three-channel recorders described in the next section, the mounting is greatly simplified.

6.1.5.2. Three-channel recorders. Where large numbers of electrocardiograms are recorded and mounted daily, substantial savings in personnel can be achieved by the use of *automatic three-channel recorders.* These devices not only record three leads simultaneously on a three-channel recorder, but they also switch automatically to the next group of three leads. An electrocardiogram with the 12 standard leads, therefore, can be recorded automatically as a sequence of four groups of three traces. The time required for the actual recording is only about 10 seconds. The groups of leads recorded and the time at which the switching occurs are automatically identified by code markings at the margin of the recording paper. At the end of the recording, standardization pulses are inserted in all three recording channels. Although the actual recording time is reduced substantially compared to single-channel recorders, more time is required to apply the electrodes to the patient because separate electrodes must necessarily be used for each chest position. The mounting of the electrocardiogram, however, is simplified substantially, for no cutting or mounting of the individual lead selections is required. A modern recorder of this type is shown in Figure 6.10.

6.1.5.3. Vector electrocardiographs (vectorcardiographs). As noted in Section 6.1.3, the voltage generated by the activity of the heart can be described as a vector whose magnitude and spatial orientation change with time. In the type of electrocardiography described thus far, only the magnitude of the voltage is recorded. *Vectorcardiography,* on the other hand, presents an image of both the magnitude and the spatial orientation of the heart vector. The heart vector, however, is a three-dimensional variable, and three "views" or projections on orthogonal planes are necessary to describe the variable fully in two-dimensional figures. Special lead placement systems must be used to pick up the ECG signals for vector electrocardiograms, the *Frank system* being the one most frequently employed. The vectorcardiogram is usually displayed on a cathode-ray tube, similar to those used for patient monitors. Each QRS complex is displayed as a sequence of "loops" on this screen, which is then photographed with a Polaroid camera. Vectorcardiographs that use computer techniques to slow down the ECG signals and allow the recording of the vectorcardiogram with a mechanical X-Y recorder are also available.

Figure 6.10. Automatic three-channel ECG recorder with keyboard for entering patient data and telephone coupler to send ECG and data to a remote computer via telephone lines. (Courtesy of Hewlett-Packard Co., MA.)

6.1.5.4. Electrocardiograph systems for stress testing. Coronary insufficiency frequently does not manifest itself in the electrocardiogram if the recording is taken during rest. In the *Masters test* or *two-step exercise test,* a physiological stress is imposed on the cardiovascular system by letting the patient repeatedly walk up and down a special pair of 9-inch high steps prior to recording his electrocardiogram. Based on the same principle is the *exercise stress test,* in which the patient walks at a specified speed on a treadmill whose inclination can be changed. While the Masters test is normally conducted using a regular single-channel electrocardiograph, special systems are available for the exercise stress test. These systems, however, are usually made up of a number of individual instruments which are described in this book.

An exercise stress test system typically consists of the following parts:

1. A treadmill which may incorporate an automatic programmer to change the speed and inclination in order to apply a specific physiological stress.
2. An ECG radiotelemetry system to allow recording of the ECG without artifacts while the patient is on the treadmill.
3. An ECG monitor with a cathode-ray-tube display and heart rate meter.
4. An ECG recorder.
5. An automatic or semiautomatic sphygmomanometer for the indirect measurement of blood pressure.

Because the exercise stress test involves a certain risk for patients with known or suspected cardiac disorders, a dc defibrillator is usually kept available while the test is performed.

6.1.5.5. Electrocardiographs for computer processing. The automatic analysis of electrocardiograms by computers is used increasingly (see Chapter 15). This technique requires that the ECG signal from the standard leads be transmitted sequentially to the computer by some suitable means, together with additional information on the patient. The automatic three-channel recorders can frequently be adapted for this purpose. The ECG signals can either be recorded on a tape for later computer entry or can be directly transmitted to the computer through special lines or regular telephone lines using a special acoustical coupler (see Chapter 12). Information regarding the patient is entered with thumbwheel switches or from a keyboard and is transmitted along with the ECG signal. During the transmission of the signal, the electrocardiogram is simultaneously recorded to verify that the transmitted signals are free of artifacts.

6.1.5.6. Continuous ECG recording (Holter recording). Because a normal electrocardiogram represents only a brief sample of cardiac activity, arrhythmias which occur intermittently or only under certain conditions, such as emotional stress, are frequently missed. The technique of continuous ECG recording, which was introduced by Norman Holter, makes it possible to capture these kinds of arrhythmias. To obtain a continuous ECG, the electrocardiogram of a patient is recorded during his normal daily activity by means of a special magnetic tape recorder. The smallest device of this type can actually be worn in a shirt pocket and allows recordings of the ECG for four hours. Other recorders, about the size of a camera case, are worn over the shoulder and can record the electrocardiogram for up to 24 hours. The recorded tape is analyzed using a special scanning device which plays back the tape at a higher speed than that used for recording. By this method a 24-hour tape can be reviewed in as little as 12 minutes. During the playback, the beat-to-beat interval of the electrocardiogram is displayed on a cathode-ray tube as a picket-fence-like pattern in which arrhythmia epsiodes are clearly visible. Once such an episode has been discovered, the tape is backed up and slowed down to obtain a normal electrocardiogram strip for the time interval during which the arrhythmias occurred. A special time clock is synchronized by the tape drive to correlate the onset of the episode with the activity of the patient.

6.2. MEASUREMENT OF BLOOD PRESSURE

As one of the physiological variables that can be quite readily measured, blood pressure is considered a good indicator of the status of the cardiovascular system. A history of blood pressure measurements has saved many a person from an untimely death by providing warnings of dangerously high blood pressure (*hypertension*) in time to provide treatment.

In routine clinical tests, blood pressure is usually measured by means of an indirect method using a *sphygmomanometer* (from the Greek word, *sphygmos,* meaning pulse). This method is easy to use and can be automated. It has, however, certain disadvantages in that it does not provide a continuous recording of pressure variations and its practical repetition rate is limited. Furthermore, only systolic and diastolic arterial pressure readings can be obtained, with no indication of the details of the pressure waveform. The indirect method is also somewhat subjective, and often fails when the blood pressure is very low (as would be the case when a patient is in shock).

Methods for direct blood pressure measurement, on the other hand, do provide a continuous readout or recording of the blood pressure waveform and are considerably more accurate than the indirect method. They require, however, that a blood vessel be punctured in order to introduce the sensor. This limits their use to those cases in which the condition of the patient warrants invasion of the vascular system.

This section is divided into three parts. First, indirect or noninvasive methods are discussed. Since there has been much progress in the automating of indirect techniques, automated methods are covered in a separate section. Finally, direct or invasive blood pressure measurements are discussed.

6.2.1. Indirect Measurements.

As stated earlier, the familiar indirect method of measuring blood pressure involves the use of a sphygmomanometer and a stethoscope. The

Figure 6.11. Wall-mounted sphygmomanometer. (Courtesy of W.A. Baum, Inc., Copiague, NY.)

sphygmomanometer consists of an inflatable pressure cuff and a mercury or aneroid manometer to measure the pressure in the cuff. The cuff consists of a rubber bladder inside an inelastic fabric covering that can be wrapped around the upper arm and fastened with either hooks or a Velcro fastener. The cuff is normally inflated manually with a rubber bulb and deflated slowly through a needle valve. The stethoscope is described in detail in Section 6.5. A wallmounted sphygmomanometer is shown in Figure 6.11. These devices are also manufactured as portable units.

The sphygmomanometer works on the principle that when the cuff is placed on the upper arm and inflated, arterial blood can flow past the cuff only when the arterial pressure exceeds the pressure in the cuff. Furthermore, when the cuff is inflated to a pressure that only partially occludes the brachial artery, turbulence is generated in the blood as it spurts through the tiny arterial opening during each systole. The sounds generated by this turbulence, *Korotkoff sounds,* can be heard through a stethoscope placed over the artery downstream from the cuff.

To obtain a blood pressure measurement with a sphygmomanometer and a stethoscope, the pressure cuff on the upper arm is first inflated to a pressure well above systolic pressure. At this point no sounds can be heard through the stethoscope, which is placed over the brachial artery, for that artery has been collapsed by the pressure of the cuff. The pressure in the cuff is then gradually reduced. As soon as cuff pressure falls below systolic pressure, small amounts of blood spurt past the cuff and Korotkoff sounds begin to be heard through the stethoscope. The pressure of the cuff that is indicated on the manometer when the first Korotkoff sound is heard is recorded as the systolic blood pressure.

Figure 6.12. Measurement of blood pressure using sphygmomanometer. (Courtesy of W.A. Baum, Inc., Copiague, NY.)

As the pressure in the cuff continues to drop, the Korotkoff sounds continue until the cuff pressure is no longer sufficient to occlude the vessel during any part of the cycle. Below this pressure the Korotkoff sounds disappear, marking the value of the diastolic pressure.

This familiar method of locating the systolic and diastolic pressure values by listening to the Korotkoff sounds is called the *auscultatory method* of sphygmomanometry. An alternative method, called the *palpatory method,* is similar except that the physician identifies the flow of blood in the artery by feeling the pulse of the patient downstream from the cuff instead of listening for the Korotkoff sounds. Although systolic pressure can easily be measured by the palpatory method, diastolic pressure is much more difficult to identify. For this reason, the auscultatory method is more commonly used. Figure 6.12 shows a blood pressure measurement using the auscultatory method.

6.2.2. Automated Indirect Methods

Because of the trauma imposed by direct measurement of blood pressure (described below) and the lack of a more suitable method for indirect measurement, attempts have been made to automate the indirect procedure. As a result, a number of automatic and semiautomatic systems have been developed. Most devices are of a type that utilizes a pressure transducer connected to the sphygmomanometer cuff, a microphone placed beneath the cuff (over the artery), and a standard physiological recording system on which cuff pressure and the Korotkoff sounds are recorded. The basic procedure essentially parallels the manual method. The pressure cuff is automatically inflated to about 220 mm Hg and allowed to deflate slowly. The microphone picks up the Korotkoff sounds from the artery near the surface, just below the compression cuff. One type of instrument either superimposes the signal of the Korotkoff sounds on the voltage recording representing the falling cuff pressure or records the two separately. The pressure reading at the time of the first sound represents the systolic pressure; the diastolic pressure is the point on the falling pressure curve where the signal representing that last sound is seen. This instrument is actually only semiautomatic because the recording thus obtained must still be interpreted by the observer. False indications—caused, for instance, by motion artifacts—can often be observed on the recording. Fully automated devices use some type of signal-detecting circuit to determine the occurrence of the first and last Korotkoff sounds and retain and display the cuff pressure reading for these points, either electronically or with mercury manometers that are cut off by solenoid valves. One of the recent innovations of these techniques is the "do-it-yourself" blood pressure machine to be found in some supermarkets. These devices, by necessity, are more susceptible to false indications caused by artifacts.

Many of the commercially available automatic blood pressure meters work well when demonstrated on a quiet, healthy subject but fail when used to measure blood pressure during activity or when used on patients in circulatory shock. Methods other than those utilizing the Korotkoff sounds have been tried in detecting the blood pulse distal to the occlusion cuff. Among them is impedance plethysmography (see Section 6.4), which indicated directly the pulsating blood flow in the artery, and ultrasonic Doppler methods, which measure the motions of the arterial walls. An early example of an automatic blood pressure meter is the *programmed electrosphygmomanometer PE-300,* illustrated in Figures 6.13 and 6.14 in block diagram and pictorial form. This instrument is designed for use in conjunction with an occluding cuff, microphone, or pulse transducer, and a recorder for the automatic measurement of indirect systolic and diastolic blood pressures from humans and many animal subjects.

The PE-300 incorporates a transducer-preamplifier that provides two output signals, a voltage proportional to the cuff pressure, and the amplified Korotkoff sounds or pulses. These signals can be monitored individually or with the sounds or pulses superimposed on the calibrated cuff-recorder. The combined signal can be recorded on a graphic pen recorder.

Figure 6.13. Programmed electrosphygmomanometer (block diagram). (Courtesy of Narco BioSystems, Inc., Houston, TX.)

Figure 6.14. Electrosphygmomanometer. (Courtesy of Narco BioSystems, Inc., Houston, TX.)

The self-contained cuff inflation system can be programmed to inflate and deflate an occluding cuff at various rates and time intervals. Equal and linear rates of cuff inflation and deflation permit two blood pressure determinations per cycle. The PE-300 can be programmed for repeat cycles at adjustable time intervals for monitoring of blood pressure over long periods of time. Single cycles may be initiated by pressing a panel-mounted switch. Provision is also made for remote control via external contact closure. The maximum cuff pressure is adjustable, and the front-panel meter gives a continuous visual display of the cuff pressure.

The electronic sphygmomanometer shown in Figure 6.15 is an example of a device incorporating a large gage for easy reading. The scale is 6 in. (over 15 cm) in diameter. In this example the cuff has to be inflated manually and so this instrument is sometimes called "semiautomatic." The Korotkoff sounds are automatically detected by microphones and a light flashes at systolic pressure, which stops at the diastolic value.

While the clinical diagnostic value of systolic and diastolic blood pressure has been clearly established, the role of *mean arterial pressure* (MAP) as an indication of blood pressure trend has become more widely accepted with the expanded use of direct pressure monitoring using arterial cannulae with electronic transducers and displays. Most electrical monitors now provide both diagnostic systolic/diastolic waveform information and the added option of a single-value MAP indication. It is now generally recognized that MAP is a direct indication of the pressure available for tissue perfusion, and that a continuously increasing or decreasing MAP can ultimately result in a hypertensive or hypotensive crisis.

Mean arterial pressure is a weighted average of systolic and diastolic pressure. Generally, MAP falls about one-third of the way between the diastolic low and the systolic peak. A simple formula for calculating MAP is: MAP = 1/3(systolic - diastolic) + diastolic.

Figure 6.15. Electronic sphygmomanometer. (Courtesy of Applied Science Laboratories, Waltham, MA.)

In the Dinamap illustrated in Figure 6.16, the mean arterial blood pressure is determined by the oscillometric method. The pressure pulsations or oscillations introduced within a cuff bladder are sensed by a solid-state pressure transducer located within the enclosure. As the air pressure in the cuff is decreased, pressure oscillations increase in amplitude and reach a maximum as the cuff pressure passes through the pressure equal to the mean arterial blood pressure. This phenomenon can also be observed as it produces pulsations in the mercury column of a conventional sphygmomanometer or the needle oscillations in an aneroid sphygmomanometer.

Figure 6.16. Dinamap for automatic detection of mean arterial blood pressure. (Courtesy of Applied Medical Research, Tampa, FL.)

Since the indications associated with the indirect measurement of mean arterial pressure pass through a maximum at the point of interest, as opposed to the phenomenon for the indirect determination of systolic and diastolic pressure, which is at a minimum at the point of interest, the Dinamap can determine arterial pressures over a wide range of physiological states. It works effectively on most patients on whom systolic and diastolic indirect pressures are impossible to determine or are subject to such variabilities as to be of questionable clinical value.

An internal microprocessor rejects most artifacts caused by patient movement or external interference. Under program control, all normal operating variables, such as inflation pressures, deflation rates, alarm limits, and abnormal operation alarms, are automatically determined and controlled without operator adjustments. Adjustable alarm limits and measurement cycle times are simply set via front panel switches by the user as required for varying clinical conditions.

Because, in most clinical situations, systolic and diastolic pressures correlate with each other and MAP is determined from the systolic/diastolic pair, critical patient arterial pressure trends can be monitored by observation of MAP. Adjustable alarm limits, as required for a given clinical situation, can then alert staff of possible patient problems. These units can be used in operating rooms, recovery rooms, and intensive-care units.

The ability to measure blood pressure automatically with portable equipment makes it possible to take measurements while the patient is pursuing his or her normal activities. A system that does this is shown in Figure

Figure 6.17. Ambulatory automatic blood pressure monitor. (Courtesy of Del Mar Avionics, Irvine, CA.)

6.17. This device is a 24-hour automatic noninvasive blood pressure and Holter (see Section 6.1.5.6) monitoring system with trend writeouts. The three major components of the ambulatory system are shown in the photograph. The Pressurometer II Model 1977 at the front is the blood pressure measuring device. The recording unit is the Model 446A Electrocardiocorder, which records blood pressure and ECG on a 24-hour basis. The patient wears the units with belts and straps. The cuff is attached comfortably and securely on the left arm.

The Model 1977 utilizes a standard pneumatic cuff. A transducer for the detection of the Korotkoff sounds is held in place with an adhesive disk. Cuff pressure is applied automatically and the patient's systolic and diastolic pressures are measured in excess of 100 preprogrammed intervals in a 24-hour period. The preselected intervals can be overridden by means of manual switching and the unit can be operated manually for checking and calibration. When used with the 446A recorder, the Korotkoff sounds are gated by ECG R-wave signals. The recordings can be fed into a companion trend computer, which gives a digital readout of the data on the recording. The entire system is powered by a portable rechargeable nickelcadmium battery pack which permits up to 26 hours of recording. The computer is a plug-in module and chart-paper documentation is also available.

An important feature of the system is that it can be used with an Electrocardioscanner, which scans all the data at a rate 120 times as fast as they were recorded (the entire 24-hour record can be scanned in 12 minutes) quantitating ectopic beats and total heart beats and printing hourly trends on heart rate and other quantities. It can rewind itself and will search out operator-selected patient abnormalities.

Another approach utilizes ultrasound to measure the pulsatile motion of the brachial artery wall. High-frequency sound energy is transmitted into the patient's arm and is reflected back from the arterial walls. By means of the Doppler effect (see explanation in Chapter 9), the movement of the arterial walls can be detected as they snap open and closed with each pulsation of blood.

An advantage of this type of instrument is that results closer to direct measurements (Section 6.2.3) can be obtained. Also, it can be used for patients under shock and in intensive care units, when direct measurement would not be suitable for the patient. Because vessel-wall movement is sensed, blood flow is not a requirement for measurement.

One such instrument is the Arteriosonde, which has a cloth cuff and air bag with an electric air pump to supply the pressure. The pump can be regulated by a front-panel control. The cuff is placed on the arm in the same fashion as the sphygmomanometer except that there is a transducer array under the cuff. These transducers are arranged as alternate transmitters and receivers. The motion of the artery produces a *Doppler shift*, which identifies the instant the artery is opened and closed with each beat between systolic and diastolic pressure.

The first signal is used to stop the mercury fall in the first of two manometers to indicate systolic pressure. The second manometer is stopped at the point of disappearance of the pulses to indicate diastolic pressure. Hence, both readings can be noted simultaneously.

6.2.3. Direct Measurements

In 1728, Hales inserted a glass tube into the artery of a horse and crudely measured arterial pressure. Poiseuille substituted a mercury manometer for the piezometer tube of Hales, and Ludwig added a float and devised the *kymograph,* which allowed continuous, permanent recording of the blood pressure. It is only quite recently that electronic systems using strain gages as transducers have replaced the kymograph.

Regardless of the electrical or physical principles involved, direct measurement of blood pressure is usually obtained by one of three methods:

1. Percutaneous insertion.
2. Catheterization (vessel cutdown).
3. Implantation of a transducer in a vessel or in the heart.

Other methods, such as clamping a transducer on the intact artery, have also been used, but they are not common.

Figure 6.18 should give a general idea of both methods. Typically, for percutaneous insertion, a local anesthetic is injected near the site of invasion. The vessel is occluded and a hollow needle is inserted at a slight angle toward the vessel. When the needle is in place, a catheter is fed through the hollow needle, usually with some sort of a guide. When the catheter is securely in place in the vessel, the needle and guide are withdrawn. For some measurements, a type of needle attached to an airtight tube is used, so that the needle can be left in the vessel and the blood pressure sensed directly by attaching a transducer to the tube. Other types have the transducer built into the tip of the catheter. This latter type is used in both percutaneous and full catheterization models.

Catheterization was first developed in the late 1940s and has become a major diagnostic technique for analyzing the heart and other components of the cardiovascular system. Apart from obtaining blood pressures in the heart chambers and great vessels, this technique is also used to obtain blood samples from the heart for oxygen-content analysis and to detect the location of abnormal blood flow pathways. Also, catheters are used for investigations with injection of radiopaque dyes for X-ray studies, colored dyes for indicator dilution studies, and of vasoactive drugs directly into the heart and certain vessels. Essentially, a *catheter* is a long tube that is in-

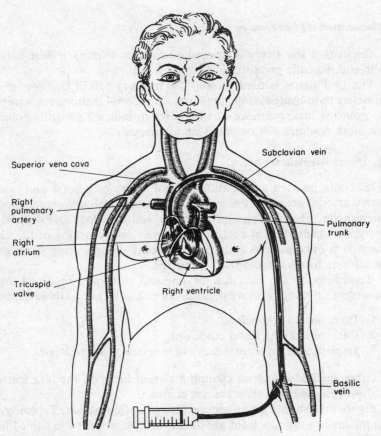

Labels on figure:

Superior vena cava

Right pulmonary artery

Right atrium

Tricuspid valve

Subclavian vein

Pulmonary trunk

Right ventricle

Basilic vein

Figure 6.18. Cardiac catheterization. The tube is shown entering the basilic vein in this case. (From W.F. Evans, *Anatomy and Physiology, The Basic Principles,* Englewood Cliffs, NJ., Prentice-Hall, Inc., 1971, by permission.)

troduced into the heart or a major vessel by way of a superficial vein or artery. The sterile catheter is designed for easy travel through the vessels.

Measurement of blood pressure with a catheter can be achieved in two ways. The first is to introduce a sterile saline solution into the catheter so that the fluid pressure is transmitted to a transducer outside the body (extracorporeal). A complete fluid pressure system is set up with provisions for checking against atmospheric pressure and for establishing a reference point. The frequency response of this system is a combination of the frequency response of the transducer and the fluid column in the catheter. In the second method, pressure measurements are obtained at the source. Here, the transducer is introduced into the catheter and pushed to the point at which the pressure is to be measured, or the transducer is mounted at the tip of the catheter. This device is called a *catheter-tip blood pressure transducer*. For mounting at the end of a catheter, one manufacturer uses an unbonded resistance strain gage in the transducer, whereas another uses a variable inductance transducer (see Chapter 2). Each will be discussed later.

Implantation techniques involve major surgery and thus are normally employed only in research experiments. They have the advantage of keeping the transducer fixed in place in the appropriate vessel for long periods of time. The type of transducer employed in that procedure is also described later in this section.

Transducers can be categorized by the type of circuit element used to sense the pressure variations, such as capacitive, inductive, and resistive. Since the resistive types are most frequently used, the other two types are discussed only briefly.

In the *capacitance manometer*, a change in the distance between the plates of a capacitor changes its capacitance. In a typical application, one of the plates is a metal membrane separated from a fixed plate by some one-thousandth of an inch of air. Changes in pressure that change the distance between the plates thereby change the capacitance. If this element is contained in a high-frequency resonant circuit, the changes in capacitance vary the frequency of the resonant circuit to produce a form of frequency modulation. With suitable circuitry, blood pressure information can be obtained and recorded as a function of time.

An advantage of this type of transducer is that its total contour can be long and thin so that it can be easily introduced into the bloodstream without deforming the contour of the recorded pressure waveform. Because of the stiff structure and the small movement of the membrane when pressure is applied, the volume displacement is extremely small (in the region of 10^{-6} cm^3/100 mm Hg of applied pressure).

Disadvantages of this type of transducer are instability and a proneness to variations with small changes in temperature. Also, lead wires introduce errors in the capacitance, and this type of transducer is more difficult to use than resistance types.

A number of different devices use inductance effects. They measure the distortion of a membrane exposed to the blood pressure. In some of these types, two coils are used—a primary and secondary. When a spring-loaded core that couples the coils together magnetically is moved back and forth, the voltage induced into the secondary changes in proportion to the pressure applied.

A better-known method employs a *differential transformer*, described in detail in Chapter 2. In this device two secondary coils are wound oppositely and connected in series. If the spring-loaded core is symmetrically positioned, the induced voltage across one secondary coil opposes the voltage of the other. Movement of the core changes this symmetry, and the result is a signal developed across the combined secondary coils. The core can be spring-loaded to accept pressure from one side, or it can accept pressure from both sides simultaneously, thus measuring the difference of pressure between two different points.

The *physiological resistance transducer* is a direct adaptation of the strain gages used in industry for many years. The principle of a strain gage is that if a very fine wire is stretched, its resistance increases. (A detailed discussion of strain gages is given in Chapter 2.) If voltage is applied to the resistance, the resulting current changes with the resistance variations according to Ohm's law. Thus, the forces responsible for the strain can be recorded as a function of current. The method by which the blood pressure produces the strain is discussed in Section 6.2.4.

To obtain the degree of sensitivity required for blood pressure transducers, two or four strain gages are mounted on a diaphragm or membrane, and these resistances are connected to form a bridge circuit. Figure 6.19 shows such a circuit configuration.

Figure 6.19. Resistance strain-gage bridge.

In general, the four resistances are initially about equal when no pressure or strain is applied. The gages are attached to the pressure diaphragm in such a way that as the pressure increases, two of them stretch while the other two contract. An excitation voltage is applied as shown. When pressure changes unbalance the bridge a voltage appears between terminals A and B proportional to the pressure. Excitation can be either direct current or alternating current, depending on the application.

Resistance-wire strain gages can be *bonded* or *unbonded* (see Chapter 2). In the bonded type, the gage is "bonded" to the diaphragm and stretches or contracts with bending. The unbonded type consists of two pairs of wires, coiled and assembled in such a way that displacement of a membrane connected to them causes one pair to stretch and the other to relax. The two pairs of wires are not bonded to the diaphragm material but are attached only by retaining lugs. Because the wires are very thin, it is possible to obtain relatively large signals from the bridge with small movement of the diaphragm.

Development of semiconductors that change their resistance in much the same manner as wire gages has led to the *bonded silicon element* bridge. Only small displacements (on the order of a few micro meters) of the pressure-sensing diaphragm, are needed for sizable changes of output voltage with low-voltage excitation. For example, with 10 V excitation, a range of 300 mm Hg is obtained with a 3-μm deflection, producing a 30-mV signal.

Semiconductor strain-gage bridges are often temperature-sensitive, however, and have to be calibrated for baseline and true zero. Therefore, it is usually necessary to incorporate external resistors and potentiometers to balance the bridge initially, as well as for periodic correction.

In Chapter 2 the gage factor for a strain gage is defined as the amount of resistance change produced by a given change in length. Wire strain gages have gage factors on the order of 2 to 4, whereas semiconductor strain gages have gage factors ranging from 50 to 200. For silicon, the gage factor is typically 120. The use of semiconductors is restricted to those configurations that lend themselves to this technique.

When strain gages are incorporated in pressure transducers, the sensitivity of the transducer is expressed, not as a gage factor, but as a voltage change that results from a given pressure change. For example, the sensitivity of a pressure transducer can be given in microvolts per (applied) volt per millimeter of mercury.

6.2.4. Specific Direct Measurement Techniques

In Section 6.2.3 methods of direct blood pressure were classified in two ways, first by the clinical method by which the measuring device was coupled to the patient and, second, by the electrical principle involved. In the following discussion, the first category is expanded, with the electrical principles involved being used as subcategories where necessary. The four categories are as follows:

1. A catheterization method involving the sensing of blood pressure through a liquid column. In this method the transducer is external to the body, and the blood pressure is transmitted through a saline solution column in a catheter to this transducer. This method can use either an unbonded resistance strain gage to sense the pressure or a linear variable differential transformer. Externally, these two devices are quite similar in appearance.

2. A catheterization method involving the placement of the transducer through a catheter at the actual site of measurement in the bloodstream (e.g., to the aorta), or by mounting the transducer on the tip of the catheter.

3. Percutaneous methods in which the blood pressure is sensed in the vessel just under the skin by the use of a needle or catheter.

4. Implantation techniques in which the transducer is more permanently placed in the blood vessel or the heart by surgical methods.

The most important aspects of these methods are discussed separately.

6.2.4.1. Liquid-column methods.

A typical liquid-column blood pressure transducer, the Gould Statham P 23 ID, is illustrated in Figure 6.20. Figure 6.21 is a cutaway drawing to show the interior construction and the isolation features of the same transducer, which is considered a standard size in hospital practice. The heart of the P 23 transducer is the unbonded strain gage, which is connected in a standard Wheatstone bridge configuration. The metal sensing diaphragm can be seen on the left side. It is a precision-made part that must deflect predictably with a given fluid pressure. When the diaphragm is deflected downward by the pressure of the liquid being measured, the tension on two of the bridge wires is relaxed and the tension on the other two wires is tightened, changing the resistance of the gage. For negative pressures, the opposite wires are stretched and relaxed.

Figure 6.20. Fluid-column blood pressure transducer. (Courtesy of Gould, Inc., Measurement Systems Division, Oxnard, CA.)

The transducer is connected through the cable to an instrument which contains zero-balance and range controls, amplifier circuits, and a readout. The shielded cable is attached to the case through a liquid-tight seal that permits immersion of the transducer for cleaning. The transducer case is vented through the cable so that measurements are always referenced to atmospheric pressure.

Figure 6.21. Interior construction of P23ID Blood Pressure Transducer. (Courtesy of Gould Inc., Measurement Systems Division, Oxnard, CA.)

NON-CONDUCTIVE DOME

LIQUID COLUMN

METAL SENSING DIAPHRAGM

LIQUID COLUMN

STANDARD ISOLATION *

ISOLATED OUTER CASE WITH INTEGRAL COUPLING THREADS *

ELECTRICAL STANDOFF FOR SECONDARY CONNECTION

INSULATED ELECTRICAL CABLE

.710" (18 mm) DIA

.870" (22 mm) DIA

3.25" [85 mm]

ARMATURE

INTERNAL FRAME

UNBONDED STRAIN GAGE

REDUNDANT ISOLATION *

LIQUID COLUMN
CONDUCTIVE MATERIAL
NON-CONDUCTIVE MATERIAL

The dome is the reservoir for the liquid that transmits blood pressure to the diaphragm. It is made of transparent plastic to facilitate the detection and removal of bubbles, since even the most minute bubble can degrade the frequency response of the pressure-monitoring system. The dome is fitted with two ports. One port is coupled through tubing to the cannula; the other is used for venting air from the dome.

It should be noted in Figure 6.21 that there are three modes of isolation: (1) external isolation of the case with a plastic sheath, which provides protection from extraneous voltages; (2) standard internal isolation of the sensing (bridge) elements from the inside of the transducer case and the frame; and (3) additional isolation (internal) of the frame from the case and the diaphragm in case of wire breakage. Thus, isolation of the patient/fluid column from electrical excitation circuitry is assured, even in the event of failure of the standard internal isolation.

This transducer is 56 mm (2.21 in.) long, with a maximum diameter at the base of 18 mm (0.71 in.). Its rated excitation voltage is 7.5 V which may be dc or an ac carrier.

Another type of transducer of smaller design is the P 50, shown in Figure 6.22. This unit can be mounted or attached to the patient near the measurement site (e.g., on the forearm of the patient). To achieve this miniaturization, the design has to be quite different. The sensing element of the P 50 is a tiny silicon beam upon which strain elements are diffused. This is, therefore, a bonded strain gage instead of the unbonded type used in the P 23 (see Section 2.3.1).

Figure 6.22. Bonded type blood pressure transducer for attaching to patient. (Courtesy of Gould Inc., Measurement Systems Division, Oxnard, CA.)

Both types of transducer described have pressure ranges of −50 to +300 mm Hg, with sensitivity for 7.5-V excitation of 50 μV/V/cm Hg.

These transducers can be flushed to remove air bubbles and to prevent blood from clotting at the end of the catheter. The fluid column used with a transducer of this type has a natural frequency or resonance of its own that can affect the frequency response of the system. Care must be taken in selecting a transducer and catheter to be used together so that the frequency response of the complete system will be adequate. There are general-purpose models for arterial pressure (0 to 330 mm Hg) and venous pressure (0 to 50 mm Hg), and special models with differing sensitivities, volume displacement characteristics, and mechanical arrangements.

Pressure transducers are normally mounted on a suitable manifold near the patient's bed. It is important to keep the transducer at the same height as the point at which the measurements are to be made in order to avoid errors due to hydrostatic pressure differences. If a *differential pressure* is desired, two transducers of this type may be used at two different points, and the difference in pressure may be obtained as the difference of their output signals. Figure 6.23 shows a typical infusion manifold incorporating a transducer, a flushing system, and syringes for blood specimen withdrawal.

The signal-conditioning and display devices for these transducers are available in a variety of forms. However, each must provide a method of excitation for the strain-gage bridge, a means of zeroing or balancing the bridge, necessary amplification of the output signal, and a display device, such as a monitor scope, a recorder, panel meter, or digital readout device. Most modern systems permit many possible combinations.

Another type of blood pressure transducer is the *linear variable differential transformer* (LVDT) device, shown in an exploded view in Figure 6.24. Superficially, these transducers look similar to the unbonded strain-gage type. Indeed, with respect to the plastic dome used for visibility, the two pressure fittings for attachment to the catheter and for flushing, and the cable coming out of the bottom, they are similar. Such transducers also come in a variety of models with a range of characteristics for venous or arterial pressure, for different sensitivities, and for alternative volume displacements. The various models also have different natural frequencies and frequency responses.

It should be noted from the exploded view that these units disassemble into three subassemblies—the dome and pressure fittings subassembly, the center portion consisting of a stainless-steel diaphragm and core assembly, and the LVDT subassembly. There are two basic diaphragm and core assemblies with appropriate domes that are interchangeable in the coil-connector assembly. The first is used for venous and general-purpose clinical measurements and has a standard-size diaphragm with an internal fluid volume between the dome and diaphragm of less than 0.5 cm³. The second design, with higher frequency response characteristics for arterial pressure contours, has a reduced diaphragm area and an internal volume of approximately 0.1 cm³.

Figure 6.23. Infusion manifold with transducer, flushing system and syringe. (Courtesy of Michael Tomeo, UCLA Medical Center.)

Labels in figure:
- Fluid reservoir and pressure pack pump system
- 3 way stopcock for flushing dome
- IV pole
- Pressure transducer
- Bedside monitor
- Irrigation syringe
- Infusion manifold located at level of mid-axillary line
- Arterial catheter stopcock-at patient

Figure 6.24. LVDT blood pressure transducer—exploded view. (Courtesy of Biotronex Laboratory, Inc., Silver Springs, MD.)

The Biotronex BL-9630 transducer is a linear variable differential transformer in which the primary coil is excited by an ac carrier (5 to 20 V peak to peak) in the range of 1500 to 15,000 Hz. Axial displacement of a movable iron core, attached to the diaphragm, cuts the magnetic lines of flux generated by the primary coil. Voltages induced in the secondary sensing coils are returned to the carrier amplifier, where they are differentially amplified and demodulated to remove the carrier frequency. The output of the carrier amplifier is a dc voltage proportional to diaphragm displacement. Linearity of the gage is better than ± 1 percent of full range. Ordinary jarring and handling will not harm the gage. A positive mechanical stop is provided to prevent damage by as much as a 100 per-cent overpressure. The LVDT offers much higher signal levels than do conventional strain-gage transducers for a given excitation voltage.

6.2.4.2. Measurement at the site. To avoid the problems inherent in measuring blood pressure through a liquid column, a "catheter-tip" manometer can be fed through the catheter to the site at which the blood pressure is to be measured. This process requires a small-diameter transducer that is fairly rigid but flexible.

One such transducer makes use of the variable-inductance effect mentioned earlier. The tip is placed directly in the bloodstream so that the blood presses on a membrane surrounded by a protective cap. The membrane is connected to a magnetic slug that is free to move within a coil assembly and thus changes the inductance of the coil as a function of the pressure on the membrane.

Another type has a bonded strain-gage sensor built into the tip of a cardiac catheter. The resistance changes in the strain gage are a result of pressure variations at the site itself rather than through a fluid column. This gage can also be calibrated with a liquid-system catheter at the same location.

6.2.4.3. Floatation catheter. The construction of specialized, multiple-lumen "floatation" catheters has made insertion and continuous monitoring of pulmonary artery pressures feasible in most clinical settings. This type of catheter was designed by Drs. Swan and Ganz of the Cedars–Sinai Medical Center in Los Angeles and bears their names. Although specialized models are available, the basic catheter is approximately 110 cm in length and consists of a double-lumen tube with an inflatable balloon tip (Figure 6.25).

The catheter may be inserted percutaneously or via a venous cutdown. By using continuous pressure and electrocardiographic (ECG) monitoring,

Figure 6.25. (a) Swan-Ganz monitoring catheter for measurement of pulmonary artery and pulmonary capillary wedge pressures, full view; (b) balloon. (Courtesy of Edwards Laboratories, Division of American Hospital Supply Corporation, Santa Ana, CA.)

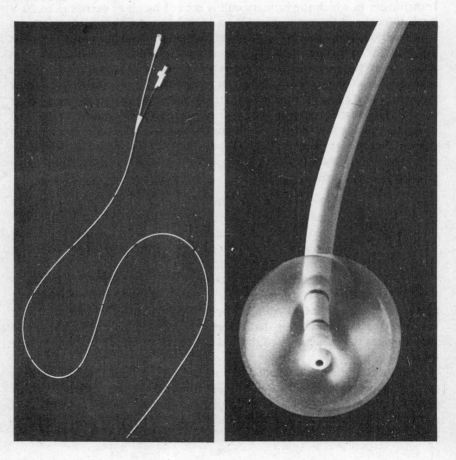

the catheter is threaded into the subclavian vein with the balloon deflated. At this point, the balloon is partially inflated to half capacity (0.4 to 0.6 cm³ of CO_2 or air) and carried downstream to the right atrium by the flow of blood. The balloon is then fully inflated (0.8 cm³) and advanced again so that the blood flow propels it through the tricuspid valve into the right ventricle. From there it is carried through the pulmonary valve into the pulmonary artery, where the balloon wedges in a distal artery branch. The position of the catheter is verified by the pressure tracing, which shifts from a pulmonary artery pressure indicator to the "wedged" pressure waveform position. Under ideal circumstances it should take the physician no more than 1 minute to float the catheter from full balloon inflation in the right atrium to the wedge position. During insertion, the fully inflated balloon covers the hard tip of the catheter, distributing pressure forces evenly across a broad area of the endocardium.

6.2.4.4. *Percutaneous transducers.* An example of a percutaneous blood pressure transducer is shown in Figure 6.26. It shows a transducer connected to a hypodermic needle that has been placed in a vessel of the arm. The three-way stopcock dome permits flushing of the needle, administering of drugs, and withdrawing of blood samples. This transducer can measure arterial or venous pressures, or the pressures of other physiological fluids, by direct attachment to a needle at the point of measurement. It can be used with a continuously self-flushing system without degradation of signal. The transparent plastic dome permits observation of air-bubble formation and consequent ejection. It is designed for use with a portable blood pressure monitor, which provides bridge excitation, balancing, and amplification. The meter scale is calibrated directly into millimeters of mercury. This transducer also has the advantage that it can be connected to a standard intravenous infusion bottle.

6.2.4.5. *Implantable transducers.* Figure 6.27 shows a type of transducer that can be implanted into the wall of a blood vessel or into the wall of the heart itself. This transducer is particularly useful for long-term investigations in animals.

The transducer's body is made of titanium, which has excellent corrosion-resistance characteristics, a relatively low thermal coefficient of expansion, and a low modulus of elasticity, which results in greater strain per unit stress. Four semiconductor strain gages are bonded to the inner surface of the pressure-sensing diaphragm. Transducers of this type come in a number of sizes (from 3 to 7 mm in diameter) for blood pressure measurement. A popular size is 4.5 mm in diameter. Larger sizes are available for pleural pressure. The thickness of the body is 1.2 to 1.3 mm in the various models.

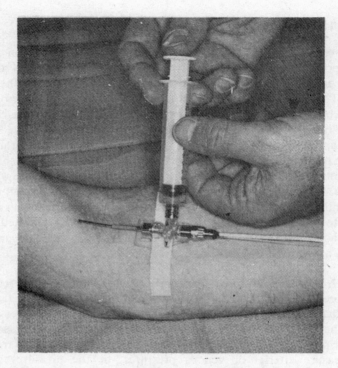

Figure 6.26. Percutaneous blood pressure measurement. Transducer in arm with three-way stopclock dome for administering drugs and withdrawing blood samples. (Courtesy of Gould Inc., Measurement Systems Division; Oxnard, CA.)

Figure 6.27. Implantable pressure transducer. (Courtesy of Konigsberg Instruments, Pasadena, CA.)

The four semiconductors are connected in bridge fashion as shown in Figure 6.19. As blood pressure increases on the diaphragm, the inner surface is stressed. The strain gages are located so that two of them are strained in tension while two are in compression. When the bridge is excited, an output voltage proportional to the blood pressure can be obtained.

Additional resistors, connected externally to the bridge, provide temperature compensation, although these bridges are not extremely sensitive to temperature. Since they operate in the bloodstream at a fairly constant 37 °C, the temperature effects are not serious.

These transducers can be excited with ac or dc and easily lend themselves to telemetry application. In service, they have proven very reliable. Cases of chronic implants (in excess of 2 years) have been reported with no detrimental effect on the animal, the gage, or the wires. The wires are usually insulated with a plastic compound, polyvinylchloride, which is fairly impervious to body fluids.

There are many examples of the use of this type of transducer in animal research, including the implantation in both ventricles of the heart, the aorta, the carotid artery, and the femoral artery. In addition to blood pressures, they have also been used for measuring abdominal, esophageal, thoracic, intrauterine and intracranial pressures.

To implant a transducer in an artery, a longitudinal incision is made; the transducer is inserted with its housing in intimate contact with the arterial walls. The wound is closed with interrupted sutures. For cardiac implants, a stab wound in the ventricle permits ready insertion, with the transducer placed free of both the myocardium and (in the left ventricle) the chordae tendonae. A technique used for long-term studies of the blood pressure in the aorta is to insert the transducer from the opposite side and use a small intercostal artery to bring the wire through. This creates a

Figure 6.28. Transducer implanted in the aorta.

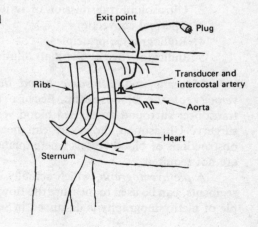

stronger bind in active animals. The wire is held to the artery by a purse-string suture. Figure 6.28 shows such a preparation. In this case the plug was inserted into a biotelemetry transmitter so that the blood pressure data could be received remotely. The use of these transducers and telemetry have been useful in gathering information on exercise, the effect of drugs and extreme environments, and acceleration and impact studies (see Chapter 12).

6.3. MEASUREMENT OF BLOOD FLOW AND CARDIAC OUTPUT

An adequate blood supply is necessary for all organs of the body; in fact, an impaired supply of blood is the cause of various diseases. The ability to measure blood flow in the vessel that supplies a particular organ would therefore be of great help in diagnosing such diseases. Unfortunately, blood flow is a rather elusive variable that cannot be measured easily.

The rate of flow of a liquid or gas in a pipe is expressed as the volume of the substance that passes through the pipe in a given unit of time. Flow rates are therefore usually expressed in liters per minute or milliliters per minute (cm^3/min).

Methods used in industry for flow measurements of other liquids, like the turbine flowmeter and the rotameter, are not very suitable for the measurement of blood flow because they require cutting the blood vessel. These methods also expose the blood to sharp edges, which are conducive to blood-clot formation.

Practically all blood flow meters currently used in clinical and research applications are based on one of the following physical principles:

1. Electromagnetic induction.
2. Ultrasound transmission or reflection.
3. Thermal convection.
4. Radiographic principles.
5. Indicator (dye or thermal) dilution.

Magnetic and *ultrasonic blood flow meters* actually measure the *velocity* of the bloodstream. Because these techniques require that a transducer surround an excised blood vessel, they are mainly used during surgery. Ultrasound, however, can be used transcutaneously to detect obstructions of blood vessels where quantitative blood flow measurements are not required.

A *plethysmograph,* which actually indicates volume changes in body segments, can be used to measure the flow of blood in the limbs. The principle of plethysmography is discussed in Section 6.4.

6.3.1. Magnetic Blood Flow Meters.

Magnetic blood flow meters are based on the principle of magnetic induction. When an electrical conductor is moved through a magnetic field, a voltage is induced in the conductor proportional to the velocity of its motion. The same principle applies when the moving conductor is not a wire, but rather a column of conductive fluid that flows through a tube located in the magnetic field. Figure 6.29 shows how this principle is used in magnetic blood flow meters. A permanent magnet or electromagnet positioned around the blood vessel generates a magnetic field perpendicular to the direction of the blood flow. The voltage induced in the moving blood column is measured with stationary electrodes located on opposite sides of the blood vessel and perpendicular to the direction of the magnetic field.

Figure 6.29. Magnetic blood flow meter, principle.

The most commonly used types of implantable magnetic blood flow probes are shown in Figures 6.30 through 6.32. The *slip-on* or *C type* is applied by squeezing an excised blood vessel together and slipping it through the slot of the probe. In some transducer models the slot is then closed by inserting a keystone-shaped segment of plastic, as shown. Contact is provided by two slightly protruding platinum disks that touch the wall of the blood vessel. For proper operation, the orifice of the probe must fit tightly around the vessel. For this reason, probes of this type are manufactured in sets, with diameters increasing in steps of 0.5 or 1 mm from about 2 to 20 mm. The probes shown in Figure 6.30 can be implanted for chronic use. In contrast, Figure 6.31 shows a model with a long handle for use during surgery.

Figure 6.30. Samples of large and small lumen diameter blood flow probes. (Courtesy of Micron Instruments, Los Angeles, CA.)

Figure 6.31. Blood flow probe—clip-on type for use during surgery. (Courtesy of Biotronex, Silver Springs, MD.)

In the *cannula-type transducer,* the blood flows through a plastic cannula around which the magnet is arranged. The contacts penetrate the walls of the cannula. This type of transducer requires that the blood vessel be cut and its ends slipped over the cannula and secured with a suture. A similar type of transducer (Figure 6.32) is also used to measure the blood flow in extracorporeal devices, such as dialyzers. Magnetic blood flow meters actually measure the mean blood velocity. Because the cross-sectional area at the place of velocity measurement is well defined with either type of transducer, these transducers can be calibrated directly in units of flow.

Figure 6.32. Extracorporeal blood flow probe. (Courtesy of Biotronex, Silver Springs, MD.)

Magnetic blood flow transducers are also manufactured as catheter-tip transducers. For this type, the normal transducer design is essentially turned "inside out," with the electromagnet being located inside the catheter, which has the electrodes at the outside. Catheter transducers cannot be calibrated in flow units, however, because the cross section of the blood vessel at the place of measurement is not defined.

The output voltage of a magnetic blood flow transducer is very small, typically in the order of a few microvolts. In early blood flow meters, a constant magnetic field was used, which caused difficulties with electrode polarization and amplifier drift. To overcome these problems, all contemporary magnetic blood flow meters use electromagnets that are driven by alternating currents. Doing this, however, creates another problem: the change of the magnetic field causes the transducer to act like a transformer and induces error voltages that often exceed the signal levels by several orders of magnitude. Thus, for recovering the signal in the presence of the error voltage, amplifiers with large dynamic range and phase-sensitive or gated detectors have to be used. To minimize the problem, several different waveforms have been advocated for the magnet current, as shown in Figure 6.33. With a sinusoidal magnet current, the induced voltage is also

Figure 6.33. Waveforms used in magnectic blood flow meters and error signals induced by the current: (a) sine wave; (b) square wave; (c) trapezoidal wave.

Figure 6.34. Magnetic blood flow meter, block diagram.

sinusoidal but is 90° out of phase with the flow signal. With a suitable circuit, similar to a bridge, the induced voltage can be partially balanced out. With the magnet current in the form of a square wave, the induced voltage should be zero once the spikes from the polarity reversal have passed. In practice, however, these spikes are often of extremely high amplitude, and the circuitry response tends to extend their effect. A compromise is the use of a magnet current having a trapezoidal waveform. None of the three waveforms used seems to have demonstrated a definite superiority.

The block diagram of a magnetic blood flow meter is shown in Figure 6.34. The oscillator, which drives the magnet and provides a control signal for the gate, operates at a frequency of between 60 and 400 Hz. The use of a gated detector makes the polarity of the output signal reverse when the flow direction reverses. The frequency response of this type of system is usually high enough to allow the recording of the flow pulses, while the mean or average flow can be derived by use of a low-pass filter. Figure 6.35 shows a single-channel magnetic blood flow meter that can be used with a variety of different transducers.

Figure 6.35. Magnetic blood flow meter. (Courtesy of Micron Instruments, Los Angeles, CA.)

6.3.2. Ultrasonic Blood Flow Meters.

In an *ultrasonic blood flow meter,* a beam of ultrasonic energy is used to measure the velocity of flowing blood. This can be done in two different ways. In the *transit time ultrasonic flow meter,* a pulsed beam is directed through a blood vessel at a shallow angle and its transit time is then measured. When the blood flows in the direction of the energy transmission, the transit time is shortened. If it flows in the opposite direction, the transit time is lengthened.

Figure 6.36. Ultrasonic blood flow meter, Doppler type.

More common are ultrasonic flow meters based on the Doppler principle (Figure 6.36). An oscillator, operating at a frequency of several megahertz, excites a piezoelectric transducer (usually made of barium titanate). This transducer is coupled to the wall of an exposed blood vessel and sends an ultrasonic beam with a frequency F into the flowing blood. A small part of the transmitted energy is scattered back and is received by a second transducer arranged opposite the first one. Because the scattering occurs mainly as a result of the moving blood cells, the reflected signal has a different frequency due to the Doppler effect. Its frequency is either $F + F_D$ or $F - F_D$, depending on the direction of the flow. The Doppler component F_D is directly proportional to the velocity of the flowing blood. A fraction of the transmitted ultrasonic energy, however, reaches the second transducer directly, with the frequency being unchanged. After amplification of the composite signal, the Doppler frequency can be obtained at the output of a detector as the difference between the direct and the scattered signal components.

Figure 6.37. Percutaneous Doppler device with probe and earphones. (Courtesy of Veterans Administration Biomedical Engineering and Computing Center, Sepulveda, CA.)

With blood velocities in the range normally encountered, the Doppler signal is typically in the low audio frequency range. Because of the velocity profile of the flowing blood, the Doppler signal is not a pure sine wave, but has more the form of narrow-band noise. Therefore, from a loudspeaker or earphone, the Doppler signal of the pulsating blood flow can be heard as a characteristic "swish—swish—." When the transducers are placed in a suitable mount (which defines the area of the blood vessel), a frequency meter used to measure the Doppler frequency can be calibrated directly in flow-rate units. Unfortunately, Doppler flow meters of this simple design cannot discriminate the direction of flow. More complicated circuits, however, which use the insertion of two quadrature components of the carrier, are capable of indicating the direction of flow.

Transducers for ultrasonic flow meters can be implanted for chronic use. Some commercially available flow meters of this type incorporate a telemetry system to measure the blood flow in unrestrained animals.

Figure 6.37 is an illustration of a simple Doppler device, with the two transducers mounted in a hand-held probe which is now widely used to trace blood vessels close to the surface and to determine the location of vascular obstructions. In order to facilitate transmission of ultrasonic energy, the probe must be coupled to the skin with an aqueous jelly. Such devices can be used to detect the motion of internal structures in the body—for example, the fetal heart. (See Chapter 9 for further discussion of ultrasonic diagnosis.)

6.3.3. Blood Flow Measurement by Thermal Convection

A hot object in a colder-flowing medium is cooled by thermal convection. The rate of cooling is proportional to the rate of the flow of the medium. This principle, often used to measure gas flow, has also been applied to the measurement of blood velocity. In one application, a thermistor in the bloodstream is kept at a constant temperature by a servo system. The electrical energy required to maintain this constant temperature is a measure of the flow rate. In another method an electric heater is placed between two thermocouples or thermistors that are located some distance apart along the axis of the vessel. The temperature difference between the upstream and the downstream sensor is a measure of the blood velocity. A device of the latter type is sometimes called *a thermostromuhr* (literally, from the German "heat current clock"). Thermal convection methods for blood flow determination, although among the oldest ones used for this purpose, have now been widely replaced by the other methods described in this chapter.

6.3.4. Blood Flow Determination by Radiographic Methods

Blood is not normally visible on an X-ray image because it has about the same radio density as the surrounding tissue. By the injection of a contrast medium into a blood vessel (e.g., an iodated organic compound), the circulation pattern can be made locally visible. On a sequential record of the X-ray image (either photographic or on a videotape recording), the progress of the contrast medium can be followed, obstructions can be detected, and the blood flow in certain blood vessels can be estimated. This technique, known as *cine* (or *video*) *angiography,* can be used to assess the extent of damage after a stroke or heart attack.

Another method is the injection of a radioactive isotope into the blood circulation, which allows the detection of vascular obstructions (e.g., in the lung) with an imaging device for nuclear radiation, such as a scanner or gamma camera (see Chapter 14).

Vascular obstructions in the lower extremities can sometimes be detected by measuring differences in the skin temperature caused by the reduced circulation. This can be accomplished by one of the various methods of skin surface temperature measurement described in Chapter 9.

6.3.5. Measurement by Indicator Dilution Methods

The indicator or dye dilution methods are the only methods of blood flow measurement that really measure the blood flow and not the blood velocity. In principle, any substance can be used as an indicator if it mixes readily with blood and its concentration in the blood can be easily determined after mixing. The substance must be stable but should not be retained by the body. It must have no toxic side effects.

An indocyanine dye, Cardiogreen, used in an isotonic solution was long favored as a indicator. Its concentration was detemined by measuring the light absorption with a densitometer (colorimeter). Radioactive isotopes (radioiodited serum albumen) have also been employed for this purpose. The indicator most frequently used today, however, is isotonic saline, which is injected at a temperature lower than the body temperature. The concentration of the saline after mixing with the blood is determined with a sensitive thermistor thermometer (see Chapter 9).

The principle of the dilution method is shown in Figure 6.38. The upper left drawing shows a model of a part of the blood circulation under the (very simplified) assumption that the blood is not recirculated. The indicator is injected into the flow continuously, beginning at time t, at a constant infusion rate I (grams per minute). A detector measures the concentration downstream from the injection point. Figure 6.38 (a) shows the output of a recorder that is connected to the detector. At a certain time after the injection, the indicator begins to appear, the concentration increases, and, finally, it reaches a constant value, C_0 (milligrams per liter). From the measured concentration and the known injection rate, I (in milligrams per minute), the flow can be calculated as

$$F \text{ (liters per minute)} = \frac{I \text{ (milligrams per minute)}}{C_0 \text{ (milligrams per liter)}}$$

The earliest method for determining cardiac output, the *Fick method,* is based on this simple model. The indicator is the oxygen of the inhaled air that is "injected" into the blood in the lungs. The "infusion rate" is determined by measuring the oxygen content of the exhaled air and subtracting it from the known oxygen content of the inhaled room air. The oxygen metabolism only approximately resembles the model of the open circulation, because only part of the oxygen is consumed in the systemic circulation and the returning venous blood still contains some oxygen. Therefore, the oxygen concentration in the returning venous blood has to be determined and subtracted from the oxygen concentration in the arterial blood leaving the lungs. The measurements are averaged over several minutes to reduce the influence of short-term fluctuations. An automated system is available that measures the oxygen concentration (by colorimetry) and the oxygen consumption, and continuously calculates the cardiac output from these measurements.

When a dye or isotope is used as an indicator, the concentration does not assume a steady-state value but increases in steps whenever the recirculated indicator again passes the detector [points R in Figure 6.38 (b)].

Figure 6.38. Flow measurements by indicator dilution methods, principle. (The indicator is injected at time $t = i$.)

The recirculation often occurs before the concentration has reached a plateau. Consequently, a slightly different method is usually used, and the indicator is injected as a bolus instead of being infused at a constant rate. Figure 6.38(c) shows the concentration for this case, again under the assumption that it is an open system. The concentration increases at first, reaches a peak, P, and then decays as an exponential function. This "washout curve" is mainly a result of the velocity profile of the blood, which causes a "spread" of the bolus. To calculate the flow, the area under the concentration curve has to be determined. This is given by the integral:

$$\int_{t=i}^{t=\infty} C \, dt \quad \left(\frac{\text{milligrams}}{\text{liter}} \times \text{minutes} \right)$$

From the value of this integral, and from the amount B of the injected indicator (in milligrams), the flow can be calculated:

$$F \left(\frac{\text{liters}}{\text{minute}} \right) = \frac{B}{\int_{t=i}^{t=\infty} C \, dt} \quad \left(\frac{\text{milligrams}}{\text{milligrams/liter} \times \text{minutes}} \right)$$

Because of the recirculation, the concentration does not show a monotonous decay as in Figure 6.38(b); instead, after some time, a "hump" (R in the figure) occurs. Normally, the portion of the curve preceding the recirculation hump is exponential, and the decay curve can be determined, despite the recirculation, by exponential extrapolation (*Hamilton method*). This was originally done by manually replotting the curve on semilogarithmic paper, which resulted in a straight line for the exponential part of the curve. This line was then extended, the extended part replotted on the original plot, and the extrapolated curve integrated with a planimeter.

To simplify this complicated and time-consuming operation, various special-purpose analog computers were used which employed several different algorithms or determining the area under the curve despite the recirculation distortion. The use of cold saline as an indicator avoids these problems. Because the volume injected is normally only 10 ml, the circulating blood is rewarmed rapidly and no measurable recirculation occurs. Injection of the cool saline and measurement of the blood temperature are frequently performed with a single catheter of special design. This device is called the *Swan-Ganz catheter,* the principle of which is shown in Figure 6.39. It is a special adaptation of the pulmonary artery floatation catheter described in Section 6.2.4.3. This catheter contains four separate lumens. One lumen terminates about 30 cm (12 in.) from the tip and is used to inject

Figure 6.39 labels:
- Inflatable balloon
- Thermistor
- Opening for saline injection
- Opening for inflation of balloon
- Lumen for wires
- Lumen for saline injection
- Wires to thermistor
- Lumen for balloon inflation
- Lumen for pressure measurement

Figure 6.39. Swan-Ganz catheter for the measurement of cardiac output by the thermal dilution method. (Not drawn to scale.) The opening for saline injection is actually located 30 cm distal from the catheter tip and the lumens vary in diameter.

the cooled saline. The second lumen contains two thin wires that lead to a tiny electrical temperature sensor close to the top of the catheter. The third lumen ends at the catheter tip and can be used to measure the blood pressure at this point with one of the pressure transducers described in Section 6.2. The fourth lumen is used to inflate a small rubber ballon at the tip of the catheter. Once the catheter has been inserted into a vein, the ballon is inflated and the returning venous blood carries the catheter until its tip is positioned in the pulmonary artery. The position of the catheter can be checked by measuring the pressure at its tip. Thus, the catheter can, if necessary, be inserted without fluoroscopic control.

The thermistor is connected into a bridge circuit which permits measurement and recording of the blood temperature during injection. A relatively simple analog computer, which consists essentially of an electronic integrator and necessary controls, permits direct reading of the cardiac output. The complete thermodilution catheter and the cardiac output computer are illustrated in Figure 6.40.

Figure 6.40. Cardiac output catheter and computer: (a) complete thermodilution Swan-Ganz floatation catheter; (b) cardiac output computer. (Courtesy of Edwards Laboratories, Division of American Hospital Supply Corporation, Santa Ana, CA.)

6.4. PLETHYSMOGRAPHY

Related to the measurement of blood flow is the measurement of volume changes in any part of the body that result from the pulsations of blood occuring with each heartbeat. Such measurements are useful in the diagnosis of arterial obstructions as well as for pulse-wave velocity measurements. Instruments measuring volume changes or providing outputs that can be related to them are called *plethysmographs,* and the measurement of these volume changes, or phenomena related thereto, is called *plethysmography.*

A "true" plethysmograph is one that actually responds to changes in volume. Such an instrument consists of a rigid cup or chamber placed over the limb or digit in which the volume changes are to be measured, as shown in Figure 6.41. The cup is tightly sealed to the member to be measured so that any changes of volume in the limb or digit reflect as pressure changes inside the chamber. Either fluid or air can be used to fill the chamber.

Figure 6.41. Plethysmograph. (Redrawn from A.C. Guyton, *Textbook of Medical Physiology,* 4th ed., W.B. Saunders Co., 1971, by permission.)

Plethysmographs may be designed for constant pressure or constant volume within the chamber. In either case, some form of pressure or displacement transducer must be included to respond to pressure changes within the chamber and to provide a signal that can be calibrated to represent the volume of the limb or digit. (See the description of the pressure transducers in Section 6.2.2. and displacement transducers in Chapter 2.) The baseline pressure can be calibrated by use of a calibrating syringe.

This type of plethysmograph can be used in two ways (see Figue 6.41). If the cuff, placed upstream from the seal, is not inflated, the output signal is simply a sequence of pulsations proportional to the individual volume changes with each heartbeat.

The plethysmograph illustrated in Figure 6.41 can also be used to measure the total amount of blood flowing into the limb or digit being measured. By inflating the cuff (placed slightly upstream from the seal) to a pressure just above venous pressure, arterial blood can flow past the cuff, but venous blood cannot leave. The result is that the limb or digit increases its volume with each heartbeat by the volume of the blood entering during that beat. The output tracing for this measurement is shown in Figure 6.42. The slope of a line along the peaks of these pulsations represents the overall rate at which blood enters the limb or digit. Note, however, that after a few seconds the slope tends to level off. This is caused by a back pressure that builds up in the limb or digit from the accumulation of blood that cannot escape.

Figure 6.42. Blood volume record from plethysmograph. (From A.C. Guyton, *Textbook of Medical Physiology,* 4th ed., W.B. Saunders Co., 1971, by permission.)

Another device that quite closely approximates a "true" plethysmograph is the *capacitance plethysmograph* shown in Figure 6.43. In this device, which is generally used on either the arm or leg, the limb in which the volume is being measured becomes one plate of a capacitor. The other plate is formed by a fixed screen held at a small distance from the limb by an insulating layer. Often a second screen surrounds the outside plate at a fixed distance to act as a shield for greater electrical stability. Pulsations of the blood in the arm or leg cause variations in the capacitance, because the distance between the limb and the fixed screen varies with these pulsations. Some form of capacitance-measuring device is then used to obtain a continuous measure of these variations. Since the length of the cuff is fixed, the variations in capacitance can be calibrated as volume variations. The device can be calibrated by using a special cone of known volume on which the diameter can be adjusted to provide the same capacitance reading as the limb on which measurements are made. Since the capacitance plethysmograph essentially integrates the diameter changes over a segment of the limb, its readings are reasonably close to those of a "true" plethysmograph. Also, as with the "true" plethysmograph, estimates of the total volume of blood entering an arm or leg over a given period of time can be made by placing an occluding cuff just upstream from the capacitance device and by

Figure 6.43. Capacitance plethysmograph. (Designed by one of the authors for V.A. Hospital, San Francisco, CA.)

pressurizing the cuff to a pressure greater than venous pressure but below arterial pressure.

Several devices, called plethysmographs, actually measure some variable related to volume rather than volume itself. One class of these "pseudo-plethysmographs" measures changes in diameter at a certain cross section of a finger, toe, arm, leg, or other segment of the body. Since volume is related to diameter, this type of device is sufficiently accurate for many purposes.

A common method of sensing diameter changes is through the use of a *mercury strain gage,* which consists of a segment of small-diameter elastic tubing, just long enough to wrap around the limb or digit being measured. When the tube is filled with mercury, it provides a highly compliant strain gage that changes its resistance with changes in diameter. With each pulsation of blood that increases the diameter of the limb or digit, the strain gage elongates and, in stretching, becomes thinner, thus increasing its resistance. The major difficulty in using the mercury strain gage is its extremely low impedance. This drawback necessitates the use of a low-impedance bridge to measure small resistance variations and convert them into voltage changes that can be recorded. A mercury strain gage plethysmograph is shown in Figure 6.44. A difficulty that is common to all diameter-measuring pseudoplethysmographs is that of interpreting single-point diameter changes as volume changes.

Figure 6.44. Mercury strain gage plethysmograph. (Courtesy of Parks Electronics Laboratory, Beaverton, OR.)

Another step away from the true plethysmograph is the *photoelectric plethysmograph*. This device operates on the principle that volume changes in a limb or digit result in changes in the optical density through and just beneath the skin over a vascular region. A photoelectric plethysmograph is shown in Figure 6.45. A light source in an opaque chamber illuminates a small area of the fingertip or other region to which the transducer is applied. Light scattered and transmitted through the capillaries of the region is picked up by the photocell, which is shielded from all other light. As the capillaries fill with blood (with each pulse), the blood density increases, thereby reducing the amount of light reaching the photocell. The result causes resistance changes in the photocell that can be measured on a Wheatstone bridge and recorded. Pulsations recorded in this manner are

Figure 6.45. Photoelectric plethysmograph. (Courtesy of Narco BioSystems, Inc., Houston, TX.)

somewhat similar to those obtained by a true plethysmograph, but the photocell device cannot be calibrated to reflect absolute or even relative volumes. As a result, this type of measurement is primarily limited to detecting the fact that there are pulsations into the finger, indicating heart rate and determining the arrival time of the pulses. One serious difficulty experienced with this type of device is the fact that even the slightest movement of the finger with respect to the photocell or light source results in a severe amount of movement artifact. Furthermore, if the light source produces heat, the effect of the heat may change local circulation beneath the light source and photocell.

A more reliable device is the *impedance plethysomgraph,* in which volume changes in a segment of a limb or digit are reflected as impedance changes. These impedance changes are due primarily to changes in the conductivity of the current path with each pulsation of blood. Impedance plethysmographic measurements can be made using a two-electrode or a four-electrode system. The electrodes are either conductive bands wrapped around the limb or digit to be measured or simple conductive strips of tape attached to the skin. In either case, the electrodes contact the skin through a suitable electrolyte jelly or paste to form an electrode interface and to remove the effect of skin resistance. In a two-electrode system, a constant current is forced through the tissue between the two electrodes, and the resulting voltage changes are measured. In the four-electrode system, the constant current is forced through two outer, or current electrodes, and the voltage between the two inner, or measurement, electrodes is measured. The internal body resistances between the electrodes form a physiological voltage divider. The advantage of the four-electrode system is a much smaller amount of current through the measuring electrodes, thus reducing the possiblility of error due to changes in electrode resistance. Currents used for impedance plethysmography are commonly limited to the low-microampere range. The driving current is ac, sometimes a square wave, and usually of a high-enough frequency (around 10 kHz or higher) to reduce the effect of skin resistance. At these frequencies the capacitive component of the skin electrode interface becomes a significant factor.

Several theories attempt to explain the actual cause of the measured impedance changes. One is that the mere presence of additional blood filling a segment of the body lowers the impedance of that segment. Tests reported by critics of this method, however, claim that the actual impedance difference between the blood-filled state and more "empty" state is not significant.

A second theory is that the increase in diameter due to additional blood in a segment of the body increases the cross-sectional area of the segment's conductive path and thereby lowers the resistance of the path. This may be true to some extent, but again the percentage of area change is very small.

Critics of impedance plethysmography argue that the measured impedance changes are actually changes in the impedance of the skin-electrode interface, caused by pressure changes on the electrodes that occur with each blood pulsation.

Whatever the reason, however, impedance plethysmography does produce a measure that closely approximates the output of a true plethysmograph. Its main difficulty is the problem of relating the output resistance to any absolute volume measurement. As with the photocell plethysmograph, detection of the presence of arterial pulsations, measurment of pulse rate, and determination of time of arrival of a pulse at any given point in the peripheral circulation can all be satisfactorily handled by impedance plethysmography. Also, the impedance plethysmograph can measure time-variant changes in blood volume.

A special form of impedance plethysmography is *rheoencephalography,* the measurement of impedance changes between electrodes positioned on the scalp. Although primarily limited to research applications, this technique provides information related to cerebral blood flow and is sometimes used to detect circulatory differences between the two sides of the head. Theoretically, such information might help in locating blockages in the internal carotid system, which supplies blood to the brain.

Another special type of plethysmograph is the *oculo pneumo plethysmograph,* shown in Figure 6.46. As the name implies, this instrument measures every minute volume changes that occur in the eye with each

Figure 6.46. Oculo pneumo plethysmograph. (Courtesy of Electro-Diagnostic Instruments, Burbank, CA.)

arterial blood pulsation. A small eye cup is placed over the sclera of each eye and is connected to a transducer positioned over the patient's head by a short section of flexible tubing. A vacuum, which can be varied from zero to − 300 mm Hg, is applied to hold the eye cups in place. Pulsations are recorded on two channels of a three-channel pen recorder, one for each eye. The third channel is used to record the vacuum. By periodically allowing the vacuum to build up to − 300 mm Hg and deplete to zero, the instrument can also be used as a recording suction *ophthalmodynamometer,* an instrument for measuring arterial blood pressure within the eye. Ocular plethysmography and blood pressure measurements are of particular interest because the eye provides a site for noninvasive access to the cerebral circulation system. Occlusion of one of the internal carotid arteries or other interference in the blood supply to one hemisphere of the brain can be detected by nonsymmetric pressures and pulsations at the eyes.

In certain rodents the tail is a convenient region for measurement of circulatory factors. For these measurements, a *caudal plethysmograph* is used. Caudal plethysmographs can utilize any of the previously described methods of sensing volume changes or the presence of blood pulsations. The same limitations encountered in human plethysmographic procedures are also found in caudal plethysmography. In addition, a special physiological factor must be considered in measuring blood pulsations from the tail of a rodent. Many animals use their tails as radiators in the control of body temperature. At low temperatures, very little blood actually flows through the vessels of the tail, and plethysmographic measurements become very difficult. If the animal is heated to a temperature at which the tail is used for cooling, however, sufficient blood flow for good plethysmographic measurements is usually found. Sometimes the necessary temperature for good caudal measurements is so near the point of overheating that traumatic effects are encountered.

6.5. MEASUREMENT OF HEART SOUNDS

In the early days of auscultation a physician listened to heart sounds by placing his ear on the chest of the patient, directly over the heart. It was probably during the process of treating a well-endowed, but bashful young lady that someone developed the idea of transmitting heart sounds from the patient's chest to the physician's ear via a section of cardboard tubing. This was the forerunner of the stethoscope, which has become a symbol of the medical profession.

The *stethoscope* (from the Greek word, *stethos,* meaning chest, and *skopein,* meaning "to examine") is simply a device that carries sound energy from the chest of the patient to the ear of the physician via a column of air. There are many forms of stethoscopes, but the familiar configuration has two earpieces connected to a common bell or chest piece. Since the system is strictly acoustical, there is no amplification of sound, except for any that might occur through resonance and other acoustical characteristics.

Unfortunately, only a small portion of the energy in heart sounds is in the audible frequency range. Thus, since the dawning of the age of electronics, countless attempts have been made to convince the medical profession of the advantage of amplifying heart sounds, with the idea that if the sound level could be increased, a greater portion of the sound spectrum could be heard and greater diagnostic capability might be achieved. In addition, high-fidelity equipment would be able to reproduce the entire frequency range, much of which is missed by the stethoscope. In spite of these apparent advantages, the *electronic stethoscope* has never found favor with the physician. The principal argument is that doctors are trained to recognize heart defects by the way they sound through an ordinary stethoscope, and any variations therefrom are foreign and confusing. Nevertheless, a number of electronic stethoscopes are available commercially.

Instruments for graphically recording heart sounds have been more successful. As stated in Chapter 5, a graphic record of heart sounds is called a *phonocardiogram*. The instrument for producing this recording is called a *phonocardiograph*. Although instruments specifically designed for phonocardiography are rare, components suitable for this purpose are readily available.

The basic transducer for the phonocardiogram is a microphone having the necessary frequency response, generally ranging from below 5 Hz to above 1000 Hz. An amplifier with similar response characteristics is required, which may offer a selective lowpass filter to allow the high-frequency cutoff to be adjusted for noise and other considerations. In one instance, where the associated pen recorder is inadequate to reproduce higher frequencies, an integrator is employed and the envelope of frequencies over 80 Hz is recorded along with actual signals below 80 Hz.

The readout of a phonocardiograph is either a high-frequency chart recorder or an oscilloscope. Because most pen galvanometer recorders have an upper-frequency limitation of around 100 or 200 Hz, photographic or light-galvanometer recorders are required for faithful recording of heart sounds. Although normal heart sounds fall well within the frequency range of pen recorders, the high-frequency murmurs that are often important in diagnosis require the greater response of the photographic device.

Some manufacturers of multiple-channel physiological recording systems claim the phonocardiogram as one of the measurements they offer. They have available as part of their system a microphone and amplifier suitable for the heart sounds, the amplifier often being the same one used for EMG (see Chapter 10). Some of these systems, however, have only a pen recorder output, which limits the high-frequency response of the recorded signal to about 100 or 200 Hz.

The presence of higher frequencies (murmurs) in the phonocardiogram indicates a possible heart disorder. For this reason, a spectral analysis of heart sounds can provide a useful diagnostic tool for discriminating between normal and abnormal hearts. This type of analysis, however, requires a digital computer with a high-speed analog-to-digital conversion capability and some form of Fourier-transform software. A typical spectrum of heart sounds is shown in Figure 6.47.

Microphones for phonocardiograms are designed to be placed on the chest, over the heart. However, heart sounds are sometimes measured from other vantage points. For this purpose, special microphone transducers are placed at the tips of catheters to pick up heart sounds from within the chambers of the heart or from the major blood vessels near the heart. Frequency-response requirements for these microphones are about the same as for phonocardiograph microphones. However, special requirements dictated by the size and configuration of the catheter must be considered in their construction. As might be expected, the difference in acoustical paths makes these heart-sound patterns appear somewhat different from the usual phonocardiogram patterns.

The *vibrocardiograph* and the *apex cardiograph,* which measure the vibrocardiogram and apex cardiogram, respectively, also use microphones

Figure 6.47. Frequency spectrum of heart sounds. (Courtesy of Computer Medical Science Corporation, Tomball, TX.)

as transducers. However, since these measurements involve the low-frequency vibrations of the heart against the chest wall, the measurement is normally one of displacement or force rather than sound. Thus, the microphone must be a good force transducer, with suitable low-frequency coupling from the chest wall to the microphone element. For the apex cardiogram, the microphone must be coupled to a point between the ribs. A soft rubber or plastic cone attached to the element of the microphone gives good results for this purpose.

Because the vibrocardiogram and the apex cardiogram do not contain the high-frequency components of the heart sounds, these signals can be handled by the same type of amplifiers and recorders as the electrocardiogram (see Section 6.1). Often, these signals are recorded along with a channel of ECG data to maintain time reference. In this case, one channel of a multichannel ECG recorder is devoted to the heart vibration signal.

For recording the Korotkoff sounds from a partially occluded artery (see Chapter 5 and Section 6.2), a microphone is usually placed beneath the occluding cuff or over the artery immediately downstream from the cuff. The waveform and frequency content of these sounds are not as important as the simple identification of their presence, so these sounds generally do not require the high-frequency response specified for the phonocardiogram. Circuitry for identification of these sounds is included in certain automated, indirect blood pressure measuring devices (see Section 6.2.2).

Measurement of the ballistocardiogram requires a platform mounted on a set of extremely flexible springs. When a person lies on the platform, the movement of his body in response to the beating of his heart and the ejection of blood causes similar movement of the platform. The amount of movement can be measured by any of the displacement or velocity transducers or accelerometers described in Chapter 2.

7

Patient Care
and Monitoring

One area of biomedical instrumentation that is becoming increasingly familiar to the general public is that of patient monitoring. Here electronic equipment provides a continuous watch over the vital characteristics and parameters of the critically ill. In the coronary care and other intensive-care units in hospitals, thousands of lives have been saved in recent years because of the careful and accurate monitoring afforded by this equipment. Public awareness of this type of instrumentation has also been greatly increased by its frequent portrayal in television programs, both factual and fictional.

Essentially, patients are monitored because they have an unbalance in their body systems. This can be caused by a heart attack or stroke, for example, or it may be the result of a surgical operation, which can drastically disturb these systems. By continual monitoring, the patient problems can be detected as they occur and remedies taken before these problems get out of hand.

In hospitals that have engineering or electronics departments, patient-monitoring units, both fixed and portable, form a substantial part of the workload of the biomedical engineer or technician. Engineers and technicians are usually involved in the design of facilities for coronary or other intensive-care units, and they work closely with the medical staff to ensure that the equipment to be installed meets the needs of that particular hospital. Ensuring the safety of patients who may have conductive catheters or other direct electrical connections to their hearts is another function of these biomedical engineers and technicians. They also work with the contractors in the installation of the monitoring equipment and, when this job is completed, supervise equipment operation and maintenance. In addition, the engineering staff participates in the planning of improvements and additions, for there are many cases in which an intensive-care unit, even after careful design and installation, fails in some respect to meet the special needs of the hospital, and an in-house solution is required.

Since the first edition of this book was written, much of the equipment then in use has become obsolete except for some basic components. The trend has been toward more automation and computerization. At first, large-scale computers were used and still are, but recent innovations are in the use of microcomputers. Although some of the illustrations in this chapter involve computerized equipment, the reader is referred to Chapter 15 for a discussion of the elements of the computer in biomedical instrumentation.

The first sections of this chapter are concerned with the various elements that compose a patient-monitoring system and the system itself. Some of the problems often encountered are discussed. Two additional topics are included which, although an integral part of the coronary care unit, do have uses in other areas of medical care: the pacemaker and the defibrillator. Many patients have a need for both of these devices while in coronary care, and many leave the unit with implanted pacemakers.

7.1. THE ELEMENTS OF INTENSIVE-CARE MONITORING

The need for intensive-care and patient monitoring has been recognized for centuries. The 24-hour nurse for the critically ill patient has, over the years, become a familiar part of the hospital scene. But only in the last few years has equipment been designed and manufactured that is reliable enough and sufficiently accurate to be used extensively for patient monitoring. Nurses are still there, but roles have changed somewhat, for they now have powerful tools at their disposal for acquiring and assimilating information about the patients under their care. They are therefore able to render better service to a larger number of patients and are better able to react promptly and properly to an emergency situation. With the capability of providing an immediate alarm in the event of certain abnormalities in the behavior of a patient's heart, monitoring equipment makes it possible to summon a physician or nurse in time to administer emergency aid, often before permanent damage can occur. With prompt warning and by providing such information as the electrocardiogram record just prior to, during, and after the onset of cardiac difficulty, the monitoring system enables the physician to give a patient the correct drug rapidly. In some cases, even this process can be automated.

Physicians do not always agree among themselves as to which physiological parameters should be monitored. The number of parameters monitored must be carefully weighed against the cost, complexity, and reliability of the equipment. There are, however, certain parameters that provide vital information and can be reliably measured at relatively low cost. For example, nearly all cardiac-monitoring units continuously measure the electrocardiogram from which the heart rate is easily derived. The electrocardiogram waveform is usually displayed and often recorded. Temperature is also frequently monitored.

On the other hand, there are some variables, such as blood pressure, in which the benefit of continuous monitoring is debatable in light of the problems associated with obtaining the measurement. Since continuous direct blood pressure monitoring requires catheterization of the patient, the traumatic experience of being catheterized may be more harmful to the patient than the lack of continuous pressure information. In fact, intermittent blood pressure measurements by means of a sphygmomanometer, either manual or automatic, might well provide adequate blood pressure information for most purposes. It is not the intent of this book to pass judgment on which measurements should be included but, rather, to familiarize the reader with the instrumentation used in patient care and monitoring.

Since patient-monitoring equipment is usually specified as a system, each manufacturer and each hospital staff has its own ideas as to what should be included in the unit. Thus, a wide variety of configurations can be found in hospitals and in the manufacturers' literature. Since cardiac monitoring is the most extensively used type of patient monitoring today, it provides an appropriate example to illustrate the more general topic of patient monitoring.

The concept of intensive coronary care had little practicality until the development of electronic equipment that was capable of reliably measuring and displaying the electrical activity of the heart on a continuous basis. With such cardiac monitors, instant detection of potentially fatal arrhythmias finally became feasible. Combined with stimulatory equipment to reactivate the heart in the event of such an arrhythmia, a full system of equipment to prevent sudden death in such cases is now available.

In the intensive coronary-care area, monitoring equipment is installed beside the bed of each patient to measure and display the electrocardiogram, heart rate, and other parameters being monitored from that patient. In addition, information from several bedside stations is usually displayed on a central console at the nurses' station.

There are a multiplicity of systems available today, but only a few are illustrated, to give the reader a general idea of their operation. Figure 7.1 shows the bedside unit of an Alpha 9 unit currently in use. The central nurses' station is illustrated in Figure 7.2. To demonstrate some of the changes in design. Figures 7.3 and 7.4 show two earlier types of nurses' stations.

As might be expected, many different room and facility layouts for intensive-coronary-care units are in use. One type that is quite popular is a U-shaped design in which six or eight cubicles or rooms with glass windows surround the nurses' central monitoring station. Although the optimum number of stations per central console has not been established, a group of six or eight seems most efficient. For larger hospitals, monitoring of 16 to 24 beds can be accomplished by two or three central stations. The exact number depends on the individual hospital, its procedures, and the physical layout of the patient-care area. In certain areas in which recruitment of trained nurses is difficult, this factor could also be considered in the selecting of the best design.

Although patient-monitoring systems vary greatly in size and configuration, certain basic elements are common to nearly all of them. A cardiac-care unit, for example, generally includes the following components:

1. Skin electrodes to pick up the ECG potentials. These electrodes are described in Chapter 4.

2. Amplification equipment similar to that described in Chapter 6 for the electrocardiograph.

3. A cathode-ray-tube (CRT) display that permits direct observation of the ECG waveforms. The bedside monitors usually contain fairly small cathode-ray-tube screens (2 to 5 in. in diameter), and each displays the ECG waveform from one patient. The central nurses' station generally has a larger screen on which electrocardiograms from several patients are displayed simultaneously.

4. A rate meter used to indicate the average number of heartbeats per minute and to provide a continuous indication of the heart rate. On most units, an audible beep or flashing light (or both) occurs with each heartbeat.

5. An alarm system, actuated by the rate meter, to alert the nurse or other observer by audible or visible signals whenever the heart rate falls below or exceeds some adjustable preset range (e.g., 40 to 150 beats per minute).

Figure 7.1. Alpha 9 bedside monitor (Courtesy of Spacelabs Inc. Chatsworth, CA.).

Figure 7.2. Nurses' central monitoring station (Courtesy of Spacelabs Inc., Chatsworth. CA.).

Figure 7.3. Eight channel nurses' station. (Courtesy of Spacelabs, Inc., Chatsworth, CA.)

Figure 7.4. Multiple central monitoring unit. (Courtesy of Spacelabs, Inc., Chatsworth, CA.)

In addition to these basic components, the following elements are useful and are often found in cardiac-monitoring systems:

1. A direct-writeout device (an electrocardiograph) to obtain, on demand or automatically, a permanent record of the electrocardiogram seen on the oscilloscope. Such documentation is valuable for comparative purposes and it usually required in the event of an alarm condition. In combination with the tape loop described below, this written record provides a valuable diagnostic tool.

2. A memory-tape loop to record and play back the electrocardiogram for the 15 to 60 seconds just prior to an alarm condition. Recording of the ECG may continue until the system is reset. In this way, the electrical events associated with the heart immediately before, during, and following an alarm situation can be displayed if a nurse or other observer was not present at the time of the occurrence.

3. Additional alarm systems triggered by ECG parameters other than the heart rate. These alarms may be activated by premature ventricular contractions or by widening of the QRS complex in the ECG (see Chapter 3). Either situation may provide advance indication of a more serious problem.

4. Electrical circuits to indicate that an electrode has become disconnected or that a mechanical failure has occurred somewhere else in the monitoring system. Such a lead failure alarm permits instrumentation problems to be distinguished from true clinical emergencies.

Although not usually considered to be a part of the biomedical instrumentation system for patient monitoring, closed-circuit television is also used in some intensive-care areas to provide visual coverage in addition to monitoring the patients' vital parameters. Where television is employed, a camera is focused on each patient. The nurses' central station has either a bank of monitors, one for each patient, or a single monitor, which can be switched to any camera as desired.

Experience has shown that in spite of its value and increasing popularity, patient-monitoring equipment is not without its problems or limitations. Although many of the difficulties originally encountered in the development of such systems have been corrected, a number of significant problems remain. A few examples are given below.

Example 1. Noise and movement artifacts have always been a problem in the measurement of the electrocardiogram (see Chapter 6). Since heart-rate meters, and subsequently alarm devices, are usually triggered by the R wave of the ECG, and many systems cannot distinguish between the R wave and a noise spike of the same amplitude, movement or muscle interference may be counted as additional heartbeats. As a result, the rate meter shows a higher heart rate than that of the patient, and a high-rate false alarm is actuated. Unfortunately, repeated false alarms tend to cause the staff of the cardiac-care unit to lose confidence in the patient-monitoring equipment and therefore to ignore the alarms or turn them off altogether. Better electrodes, which reduce patient movement artifacts, and more careful placement of electrodes to avoid areas of muscle activity can help to some extent. Electronic filtering to reduce the response of the system at frequencies at which interference might be expected is also partially effective. Some of the more sophisticated systems include circuitry that identifies additional characteristics of the ECG other than simply the amplitude of the R wave, thus further reducing the possibility of mistaking noise for the ECG signal. In spite of all these measures, the possibility of false alarm signals due to movement or muscle artifact is still a real problem.

Example 2.   The low-rate alarm can be falsely activated if the R wave of the ECG is of insufficient amplitude to trigger the rate meter. This can happen if the contact between the electrodes and the skin becomes disturbed because of improper application of the electrodes, excessive patient sweating, or drying of the electrode paste or jelly. In some cases, the indication on the oscilloscope approximates that which might appear if the heart stopped beating. Even though a false low-rate alarm indicates an equipment problem that requires attention, the danger of mistaking failure of the electrode connections for cardiac standstill can have serious consequences. To prevent this possibility, lead-failure alarms have been designed and are built into some patient-monitoring systems.

Example 3.   Because the ECG electrodes must remain attached to the skin for long periods of time during patient monitoring, inflammatory reactions at electrode locations are common. Special skin care and proper application of the electrodes can help minimize this problem.

Special electrode placement patterns are often used in patient-monitoring applications. These patterns are generally intended to approximate the standard limb lead signals (see Chapter 6) while avoiding the actual placement of electrodes on the patient's arms and legs. Instead, the RA, LA, and RL electrodes are placed at appropriate positions on the patient's chest. Because many possible chest placement patterns provide suitable approximations of the three limb leads, no standard pattern has been determined, although some hospitals and manufacturers of patient monitoring equipment may specify a particular arrangement.

7.1.1. Patient-Monitoring Displays

An important feature of any patient-monitoring system is its ability to display the physiological waveforms being monitored. Clear, faithful reproductions of the ECG, arterial blood pressure, and other variables enable the medical staff to periodically check a patient's progress and make vital decisions at times of crisis. Although paper-chart recordings are often used to provide a permanent record of the data, the principal display device for patient monitoring is the cathode-ray tube (CRT). Ranging from a small single- or dual-channel display at the patient's bedside to a large multichannel unit at the nurses' station, the CRT provides a continuous, current presentation of one or more waveforms from a given patient or simultaneous waveforms from several patients. In addition, computerized patient-monitoring systems may permit display of calculated parameters and graphic information, including trend plots and comparisons of current measurement results with past data.

Two types of CRT displays are found in patient-monitoring systems, the conventional or "bouncing-ball" display and the more recent nonfade display. Both utilize the same basic cathode-ray tube, but incorporate different methods of presenting information on the screen.

The *conventional* or *bouncing-ball display* is nothing more than an oscilloscope with the horizontal sweep driven by a slow-speed sweep generator that causes the electron beam to move from left to right at a predetermined rate, selectable from a front-panel control. Sweep rates of 25 and 50 mm/sec are often included to correspond to standard ECG chart speeds. Multiple traces are obtained by an electronic chopper that causes the electron beam to sequentially jump from trace to trace, sharing time among the various channels of data. Eight or more channels can be presented simultaneously in this manner, all of which are presented in time relationship with each other. Because of the high speed with which the beam jumps from trace to trace, the display appears to the viewer as a number of continuous patterns traced horizontally across the screen, each apparently traced by a dot of light that moves up and down to follow the waveform as all of the dots move simultaneously across the screen from left to right. This type of display is often called a bouncing-ball display because each spot of light seems to bounce up and down as it traces the ECG or other waveform being presented.

As the electron beam moves across and writes a pattern on the face of the CRT, the earlier portion of the trace begins to fade away and finally disappears. The ability of the trace to remain visible on the face of the CRT is known as *persistence*. The duration of this persistence is determined by the phosphor (coating) inside the CRT. The longest persistence tubes that are available allow the trace to be visible for approximately 1 second. In the case of patterns like the ECG or blood pressure waveforms, for example, which may occur at a rate of 60 events per minute, the persistence of the tube will allow the viewer to see only one cycle of the waveform. In addition, this displayed waveform will not be uniformly bright. The early portion of the display will always be dimmer than the more current portion. Such a "temporary display" has great limitations for the observer, who may need to evaluate the waveform for diagnostic purposes. Doing so becomes an almost impossible task. When it is necessary to perform any analysis on such waveforms, the waveforms must be permanently recorded on paper. Any event that might have occurred unseen may be lost within a second and cannot be documented on paper even with a time lag or delay between the CRT and writeout device.

For years the bouncing-ball display was the only available type of waveform display, and it was useful despite its limitations. A few of the less expensive systems still use this method, although most modern patient monitors feature nonfade displays.

Nonfade displays also use the cathode-ray tube, but in an entirely different way. In the nonfade method, the electron beam rapidly scans the entire surface of the CRT screen in a television-like raster pattern, but with the brightness level so low that the background raster is not visible. The beam is brightened only when a brightening signal is applied to the CRT by a method called *Z-axis modulation*. This brightening signal is applied only when the electron beam passes a location that is to contain a part of the displayed waveform, at which time it produces a dot on the screen. Each time the entire screen is scanned, each of the traces appears as a series of dots similar to the ECG pattern shown in Figure 7.5. However, the dots are so close together and the scan is so rapid that they appear as a continuous trace.

Fig. 7.5. ECG pattern made up of dots.

The brightening signal is produced from a digital memory in which several seconds of data from each channel of the patient monitor are stored. The memory is constantly renewed so that the oldest data are continually replaced by the most recent. The memory may be an independent digital memory controlled by hardwired logic circuitry or it may be part of a microprocessor or computer incorporated into the patient monitor (see Chapter 15).

The displayed waveforms usually contain several cycles of ECG or respiratory data, all of which are of uniform brightness. The waveforms may either slowly move across the screen from right to left, with the most recent data at the extreme right, or they may remain stationary with the newer data "erasing" the older information as it is written from left to right. Either way, the display may be stopped at any time in order to allow detailed observation of any part of the pattern. Also, in many units, a stored trace may be expanded at any time to permit more detailed observation.

In addition the nonfade display makes possible the presentation of digital numerical readouts on the face of the monitor screen. Thus, the ongoing heart rate, systolic and diastolic blood pressure, and the patient's temperature may be displayed along with the ECG and blood pressure waveform.

(a)

Figure 7.6. PDS 3000 monitoring system. (a) Bedside unit. (b) Nurses' unit. (Courtesy of General Electric Co., Medical Systems Div., Milwaukee, WI.)

(b)

An example of an intensive-care patient-monitoring system using a nonfade display is the Patient Data System PDS 3000, shown in Figures 7.6 and 7.7. Figure 7.6(a) and (b) show the bedside assembly and central monitoring unit, respectively. The bedside unit displays four nonfade waveforms, together with digital numeric readouts and transmits analog waveforms and digital data to other portions of the system. The central-station unit is equipped with a dual-channel graph. It is a distributed-intelligence system with a microcomputer (see Chapter 15) integrated into each patient's bedside monitor. The bedside microcomputers communicate with another microcomputer at the nurses' central station. The interconnection of the microcomputers form a "star" network with the central nurses' station at the center and the bedside units functioning as satellites. The communications channel from the central station to each bedside is bi-directional so that data and control signals can flow freely in each direction between microcomputers.

It should be noted that the nurses' control station accepts data from up to eight patients; provides single- or dual-channel strip-chart recordings which can be either delayed or produced in real time; identifies all recordings by bed number, time of day, and date; and provides heart rate, lead configuration, and (if monitored) blood pressure values. Figure 7.7 shows a typical hospital installation.

Figure 7.7. This view from the General Electric Patient Data System nurses' station shows two of nine beds in the Intensive Care Unit of Eisenhower Memorial Hospital's expanded facilities. The 185-bed hospital was recently expanded from 138 beds by means of a 78,000-square-foot, three-story addition in the shape of a cross. The addition also features six Coronary Care Unit beds, five new surgeries and 11 recovery beds. (Courtesy of the Eisenhower Medical Center, Palm Desert, CA.)

7.2. DIAGNOSIS, CALIBRATION, AND REPAIRABILITY OF PATIENT-MONITORING EQUIPMENT

Just as the physician must diagnose the patient, engineers or technicians may be required to diagnose the patient-monitoring equipment in the hospital. In connection with the typical intensive-care unit, there is often an associated maintenance and design group composed of engineers and technicians who usually have access to a wide variety of diagnostic devices for electronic equipment.

Not only is it necessary to keep medical instrumentation in good repair, but it is equally important to keep all equipment calibrated accurately. Many pieces of medical electronics have built-in calibration devices. For example, all electrocardiographs have a 1-mV calibration voltage available internally. Many patient monitors have built-in calibration features. In recent years, manufacturers of electronic servicing equipment have designed many items especially for the hospital and other medical applications. An excellent example of such a device is the Medical Instrumentation Calibration System illustrated in Figure 7.8.

Figure 7.8. Medical instrumentation calibration system. (Courtesy of Tektronix Inc., Beaverton, OR.)

(a)

(b)

(c)

Figure 7.9. Components of Alpha 9 monitoring system. (a) Monitor unit. (b) Heart rate module. (c) Pressure module. (Courtesy of Spacelabs Inc., Chatsworth, CA.)

The basic configuration is a special mobile cart carrying an oscilloscope and two mainframe power units. These mainframes accommodate the modular plug-in instruments, which can be any of the more than 30 available units. Typical plug-ins that might be selected are digital multimeters, function generators, frequency counters, amplifiers, and power supplies. The major primary power supply components are located in the mainframe units, where they can be shared by the plug-in instruments.

Signal interconnections between plug-ins can be made through the main-frame. All units share a common ground.

This unit is capable of repair or calibration of most types of electronic equipment used in medical applications today, including ECGs, EEGs, complete patient monitors, X-ray and cardiac-unit control systems, ultrasound systems, radio-frequency heating and diathermy equipment, and radio-frequency and direct telemetry.

It is important to have all parts of the patient-monitoring equipment designed for easy replacement or repair or both. To achieve the former, most intensive-care equipment is of a modular design, so that individual component groups, such as amplifiers, can be removed and replaced easily. An example of this feature is illustrated in Figure 7.9. These three components are all part of the bedside unit shown in Figure 7.1.

Figure 7.9(a) shows the entire monitor unit. Figure 7.9(b) shows the blood pressure unit and part (c) shows the heart rate unit. Both can be removed and replaced very rapidly in the case of malfunction.

7.3. OTHER INSTRUMENTATION FOR MONITORING PATIENTS

In addition to its use at the bedside, as discussed in Section 7.1 and illustrated in Figures 7.1 through 7.7, patient-monitoring equipment is often found in other applications in the hospital. An important example is in the operating room. Figure 7.10 shows one type of unit used during surgery. The main features of this type of system are the large multichannel oscilloscope, the capability of obtaining a permanent ECG record on the chart recorder, and plug-in signal-conditioner modules that provide versatility and choice of measurement parameters.

The chart recorder has eight channels, to be used as dictated by the specific requirements of the surgical team. The fluid writing system is pressurized and writes dry. The frequency response of such a unit is up to 40 Hz full scale. The trace is rectilinear, and the channel span is 40 mm graduated in 50 divisions. Two event channels are provided to relate information on the chart to specific events. The recorder has a large number of chart speeds selected by pushbuttons, ranging from 0.05 to 200 mm/sec.

As mentioned earlier, a variety of plug-in modules are available for use with the unit. These biomedical signal conditioners include a universal unit for various bioelectric signals, an ECG unit, an EEG unit, a biotachometer, a transducer unit, an integrator, a differentiator, and an impedance unit. These units are all compatible. Figure 7.11 shows the front plates of some of them, and Figure 7.12 shows a complete biotachometer unit.

Figure 7.10. Surgical monitoring system. (Courtesy of Gould, Inc., Brush Instruments Division, Cleveland, OH.)

Each of the signal conditioners includes two separate submodules: a coupler and a medical amplifier. The coupler contains the circuitry and controls that are essential to its nameplate function. The amplifier or "back end" contains circuitry that is exactly the same for each channel. This "back end" can be obtained separately, thus reducing a possible investment in idle circuitry. In the last few years many manufacturers of biomedical monitoring equipment have improved their systems to include such versatility.

The amplifier units are designed for broad-band amplification from dc to 10 kHz. The amplifier is a ground-isolation type that eliminates a potential shock hazard to the patient by isolating him to the extent that current through his body cannot exceed 2 μA (see Chapter 16).

Each amplifier provides a buffered output drive signal for peripheral monitoring equipment, such as tape recorders, oscilloscopes, and computers.

(a)   (b)   (c)   (c

Figure 7.11. Front panel of signal conditioner units: (a) EEG; (b) universal; (c) integrator; (d) transducer. (Courtesy of Gould, Inc., Brush Instruments Division, Cleveland, OH.)

Figure 7.12. View of biotachometer module. (Courtesy of Gould, Inc., Brush Instruments Division, Cleveland, OH.)

Each biomedical coupler unit has a high input impedance compatible with the function it performs, plus differential inputs with good common-mode rejection at 60 Hz. In general, the sensitivity varies with the particular unit. However, the universal biomedical coupler, which can be used for phonocardiography, electromyography, electrocardiography, and other measurements involving low- or medium-voltage signals, has a measurement range on an ac setting of from 20 μV per division to 25 mV full scale, and, on dc, of from 1 mV per division to 25 V full scale.

It is often the case that new innovations can be added to equipment that has been used for many years. For example, the equipment shown in Figures 7.10 through 7.12 is many years old, but the manufacturer keeps improving and adding to the system. A recent addition is the pressure computer, shown in Figure 7.13, which can be plugged into the existing frame as a modular unit. This plug-in unit is self-powered, employing all solid-state circuitry. It supplies $\pm$ 2.5 Vdc excitation for strain-gage-based transducers having sensitivities from 50 to 500 μV/volt excitation/cm Hg.

Front-panel controls allow electronic shunt calibration of transducers either with or without built-in calibration resistors, and balancing of transducers to the zero reference pressure after calibration. Other front-panel controls permit selection of overall amplifier gain, scale factor of recorder outputs, and pen position for graphic recording.

An eight-position mode switch permits the complete waveform or any derived parameter to be fed to a graphic recorder or other analog device such as an oscilloscope, FM tape recorder, or remote monitor. In addition, all derived parameters are available simultaneously (independent of the mode-switch position) at fixed gain for digital display. The digital display update rate is internally adjustable from 6 to 30 per minute.

The unit displays the complete dynamic waveform in direct mode and simultaneously derives the following parameters from the waveform: systolic pressure, diastolic pressure, pulse pressure, average (mean) pressure, rate of change of pressure (dp/dt), and pulse rate. It has a range of -30 to $+500$ mm Hg for systolic and diastolic pressure and 5 to 300 mm Hg for pulse pressure. The pressure derivative range is from 100 mm Hg/sec/ division to 15,000 mm Hg/sec full scale. Pulse rate is measured from 20 to 300 beats per minute.

Another special type of monitoring device is the *arterial diagnostic unit* (ADU) shown in Figure 7.14. This mobile cart combines several commonly used instruments for peripheral arterial evaluation. The ADU provides automated pressure-cuff inflation for rapidly determining segmental pressures and post-exercise pressure trends in noninvasive peripheral arterial evaluations. The strip chart can be used for recording Doppler-flow pulse waveforms, ECG traces, or other physiological waveforms. It has a heated stylus strip-chart recorder, a bidirectional Doppler-flow meter with external

Figure 7.13. Blood pressure computer unit. (Courtesy of Gould Inc., Instrument Systems Division, Cleveland, OH.)

Figure 7.14. Arterial diagnostic unit (Courtesy of Narco Bio-Systems, Houston, TX.)

Figure 7.15. Meddars catheterization laboratory recording systems. (Courtesy of Honeywell Inc., Test Instruments Division, Denver, CO.)

loudspeaker and headphones, an ECG telemetry transmitter, a nonfade two-channel oscilloscope with freeze capability, a compressor with regulator and pressure gages, a foot-switch activator for cuffs and recorder, a digital heart rate tachometer, and a noninvasive determination of common femoral artery pressure.

Another place in the hospital where portability can be an advantage is in the catheterization laboratory. The technique of catheterization has been described in a number of places in Chapter 6 (see Figure 6.18 for an illustration of the process). Essentially the *cath. lab* is the room in which cardiologists perform diagnostic catheterizations. If a patient is suspected of having a blockage, say, of one of the coronary arteries, he or she would be brought into the cath. lab to undergo analysis to determine if there is such a blockage and its extent, if it exists.

The catheterization technique is to introduce a catheter into the heart by the method shown in Figure 6.18 and through this catheter to inject a radiopaque dye into the cardiac chamber. The passage of the dye as it traverses the arteries is monitored fluoroscopically on a monitor. In this way, any blockage can be seen and a motion picture can be taken simultaneously.

Catheterization can be a dangerous procedure for the patient, even though fatalities are infrequent. Therefore, the patient must be monitored continuously. Many units have extensive built-in monitoring, but since cath. labs are usually small, there is an advantage to having a smaller mobile unit available. Such a unit is illustrated in Figure 7.15. This is a computerized unit capable of monitoring all the variables usually needed in the cath. lab, such as cardiovascular pressures, cardiac output, and ECG. Patient files may be reviewed by instant recall. Six channels of analog data can be recorded on continuous strip charts, and computer-generated results can be shown on the same page as the waveforms. Test results are eventually incorporated in a comprehensive final report, which includes calculated results, derived results, comments, summary, and a pictorial representation of the heart, showing pressures, oxygen saturation, and so on. During the procedure the patient's name, physiological data in digital form, blood pressure, and ECG waveforms are also displayed on the cathode-ray tube as a nonfade display. The console has a keyboard which allows an operator instant access to any information that he or she wishes to identify. There is also a 12-digit, 10-function calculator adjacent to the keyboard.

7.4. THE ORGANIZATION OF THE HOSPITAL FOR PATIENT-CARE MONITORING

The engineer or technician should be familiar with the overall organization of the hospital with respect to monitoring equipment. In the previous sections of this chapter, many types of equipment and services have been described. The following summary is provided to give an overall view.

A broad classification for patients in the hospital is to categorize them as surgical or nonsurgical. The heart of the surgical facilities is the *operating room,* where the surgery is actually performed. The monitoring equipment in this room usually includes measurement of heart rate, venous and arterial blood pressures, ECG and EEG (see Chapter 10 for a description of EEG methods), and various respiratory therapy devices (see Chapter 8). It is also necessary to have emergency equipment on hand, such as defibrillators and pacemakers (see later sections of this chapter), resuscitation devices, and stimulation equipment.

The *intensive-care unit* (ICU) can be used for postsurgical follow-up or for medical patients with very serious problems. It is usually provided with equipment similar to that of the operating room, the only difference being that there is usually only one set of equipment in the operating room, while in the ICU there are bedside monitoring units and nurses' central consoles to monitor many patients simultaneously.

Most heart-attack victims are placed in a *coronary care unit* (CCU). In some hospitals this is called a *cardiac care unit.* The monitoring equipment in these units center around blood pressure, heart rate, and ECGs.

As the heart attack patient recovers, he or she is usually moved into another unit, where monitoring is not as critical. This unit, typically called the *intermediate coronary care unit* (ICCU), may also contain telemetry equipment to monitor ambulatory patients (see Chapter 12). There are also special groups of rooms in many hospitals that do not have bedside units installed but have portable units available in the corridors for immediate use for short periods of time. These do not necessarily have special names, but *cardiac observation unit* is one name that has been used.

Another important area in the hospital is the *emergency room,* in which emergency care is provided. Here every patient is a possible crisis. For this reason, emergency rooms require equipment of the same types described for the other facilities, but usually of the portable variety. Typically, a rapid diagnosis is made and the patient is rushed off to some other facility, such as the operating room or an intensive-care unit, where the critical measurements are made. In addition to on-the-spot measurements, all the units described above must have provision for taking samples of body fluids, such as urine and blood, where indicated. These samples are usually taken by a medical technologist, technician, or nurse and sent to the laboratory, which is usually situated elsewhere in the hospital. Instrumentation for the laboratory is described in Chapter 13.

Finally, some consideration should be given to what happens to a potential patient if he or she should have a heart attack at home or in the street. Connected with most hospitals today there is a *paramedic service.* Many of these are privately operated or they may be operated by the city or county, typically by the fire department. Paramedic units are described in more detail in Chapter 12, but an introduction is appropriate in the context of this chapter. The need to provide immediate around-the-clock medical care to heart attack and accident victims in the community has resulted in the use of *mobile emergency care units.* Manned by personnel trained to administer first aid as well as emergency cardiopulmonary resuscitation techniques, these vehicles are equipped with instruments and medication similar to that used in the special care units of hospitals. Because these units are in constant radio contact with community organizations (police and fire departments) and with hospitals, they are able to reach an accident scene or the location of a stricken citizen in a short period of time. Typically, on arrival, a portable electrocardiograph (often with an oscilloscope display) is quickly applied to obtain an evaluation of the patient's ECG and heart rate. An indication of cardiac standstill or pulmonary failure will initiate emergency cardiopulmonary resuscitation procedures. After airway clearance and assisted breathing are ensured, defibrillation or cardioversion may be required by a portable defibrillator. The victim's heart may then be temporarily paced by a portable pacer. Some instruments, such as the defibrillator shown in Figure 7.22, are capable of performing the three functions— monitoring of ECG display, defibrillation (or cardioversion), and pacing. The condition of the patient may then be radioed to personnel in the special care unit of a nearby hospital while the ECG is simultaneously transmitted to the unit's display and recording equipment via telemetry (see Chapter 12). In a short time, after a detailed diagnosis is made, instructions returned by radio may prescribe specific medication or additional resuscitation techniques. If the patient is in standstill and cannot breathe, adequate blood circulation can be maintained by means of a mechanical cardiopulmonary resuscitation unit. When the patient is able to be transported to a hospital, vital signs are monitored by appropriate equipment inside the vehicle. In this way, a seriously stricken individual is able to receive timely special care away from the hospital.

7.5. PACEMAKERS

More than a half-million people fall victim to heart attacks in the United States every year and thousands more are critically injured in accidents. Taking care of these patients in special care units of hospitals involves the use of several types of specialized equipment, among which are cardiac pacemakers and defibrillators. Defibrillators and cardiopulmonary resuscitation equipment are also required away from the hospital, in an ambulance or at the scene of an emergency.

In the past few years electronic pacemaker systems have become extremely important in saving and sustaining the lives of cardiac patients whose normal pacing functions have become impaired. Depending on the exact nature of a cardiac dysfunction, a patient may require temporary artificial pacing during the course of treatment or permanent pacing in order to lead an active, productive life after treatment.

This section deals with the various types of cardiac pacemakers. In addition to describing each device, its basic purpose, the physiological conditions under which it is required, and the ways in which it is used are also discussed. Section 7.6 covers defibrillators.

The heart's electrical activity is described in Chapters 3 and 5, but a brief review at this point will be helpful in understanding the need for artificial cardiac pacing. The rhythmic action of the heart is initiated by regularly recurring action potentials (electrochemical impulses) originating at the natural cardiac pacemaker, located at the sinoatrial (SA) node. Each pacing impulse is propagated throughout the myocardium, spreading over the surface of the atria to the atrioventricular (AV) node—which is located within the septum, adjacent to the atrioventricular valves—and depolarizing the atria. After a brief delay at the AV node, the impulse is rapidly conducted to the ventricles to depolarize the ventricular musculature.

A normal sinus rhythm (NSR) depends on the continuous, periodic performance of the pacemaker and the integrity of the neuronal conducting pathways. Any change in the NSR is called an *arrhythmia* (abnormal rhythm). Should the SA node temporarily or permanently fail because of disease (SA node disease) or a congenital defect, the pacing function may be taken over by pacemaker-like cells located near the AV node. However, under certain conditions, cells in the conduction system (an *idioventricular focus*) may pace the ventricles instead. Similarly, an area in the excitable ventricular musculature may try to control the heartbeat. Unfortunately, under these conditions the heart is paced at a much slower rate than normal, ranging between 30 and 50 beats per minute (BPM). The result is a condition called *bradycardia* (slow heart), in which the heart cannot provide sufficient blood circulation to meet the body's physical demands. During the transition period from an NSR to a slow rhythm, dizziness and loss of consciousness (syncope) may occur because of diminished cardiac output.

Heart block occurs whenever the conduction system fails to transmit the pacing impulses from the atria to the ventricles properly. In *first-degree block* an excessive impulse delay at the AV junction occurs that causes the P-R interval to exceed 0.2 second for normal adults. *Second-degree block* results in the complete but intermittent inhibition of the pacing impulse, which may also occur at the AV node. Total and continuous impulse blockage is called *third-degree block*. It may occur either at the AV node or elsewhere in the conduction system. In this case, the ventricles usually continue to contract but at a sharply reduced rate (40 BPM) because of the establishment of an idioventricular escape rhythm or because of impulses that only periodically originate from the atria. In all these conditions, an artificial method of pacing is generally required to ensure that the heart beats at a rate that is sufficient to maintain proper circulation.

7.5.1. Pacemaker Systems

A device capable of generating artificial pacing impulses and delivering them to the heart is known as a *pacemaker system* (commonly called a

(a)

Figure 7.16. (a) Implanted standby pacemaker with catheter electrodes inserted
through the right cephalic vein. (b) Pacing
electrodes attached to the myocardium;
(c) Myocardial electrodes with pacemaker
generator implanted in abdomen.

(c)

pacemaker) and consists of a *pulse generator* and appropriate *electrodes*. Pacemakers are available in a variety of forms. *Internal pacemakers* may be permanently implanted in patients whose SA nodes have failed to function properly or who suffer from permanent heart block because of a heart attack. An internal pacemaker is defined as one in which the entire system is inside the body. In contrast, an *external pacemaker* usually consists of an externally worn pulse generator connected to electrodes located on or within the myocardium.

External pacemakers are used on patients with temporary heart irregularities, such as those encountered in the coronary patient, including heart blocks. They are also used for temporary management of certain arrhythmias that may occur in patients during critical postoperative periods and in patients during cardiac surgery, especially if the surgery involves the valves or septum.

Internal pacemaker systems are implanted with the pulse generator placed in a surgically formed pocket below the right or left clavicle, in the left subcostal area, or, in women, beneath the left or right major pectoralis muscle. Internal leads connect to electrodes that directly contact the inside of the right ventricle or the surface of the myocardium (see Figure 7.16). The exact location of the pulse generator depends primarily on the type of electrode used, the nature of the cardiac dysfunction, and the method (mode)

Figure 7.17. Portable external pacemaker. Patient is being temporarily paced with an external demand pacemaker and transvenous pacing catheter. (Courtesy of Medtronic, Inc., Minneapolis, MN.)

Figure 7.18. Portable external pacemaker, strapped on arm. (Courtesy of Medtronic, Inc., Minneapolis, MN.)

Figure 7.19. Detail view of external demand pacemaker showing adjustment controls. (Courtesy of Medtronic, Inc., Minneapolis, MN.)

of pacing that may be prescribed. Pacing electrodes and modes are described later in this chapter. Since there are no external connections for applying power, the pulse generator must be completely self-contained, with a power source capable of continuously operating the unit for a period of years.

External pacemakers, which include all types of pulse generators located outside the body, are normally connected through wires introduced into the right ventricle via a cardiac catheter, as shown in Figure 7.17. The pulse generator may be strapped to the lower arm of a patient who is confined to bed, or worn at the midsection of an ambulatory patient, as shown in Figures 7.17 and 7.18. A detailed view of the external pulse generator appears in Figure 7.19. Figure 7.17 depicts an older model replaced by that in Figures 7.18 and 7.19, but the idea remains the same.

7.5.2. Pacing Modes and Pulse Generators

Several pacing techniques are possible with both internal and external pace-makers. They can be classed as either *competitive* and *noncompetitive* pacing modes as shown in Figure 7.20. The noncompetitive method, which uses pulse generators that are either *ventricular programmed* or programmed by the atria, is more popular. Ventricular-programmed pacemakers are designed to operate either in a *demand* (R-wave-inhibited) or *standby* (R-wave-triggered) mode, whereas *atrial-programmed pacers* are always synchronized with the P wave of the ECG.

The first (and simplest) pulse generators were *fixed-rate* or *asynchronous* (not synchronized) devices that produced pulses at a fixed rate (set by the physician or nurse) and were independent of any natural cardiac activity. Asynchronous pacing is called *competitive* pacing because the fixed-rate impulses may occur along with natural pacing impulses generated by the heart and would therefore be in competition with them in controlling the heartbeat. This competition is largely eliminated through use of ventricular- or atrial-programmed pulse generators.

Fixed-rate pacers are sometimes installed in elderly patients whose SA nodes cannot provide proper stimuli. They are also used temporarily to determine the amplitude of impulses needed to pace or *capture* the heartbeat of a patient prior to or during the implantation of a more permanent unit. The amplitude at which capture occurs is referred to as the pacing *threshold*. While the implantable fixed-rate units tend to fail less frequently than the more sophisticated demand or standby pacers, their battery life (if the

Figure 7.20. Types of pacing modes.

batteries are not rechargeable) is generally shorter because they are in constant operation.

The problems of shorter battery life and competition for control of the heart led, in part, to the development of ventricular-programmed (demand or standby) pulse generators. The models shown in Figures 7.19 and 7.21 are of the demand type. Either type of ventricular-programmed pulse generator, when connected to the ventricles via electrodes, is able to sense the presence (or absence) of a naturally occurring R wave. The output of an R-wave-inhibited (demand) unit is suppressed (no output pulses are produced) as long as natural (intrinsic) R waves are present. Thus, its output is held back or inhibited when the heart is able to pace itself. However, should standstill occur, or should the intrinsic rate fall below the preset rate of the pacer (around 70 BPM), the unit will automatically provide an output to pace the heart after an escape interval at the designated rate. In this way, ventricular-inhibited pacers are able to pace on demand. Some external demand-mode pacers may be adjusted to operate in a fixed-rate mode by means of an accessible mode control of the type shown on the unit in Figure 7.19. Other controls allow the setting of the pacer's rate anywhere between 30 and 180 BPM, as well as the amplitude of output pacing pulses between 0.1 and 20 mA. Some external demand pacers have a sense-pace indicator that deflects for each detected R wave or pacer-initiated impulse. The ON–OFF switch of some external pacers is provided with an interlock mechanism to prevent the unit from being accidentally turned off.

A demand pacer, in the absence of R waves, automatically reverts to a fixed-rate mode of operation. For testing purposes at the time of implantation and for evaluation later, implanted demand pacers are purposely placed in a fixed-rate mode, usually by means of a magnet provided by the manufacturer. When placed over the skin layer covering the pacer, the magnet activates a magnetically operated switch that prevents the pacer from sensing R-wave activity. This process causes the pacer to operate in a fixed-rate mode at a slightly higher rate (about 10 BPM higher than the demand-mode pacing rate that had been preset). For a patient with a normal sinus rhythm, this procedure is used to ensure that an implanted demand pacer whose output is normally inhibited is capable of providing pacing pulses when needed. Evidence of the presence of pacing impulses is obtained from the electrocardiogram. Pacing impulses appear as *pacing artifacts* or *spikes*. Occasionally, they may seriously distort the recorded QRS complex.

When required, the basic pacing rate of some of the earlier implanted pacers (both fixed-rate and demand types) may be changed with the use of a needle-like screwdriver (a Keith surgical skin needle) that is inserted transcutaneously to alter the rate control in the pulse generator. The amplitude of the impulses may also be adjusted in some earlier pacers by using the same type of needle in the appropriate control. In a newer type of pacer, these adjustments are accomplished by means of coded impulses that are magnetically coupled to the implanted pulse generator from the skin surface, thus eliminating the need to puncture the skin. To adjust this pace-maker, a special programming device with an attached coil is placed over the implanted pulse generator. Appropriate controls on the programmer allow the unit to transmit coded signals that cause the pacer to change its basic rate and vary the amplitude of its impulses. The basic rate and impulse amplitude of other recent implantable pulse generators are fixed by the manufacturer and cannot be changed, however.

As explained earlier, R-wave-triggered pulse generators, like the R-wave-inhibited units, sense each intrinsic R wave. However, this pacer emits an impulse with the occurrence of each sensed R wave. Thus, the unit is triggered rather than inhibited by each R wave. The pacing impulses are transmitted to the myocardium during its absolute refractory period, how-ever, so they will have no effect on normal heart activity. Should the intrinsic heart rate fall below the preset rate of the pacer, the pacer will automatically operate synchronously at its preset rate to pace the heart. Thus, this pace-maker stands by to pace when needed. Ventricular-triggered pacing is used less frequently than inhibited-mode pacing. Evidence of pacing impulses from this type of pacer is present on the patient's ECG, although some monitoring modes that utilize greater filtering may distort and even block the pacer artifact. In this case, one should document the ventricular complex following a pacer spike and compare it to the complex in question.

In cases of complete heart block where the atria are able to depolarize but the impulse fails to depolarize the ventricles, atrial synchronous pacing may be used. Here the pulse generator is connected through wires and elec-trodes to both the atria and the ventricles. The atrial electrode couples atrial impulses to the pulse generator, which then emits impulses to stimulate the ventricles via the ventricular electrode. In this way, the heart is paced at the same rate as the natural pacemaker. When the SA node rate changes because of vagus or sympathetic neuronal control, the ventricle will change its rate accordingly but not above some maximum rate (about 125 per minute).

Pulses applied directly to the heart are usually rectangular in shape with a duration of from 0.15 to 3 msec, depending on the type of pulse generator used and the needs of the patient. Depending on the value of impulse current required to capture, pulse amplitudes may range from 5 to 15 mA for adults, while infants and children require less. If, in an emergency, pacing must be done through the intact chest wall, amplitudes 10 times as great are required. These higher values of current are often painful and may cause burns and contractions of the chest muscles and diaphragm. The amplitude of impulse required to capture the heartbeat of a patient is affected by the duration of the pulse. For example, an impulse of 2-msec duration may capture when its amplitude is only 3 mA. On the other hand, a 0.8-msec pulse may reach 6 mA before capture occurs.

The ability to capture and hence the threshold value of a pacer impulse that has a given amplitude and duration also depend on the electrical quality of the contact between the electrode and the heart. Capture will occur at a higher threshold value for a poor contact than for a good electrical contact at the electrode–heart muscle interface.

The quality of the electrode–heart muscle contact also affects a demand pacer's inhibition capability or *sensitivity*. A good contact will permit the pacer's output to remain inhibited for smaller values of sensed R waves.

The performance of the pulse generators can be checked with the use of a special tester. In one type of tester, pacing impulses are indicated by a lamp that blinks at the pacing rate. In another type, the pacer's pulse rate, amplitude, width, and interval are displayed in digital form. This type of tester is also able to generate impulses used to check the inhibition capability of a demand pacer.

Typical internal pulse generators are shown in Figure 7.21(a). The Xyrel Models 5972 and 5973 pulse generators are of the ventricular-inhibited (demand) type. Programmed from the QRS complex, they deliver their impulses only when the patient's ventricular rate falls below the basic pacing rate of the pulse generator. Rate is preset during manufacture at a typical 72 pulses per minute (ppm). The Model 5972 is a bipolar pulse generator. The 5973 is a unipolar pulse generator. *Unipolar electrodes* have one electrode placed on or in the heart and the other (reference) electrode located somewhere away from the heart, whereas *bipolar electrodes* have both electrodes on or in the heart.

The pulse generators are powered by a hermetically sealed lithium–iodine power source and utilize hermetically sealed hybrid electronic circuitry. To further protect the components of the pulse generator from intrusion of body fluids the electronics assembly and power source are encapsulated and hermetically sealed within a titanium shield.

Nominal dimensions of the circular-shaped pulse generators are 56 mm (2.2 in.) in diameter by 18 mm (0.71 in.) in thickness. Weight is a nominal 95 grams.

Both pulse generators have a self-sealing connector assembly with a corrosion-resistant titanium-alloy body and socket setscrew(s). To help prevent potential migration or rotational complications, the pulse generators have a suture pad which enables the physician to secure the pulse generator within the pocket.

The power source is rated at 5.6 V with 1.1-Ahour capacity and is expected to last for 7 to 10 years with continuous pacing at 72 pulses per minute. Two power-source-depletion indicators are programmed into the circuitry of the pulse generators—a rate decrease and a pulse duration increase. The decrease in rate occurs when voltage has been depleted to about 4.0 V. At this point, replacement of the pulse generator is indicated. The increase in pulse duration, which serves as a secondary power-source-depletion indicator, is gradual and occurs simultaneously with the depletion of the lithium–iodine power source.

Figure 7.21. Internal pacemaker. (a) Photograph of two units. (b) Block diagram. (Courtesy of Medtronic, Inc., Minneapolis, MN.)

(b)

Models 5972 and 5973 have a rate-limit circuit which prevents the rate from going above 120 ppm for most single-component failures. In the presence of strong continuous interference, the pulse generators are designed to revert to asynchronous operation. The reversion rate is approximately the same as the basic pacing rate.

The pacing function of the pulse generators can be verified during periods of sinus rhythm (when the pulse generator's output is suppressed) by means of a magnet held against the skin over the implanted pulse generator. The rate with the application of the magnet can be slightly higher than the basic pacing rate.

Radiopaque identification permits positive determination of model and series number at all times. With standard X-ray procedures, the five-character code inside the titanium shield appears as black letters and numerals on a white background.

Figure 7.21(b) is a block diagram showing components of the circuitry. The timing circuit which consists of an *RC* network, a reference voltage source, and a comparator determines the basic pacing rate of the pulse generator. Its output signal feeds into a second *RC* network, the pulse width circuit, which determines the stimulating pulse duration. A third *RC* network, the rate-limiting circuit, disables the comparator for a preset interval and thus limits the pacing rate to a maximum of 120 pulses per minute for most single-component failures. The output circuit provides a voltage pulse to stimulate the heart. The voltage monitor circuit senses cell depletion and signals the rate slowdown circuit and energy compensation circuit of this event. The rate slowdown circuit shuts off some of the current to the basic timing network to cause the rate to slow down 8 ± 3 beats per minute when cell depletion has occurred. The energy-compensation circuit causes the pulse duration to increase as the battery voltage decreases, to maintain nearly constant stimulation energy to the heart.

There is also a feedback loop from the output circuit to the refractory circuit, which provides a period of time following an output pulse or a sensed R-wave during which the amplifier will not respond to outside signals. The sensing circuit detects a spontaneous R wave and resets the oscillator timing capacitor. The reversion circuit allows the amplifier to detect a spontaneous R wave in the presence of low-level continuous wave interference. In the absence of an R wave, this circuit allows the oscillator to pace at its preset rate ± 1 beat per minute.

7.5.3. Power Sources and Electromagnetic Interference

The type of power source used for a pulse generator depends on whether the unit is an external or an implantable type. Today most of the manufactured external pulse generators are battery-powered, although earlier units that receive power from the ac power line are still in use. Because of the need to electrically isolate patients with direct-wire connections to their hearts from any possible source of power-line leakage current (see Chapter 16), and for portability, battery-powered units are preferred. Implantable pulse generators commonly use mercury batteries whose life span ranges between 2 and 3 years, after which a new pulse generator must be installed. Recognizing the need to develop longer-lasting batteries for pacing use, the industry has developed the lithium–iodine battery, which has an estimated life expectancy of 5 years. A pulse generator with rechargeable batteries whose life span is estimated at 10 years is now available.

For a short period of time once each week, the patient dons a vest, thus ensuring the correct positioning of a charging head over the implanted pulse generator. Through magnetic coupling between the charging head and the pacer, the pacer's batteries can be recharged. Afterward, the pacer signals the charging unit that the process is completed. The weekly charge provides a pacing safety margin of approximately 6 weeks.

Another technological advance in implantable power sources has been the introduction of nuclear-powered pulse generators. In these devices, heat generated by the decay of radioactive plutonium is converted into direct current that is used to power the pacemaker. These units have an estimated useful life of at least 10 years, with negligible radiation danger to the patient.

Sources of electromagnetic energy, such as microwave ovens, diathermy, electrosurgical units, and auto ignition systems, may affect the operating mode of implanted or external pacemakers. Under certain circumstances such electrical noise signals may be strong enough to mimic the R wave in demand-mode pacers, thus inhibiting their outputs. Some implantable units are shielded to minimize the effects of extraneous noise. Nevertheless, patients with demand pacers should be warned about approaching microwave ovens or other obvious sources of electrical interference.

7.6. DEFIBRILLATORS

As discussed earlier in this chapter, the heart is able to perform its important pumping function only through precisely synchronized action of the heart muscle fibers. The rapid spread of action potentials over the surface of the atria causes these two chambers of the heart to contract together and pump blood through the two atrioventricular valves into the ventricles. After a critical time delay, the powerful ventricular muscles are synchronously activated to pump blood through the pulmonary and systemic circulatory systems. A condition in which this necessary synchronism is lost is known as *fibrillation*. During fibrillation the normal rhythmic contractions of either the atria or the ventricles are replaced by rapid irregular twitching of the muscular wall. Fibrillation of atrial muscles is called *atrial fibrillation;* fibrillation of the ventricles is known as *ventricular fibrillation.*

Under conditions of atrial fibrillation, the ventricles can still function normally, but they respond with an irregular rhythm to the nonsynchronized bombardment of electrical stimulation from the fibrillating atria. Since most of the blood flow into the ventricles occurs before atrial contraction, there is still blood for the ventricles to pump. Thus, even with atrial fibrillation circulation is still maintained, although not as efficiently. The sensation produced, however, by the fibrillating atria and irregular ventricular action can be quite traumatic for the patient.

Ventricular fibrillation is far more dangerous, for under this condition the ventricles are unable to pump blood; and if the fibrillation is not corrected, death will usually occur within a few minutes. Unfortunately, fibrillation, once begun, is not self-correcting. Hence, a patient susceptible to ventricular fibrillation must be watched continuously so that the medical staff can respond immediately if an emergency occurs. This is one of the reasons for cardiac monitoring, which was discussed earlier.

Although mechanical methods (heart massage) for defibrillating patients have been tried over the years, the most successful method of defibrillation is the application of an electric shock to the area of the heart. If sufficient current to stimulate all musculature of the heart simultaneously is applied for a brief period and then released, all the heart muscle fibers enter their refractory periods together, after which normal heart action may resume. The discovery of this phenomenon led to the rather widespread use of defibrillation by applying a brief (0.25 to 1 sec) burst of 60-Hz ac at an intensity of around 6 A to the chest of the patient through appropriate electrodes. This application of an electrical shock to resynchronize the heart is sometimes called *countershock.* If the patient does not respond, the burst is repeated until defibrillation occurs. This method of countershock was known as *ac defibrillation.*

There are a number of disadvantages in using ac defibrillation, however. Successive attempts to correct ventricular fibrillation are often required. Moreover, ac defibrillation cannot be successfully used to correct atrial defibrillation. In fact, attempts to correct atrial fibrillation by this method often result in the more serious ventricular fibrillation. Thus, ac defibrillation is no longer used.

About 1960, a number of experimenters began working with direct-current defibrillation. Various schemes and waveforms were tried until, in late 1962, Bernard Lown of the Harvard School of Public Health and Peter Bent Brigham Hospital developed a new method of *dc defibrillation* that has found common use today. In this method, a capacitor is charged to a high dc voltage and then rapidly discharged through electrodes across the chest of the patient.

It was found that dc defibrillation is not only more successful than the ac method in correcting ventricular fibrillation, but it can also be used successfully for correcting atrial fibrillation and other types of arrhythmias. The dc method requires fewer repetitions and is less likely to harm the patient. A dc defibrillator is shown in Figure 7.22 with a typical dc defibrillator circuit shown in Figure 7.23.

Depending on the defibrillator energy setting, the amount of electrical energy discharged by the capacitor may range between 100 and 400 W-sec, or joules. The duration of the effective portion of the discharge is approximately 5 msec. The energy delivered is represented by the typical waveform shown in Figure 7.24 as a time plot of the current forced to flow through the thoracic cavity. The area under the curve is proportional to the energy delivered. It can be seen that the peak value of current is nearly 20 A and that the wave is essentially *monophasic,* since most of its excursion is above the baseline. An inductor in the defibrillator is used to shape the wave in order to eliminate a sharp, undesirable current spike that would otherwise occur at the beginning of the discharge.

Figure 7.22. DC defibrillator with paddles. This portable unit incorporates a defibrillator, electrocardioscope and pacemaker. (Courtesy of Gould Medical Systems, Sunnyvale, CA.)

Figure 7.23. DC defibrillator circuit.

Figure 7.24. DC defibrillator discharge waveform (Lown).

Even with dc defibrillation, there is danger of damage to the myocardium and the chest walls because peak voltages as high as 6000 V may be used. To reduce this risk, some defibrillators produce dual-peak waveforms of longer duration (approximately 10 msec) at a much lower voltage. When this type of waveform is used, effective defibrillation can be achieved in adults with lower levels of delivered energy (between 50 and 200 W-sec). A typical dual-peak waveform is shown in Figure 7.25.

Effective defibrillation at the desirable lower-voltage levels is also possible with the *truncated* waveform shown in Figure 7.26. The amplitude of this waveform is relatively constant, but its duration may be varied to obtain the amount of energy required. To properly deliver a large current discharge applied through the skin large electrodes are used. These electrodes, called *paddles,* have metal disks that usually measure from 8 to 10 cm (3 to

Figure 7.25. Dual-peak monophasic defibrillator discharge waveform.

4 in.) in diameter for external (transthoracic) use. For internal use (direct contact with the heart) or for use on infants, smaller paddles are applied. In external use, a pair of electrodes is firmly pressed against the patient's chest. Conductive jelly or a saline-soaked gauze pad (the latter is preferred) is applied between each paddle surface and the skin to prevent burning. However, if conductive jelly is applied to the paddles prior to electrode placement, care must be taken that when the paddles are applied, the jelly does not accidentally form a conductive bridge between the paddles. If it does, the defibrillation attempt may not be successful. With either of the preceding conductive materials, care must be taken that they will not dry out with repeated discharges.

To protect the person applying the electrodes from accidental electric shock, special insulated handles are provided. A thumb switch, located in one (or both) of the handles, is generally used to discharge the defibrillator when the paddles are properly positioned. This device prevents the patient, or someone else, from receiving a shock prematurely. In earlier equipment, a foot switch was used instead. The possibility of someone accidentally stepping on the foot switch in the excitement of an emergency, before the paddles are in place, makes the thumb switches in the handles preferable.

Figure 7.26. Truncated defibrillator discharge waveform.

The method by which defibrillators are programmed to become charged (or recharged after use) varies widely. For example, in some defibrillators the charging process is accomplished by means of a charge switch (or push-button) located on the front panel of the unit. A newer model, however, has the charge switch located in the handle of one of its paddles. In a few defibrillators the charging process begins automatically (and immediately) after discharge. Whatever the method, it is important that the person using the defibrillator follows the manufacturer's instructions. Additionally, to ensure the safety of the medical team that is immediately caring for the patient, the user should verbally indicate that the defibrillator is about to be discharged.

The two defibrillator electrodes applied to the thoracic walls are called either *anterior-anterior* or *anterior-posterior* paddles. With anterior-anterior paddles, both paddles are applied to the chest. Anterior-posterior paddles are applied to both the patient's chest wall and back so that the energy is delivered through the heart. This method of paddle application offers better control over arrhythmias that occur as a result of atrial activity. A pair of anterior-posterior paddles consists of the anterior paddle already described and a flat posterior paddle that has a larger electrode diameter than the anterior paddle. Internal paddles, as mentioned above, may be applied directly to the myocardium (during open-chest surgery), or they may be applied to the chest of an infant. Such paddles are flat and are usually available in several sizes, with diameters ranging from 5 to 10 cm. In these applications, the energy levels required for defibrillation may range from 10 to 50 W-sec. Special *pediatric paddles* are available with diameters ranging from 2 to 6 cm. Internal paddles can be either gas-sterilized or autoclaved.

Most defibrillators include watt-second (or joule) meters to indicate the amount of energy stored in the capacitor prior to discharge. For some defibrillators, however, this indication does not assure that the amount of energy to which the unit is set by the user will, in fact, be delivered to a patient. Some of the energy indicated on the meter is lost or dissipated as heat in components (mainly inductors) inside the unit and, to a lesser extent, at the electrode–skin interface. As a result, the patient always receives less energy than the amount indicated on the meter. For example, a user may set a defibrillator to deliver 300 W-sec of energy to a patient (as shown by the meter). The actual amount of energy delivered, however, may be only 240 W-sec, which represents a 20-percent loss of energy. In some defibrillators, the loss may reach 40 percent or more. This inherent drawback of some defibrillators makes it difficult to determine accurately the amount of energy needed for various countershock procedures. For this type of defibrillator, a calibration chart must be prepared as an aid in setting the unit to accurate levels of delivered energy.

Within the last few years, defibrillators whose delivered energy levels essentially equal their preset levels have become available. Their output waveforms are of types shown in Figures 7.25 and 7.26.

Because of the large amount of energy released into the body, an implanted pacemaker pulse generator located immediately beneath a defibrillator paddle could be damaged during a discharge. Furthermore, the lump beneath the skin may reduce the effective skin contact area of the paddle and increase the danger of burns. Thus, care should be taken to avoid placement of a paddle over or near the pulse generator.

Defibrillators are also used to convert other potentially dangerous arrhythmias to one that is easily managed. This process is referred to as *cardioversion*. For this procedure, anterior-posterior paddles are generally used. For example, a defibrillator discharge may be used to convert a *tachycardia* (fast heart) arrhythmia to a normal rhythm. Unlike the ECG for a heart in ventricular fibrillation, the electrocardiogram for a fast heart contains QRS complexes. To avoid the possibility of ventricular fibrillation resulting from the application of the dc pulse in cardioversion, the discharge must be synchronized with the electrocardiogram. The optimum time for discharge is during or immediately after the downward slope of the R wave when the heart is in its absolute refractory period (see Chapter 3). This synchronization will ensure that the countershock is not delivered during the middle of the T wave, which is called the heart's *vulnerable period*. During this time, since it is partially refractory, the heart is susceptible to ventricular fibrillation by the introduction of artificial stimuli.

Most modern defibrillators include a provision for synchronizing the discharge pulse with the patient's ECG. The ECG signal is fed to an amplifier from either a patient monitor or an electrocardiograph. In some cases, the patient's ECG electrodes are connected directly to the amplifier. When properly programmed, the defibrillator will discharge only at the desired portion of the ECG waveform. The closing of the thumb switches on the paddles applied to the patient allows the defibrillator to discharge at the next occurrence of the R wave.

8

Measurements in the Respiratory System

The exchange of gases in any biological process is termed *respiration*. To sustain life, the human body must take in oxygen, which combines with carbon, hydrogen, and various nutrients to produce heat and energy for the performance of work. As a result of this process of *metabolism,* which takes place in the cells, a certain amount of water is produced along with the principal waste product, carbon dioxide (CO_2). The entire process of taking in oxygen from the environment, transporting the oxygen to the cells, removing the carbon dioxide from the cells, and exhausting this waste product into the atmosphere must be considered within the definition of respiration.

In the human body, the tissue cells are generally not in direct contact with their external environment. Instead, the cells are bathed in fluid. This tissue fluid can be considered as the *internal environment* of the body. The cells absorb oxygen from this fluid. The circulating blood is the medium by which oxygen is brought to the internal environment. Carbon dioxide is carried from the tissue fluids by the same mechanism. The exchange of gases between the blood and the external environment takes place in the *lungs* and is termed *external respiration*.

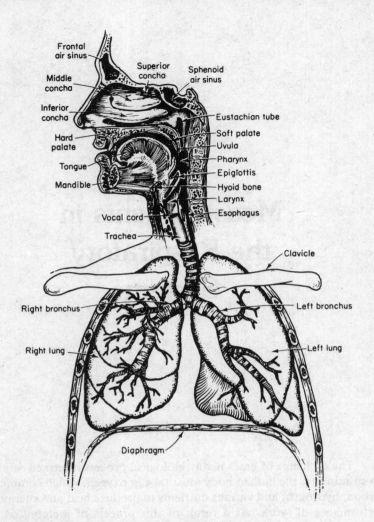

Figure 8.1. The respiratory tract. (From W.F. Evans, *Anatomy and Physiology, The Basic Principles,* Prentice-Hall, Inc., 1971, by permission.)

The function of the lungs is to oxygenate the blood and to eliminate carbon dioxide in a controlled manner. During inspiration fresh air enters the respiratory tract, becomes humidified and heated to body temperature, and is mixed with the gases already present in the region comprising the trachea and bronchi (see Figure 8.1). This gas is then mixed further with the gas residing in the alveoli as it enters these small sacs in the walls of the lungs. Oxygen diffuses from the alveoli to the pulmonary capillary blood supply, whereas carbon dioxide diffuses from the blood to the alveoli. The oxygen is carried from the lungs and distributed among the various cells of the body by the blood circulation system, which also returns the carbon dioxide to the lungs. The entire process of inspiring and expiring air, exchange of gases, distribution of oxygen to the cells, and collection of CO_2 from the cells forms what is known as the *pulmonary function*. Tests for assessing the various components of the process are called *pulmonary function tests*.

Unfortunately, no single laboratory test or even a simple group of tests is capable of completely measuring pulmonary function. In fact, the field of instrumentation for obtaining pulmonary measurements is quite complex. However, tests and instrumentation for the measurement of respiration can be divided into two categories. The first includes tests designed to measure the mechanics of breathing and the physical characteristics of the lungs; the second category is involved with diffusion of gases in the lungs, the distribution of oxygen, and the collection of carbon dioxide.

This chapter begins with a brief presentation of the physiology of the respiratory system; then the tests and instrumentation associated with each of the two categories of measurements described above are covered. Because of the complexity of the field, it is almost impossible to cover all tests or all types of instrumentation used in either category. However, an attempt has been made to include the most meaningful ones, as well as those with which the biomedical engineer or technician is most likely to become associated.

The chapter closes with a section on respiratory therapy equipment, which is used to assist patients who are unable to maintain normal respiration by natural processes.

8.1. THE PHYSIOLOGY OF THE RESPIRATORY SYSTEM

Air enters the lungs through the air passages, which include the *nasal cavities, pharynx, larynx, trachea, bronchi,* and *bronchioles,* as shown in Figure 8.1.

The lungs are elastic bags located in a closed cavity, called the *thorax* or *thoracic cavity*. The right lung consists of three lobes (upper, middle, and lower), and the left lung has two lobes (upper and lower).

The *larynx,* sometimes called the "voice box" (because it contains the vocal cords), is connected to the bronchi through the *trachea,* sometimes called the "windpipe." Above the larynx is the *epiglottis,* a valve that closes whenever a person swallows, so that food and liquids are directed to the esophagus (tube leading to the stomach) and into the stomach rather than into the larynx and trachea.

The trachea is about 1.5 to 2.5 cm in diameter and approximately 11 cm long, extending from the larynx to the upper boundary of the chest. Here it bifurcates (forks) into the right and left main stem *bronchi*. Each bronchus enters into the corresponding lung and divides like the limbs of a tree into smaller branches. The branches are of unequal length and at different angles, with over 20 of these nonsymmetrical bifurcations normally present in the human body. Farther along these branchings, where the diameter is reduced to about 0.1 cm, the air-conducting tubes are called *bronchioles*. As they continue to decrease in size to about 0.05 cm in diameter, they form the *terminal bronchioles,* which branch again into the *respiratory bronchioles,* where some alveoli are attached as small air sacs in the walls of the lung. After some additional branching, these air sacs increase in number, becoming the *pulmonary alveoli.* The alveoli are each about 0.02 cm in diameter. It is estimated that, all told, some 300 million alveoli are found in the lungs (see Figure 8.2).

Figure 8.2. Alveoli and capillary network (From W.F. Evans, *Anatomy and Physiology, The Basic Principles,* Prentice-Hall, Inc., 1971, by permission.)

Beyond about the tenth stage of branching, the bronchioles are embedded within alveolar lung tissue; and with the expansion and relaxation of the lung, their diameters are greatly affected by the lung size or lung volume. Up to this point, the diameter of the air sacs is more affected by the *pleural pressure,* the pressure inside the thorax.

The lungs are covered by a thin membrane called the *pleura,* which passes from the lung at its root onto the interior of the chest wall and upper surface of the diaphragm. The two membranous sacs so formed are called the *pleural cavities,* one on each side of the chest, between the lungs and the thoracic boundaries. These "cavities" are potential only, for the pleura covering the lung and that lining the chest are in contact in the healthy condition. Fluid or blood, as well as air, may collect in this potential space to create an actual space in certain diseases. The part of the pleural membrane lining the thoracic wall is called the *parietal pleura,* whereas that portion covering and firmly adherent to the surface of the lungs themselves is called the *pulmonary pleura* or *visceral pleura.* A small amount of fluid, just wetting the surfaces between the pleura, allows the lungs and the lobes of the lungs to slide over each other and on the chest wall easily with breathing.

Breathing is accomplished by musculature that literally changes the volume of the thoracic cavity and, in so doing, creates negative and positive pressures that move air into and out of the lungs. Two sets of muscles are involved: those in and near the diaphragm that cause the diaphragm to move up and down, changing the size of the thoracic cavity in the vertical direction, and those that move the rib cage up and down to change the lateral diameter of the thorax.

The *diaphragm* is a special dome- or bell-shaped muscle located at the bottom of the thoracic cavity, which, when contracted, pulls downward to enlarge the thorax. This action is the prinicpal force involved in inspiration. At the same time as the diaphragm moves downward, a group of external intercostal muscles lifts the rib cage and sternum. Because of the shape of the rib cage, this lifting action also increases the effective diameter of the thoracic cavity. The resultant increase in thoracic volume creates a negative pressure (vacuum) in the thorax. Since the thorax is a closed chamber and the only opening to the outside is from the inside of the lungs, the negative pressure is relieved by air entering the lungs. The lungs themselves are passive and expand only because of the internal pressure of air in the lungs, which is greater than the pressure in the thorax outside the lungs.

Normal expiration is essentially passive, for, on release of the inspiratory muscles, the elasticity of the lungs and the rib cage, combined with the tone of the diaphragm, reduces the volume of the thorax, thereby developing a positive pressure that forces air out of the lungs. In forced expiration a set of abdominal muscles pushes the diaphragm upward very powerfully while the internal intercostal muscles pull the rib cage downward and apply pressure against the lungs to help force air out.

During normal inspiration the pressure inside the lungs, the *intra-alveolar pressure,* is about —3 mm Hg, whereas during expiration the pressure becomes about + 3 mm Hg. The ability of the lungs and thorax to expand during breathing is called the *compliance,* which is expressed as the volume increase in the lungs per unit increase in intra-alveolar pressure. The resistance to the flow of air into and out of the lungs is called *airway resistance.*

As described in Chapter 5, blood from the body tissues and their capillaries is brought via the superior and inferior vena cava into the right atrium of the heart, which in turn empties into the right ventricle. The right ventricle pumps the blood into and through the lungs in a pulsating fashion, with a systolic pressure of about 20 mm Hg and a diastolic pressure of 1 to 4 mm Hg. By perfusion, the blood passes through the pulmonary capillaries, which are in the walls of the air sacs, wherein oxygen is taken up by the red blood cells and hemoglobin. The compound formed by the oxygen and the hemoglobin is called *oxyhemoglobin.* At the same time, carbon dioxide is removed from the blood into the alveoli.

From the pulmonary capillaries, the blood is carried through the pulmonary veins to the left atrium. From here it enters the left ventricle, which pumps the blood out into the aorta at pressures of 120/80 mm Hg. It is then distributed to all the organs and muscles of the body. In the tissues, the oxyhemoglobin gives up its oxygen, while carbon dioxide diffuses into the blood from the tissue and surrounding fluids. The blood then flows from the capillaries into the venous system back into the superior and inferior vena cava.

The interchange of the oxygen from the lungs to the blood and the diffusion of carbon dioxide from the blood to the lungs take place in the capillary surfaces of the alveoli. The alveolar surface area is about 80 m², of which more than three-fourths is capillary surface.

In order to understand some of the terminology used in conjunction with the tests and instrumentation involved in respiratory measurements, definition of a few medical terms is necessary. Additional definitions are included in the glossary in Appendix A.

Hypoventilation is a condition of insufficient ventilation by an individual to maintain his normal P_{CO_2} level, whereas *hyperventilation* refers to abnormally prolonged, rapid, or deep breathing. Hyperventilation is also the condition produced by overbreathing. *Dyspnea* is the sensation of inadequate or distressful respiration, a condition of abnormal breathlessness. *Hypercapnia* is an excess amount of CO_2 in the system, and *hypoxia* is a shortage of oxygen. Both hypercapnia and hypoxia can result from inadequate ventilation.

8.2. TESTS AND INSTRUMENTATION FOR THE MECHANICS OF BREATHING

The mechanics of breathing concern the ability of a person to bring air into his lungs from the outside atmosphere and to exhaust air from the lungs. This ability is affected by the various components of the air passages, the diaphragm and associated muscles, the rib cage and associated musculature, and the characteristics of the lungs themselves. Tests can be performed to assess each of these factors, but no one measurement has been devised that can adequately and completely evaluate the performance of the breathing mechanism. This section describes a number of the most prominent measurements and tests that are used clinically and in research in connection with the mechanics of breathing. In addition, the instrumentation required for these tests and measurements is described and discussed. In some cases, one instrument can be used for the performance of several tests.

8.2.1. Lung Volumes and Capacities

Among the basic pulmonary tests are those designed for determination of lung volumes and capacities. These parameters, which are a function of an individual's physical characteristics and the condition of his breathing mechanism, are given in Figure 8.3.

Figure 8.3. Lung volumes and capacities. (From W.F. Evans, *Anatomy and Physiology, The Basic Principles,* Prentice-Hall, Inc., 1971, by permission.)

The *tidal volume* (TV), or normal depth of breathing, is the volume of gas inspired or expired during each normal, quiet, respiration cycle.

Inspiratory reserve volume (IRV) is the extra volume of gas that a person can inspire with maximal effort after reaching the normal end inspiratory level. The *end inspiratory level* is the level reached at the end of a normal, quiet inspiration.

The *expiratory reserve volume* (ERV) is that extra volume of gas that can be expired with maximum effort beyond the end expiratory level. The *end expiratory level* is the level reached at the end of a normal, quiet expiration.

The *residual volume* (RV) is the volume of gas remaining in the lungs at the end of a maximal expiration.

The *vital capacity* (VC) is the maximum volume of gas that can be expelled from the lungs by forceful effort after a maximal inspiration. It is actually the difference between the level of maximum inspiration and the residual volume, and it is measured without respect to time. The vital capacity is also the sum of the tidal volume, inspiratory reserve volume, and expiratory reserve volume.

The *total lung capacity* (TLC) is the amount of gas contained in the lungs at the end of a maximal inspiration. It is the sum of the vital capacity and residual volume. Total lung capacity is also the sum of the tidal volume, inspiratory reserve volume, expiratory reserve volume, and residual volume.

The *inspiratory capacity* (IC) is the maximum amount of gas that can be inspired after reaching the end expiratory level. It is the sum of the tidal volume and the inspiratory reserve volume.

The functional residual capacity, often referred to by its abbreviation, FRC, is the volume of gas remaining in the lungs at the end expiratory level. It is the sum of the residual volume and the expiratory reserve volume. The FRC can also be calculated as the total lung capacity minus the inspiratory capacity, and it is often regarded as the baseline from which other volumes and capacities are determined, for it seems to be more stable than the end inspiratory level.

In addition to the static volumes and capacities given above, several dynamic measures are used to assess the breathing mechanism. These measures are important because breathing is, in fact, a dynamic process, and the rate at which gases can be exchanged with the blood is a direct function of the rate at which air can be inspired and expired.

A measure of the overall output of the respiratory system is the *respiratory minute volume.* This is a measure of the amount of air inspired during 1 minute at rest. It is obtained by multiplying the tidal volume by the number of respiratory cycles per minute.

A number of forced breathing tests are used to assess the muscle power associated with breathing and the resistance of the airway. Among them is the *forced vital capacity* (FVC), which is really a vital capacity measurement taken as quickly as possible. By definition, the FVC is the total amount of air that can forcibly be expired as quickly as possible after taking the deepest possible breath. If the measurement is made with respect to the time required for the maneuver, it is called a *timed vital capacity* measurement. A measure of the maximum amount of gas that can be expelled in a given number of seconds is called the *forced expiratory volume* (FEV). This is usually given with a subscript indicating the number of seconds over which the measurement is made. For example, FEV_1 indicates the amount of air that can be blown out in 1 second following a maximum inspiration, while FEV_3 is the maximum amount of air that can be expired in 3 seconds. FEV is sometimes given as a percentage of the forced vital capacity.

Since forced vital capacity measurements are often encumbered by patient hesitation and the inertia of the instrument, a measure of the *maximum midexpiratory flow* rate may be taken. This is a flow measurement over the middle half of the forced vital capacity (from the 25 percent level to the 75 percent level). The corresponding FEV measurement is called $FEV_{25\%-75\%}$.

Another important flow measurement is the *maximal expiration flow* (MEF) rate, which is the rate during the first liter expired after 200 ml has been exhausted at the beginning of the FEV. It differs from the *peak flow,* which is the maximum rate of airflow attained during a forced expiration.

Another useful measurement for assessing the integrity of the breathing mechanism is the *maximal breathing capacity* (MBC) or *maximal voluntary ventilation* (MVV). This is a measure of the maximum amount of air that can be breathed in and blown out over a sustained interval, such as 15 or 20 seconds. A ratio of the maximal breathing capacity to the vital capacity is also of clinical interest.

In detecting obstruction of the small airways in the lungs, a procedure involving measurement of the *closing volume* is often used. The closing volume level is the volume at which certain zones within the lung cease to ventilate, presumably as the result of airway closure.

The results of many of the preceding tests are generally reported as percentages of predicted normal values. In the presentation of various respiratory volumes, the term *BTPS* is often used, indicating that the measurements were made at body temperature and ambient pressure, with the gas saturated with water vapor. Sometimes, in order to use these values in the reporting of metabolism, they must be converted to standard temperature and pressure and dry measurement conditions, indicated by the term *STPD*.

With each breath, most of the air enters the lungs to fill the alveoli. However, a certain amount of air is required to fill the various cavities of the air passages. This air is called the *dead-space air,* and the space it occupies is called the *dead space*. The amount of air that actually reaches the alveolar interface with the bloodstream with each breath is the tidal volume minus the volume of the dead space. The respiratory minute volume can be broken down into the alveolar *ventilation per minute* and the *dead space ventilation per minute.*

8.2.2. Mechanical Measurements

The volume and capacity measurements just described, particularly the forced measurements, are a good indication of the compliance of the lungs and rib cage and the resistance of the air passages. However, direct measurement of these parameters is also possible and is often used in the measurement of pulmonary function.

Determination of *compliance,* which has been defined as the volume increase in the lungs per unit increase in lung pressure, requires measurement of an inspired or expired volume of gas and of intrathoracic pressure. Compliance is actually a static measurement. However, in practice, two types of compliance measurement, static and dynamic, are made. *Static compliance* is determined by obtaining a ratio of the difference in lung volume at two different volume levels and the associated difference in intra-alveolar pressure. To measure dynamic compliance, tidal volume is used as the volume measurement, while intrathoracic pressure measurements are taken during the instants of zero airflow that occur at the end inspiratory and expiratory levels with each breath (refer to Figure 8.3). The lung compliance varies with the size of the lungs; a child has a smaller compliance than an adult. Furthermore, the volume-pressure curve is not linear. Hence, compliance does not remain constant over the breathing cycle but tends to decrease as the lungs are inflated. Fortunately, over the tidal volume range in which dynamic compliance measurements are usually performed, the relationship is approximately linear and a constant compliance is assumed. Compliance values are given as liters per centimeter H_2O.

Resistance of the air passages is generally called *airway resistance,* which is a pneumatic analog of hydraulic or electrical resistance and, as such, is a ratio of pressure to flow. Thus, for the determination of airway resistance, intra-alveolar pressure and airflow measurements are required. As was the case with compliance, airway resistance is not constant over the respiratory cycle. As the pressure in the thoracic cavity becomes more negative, the airways are widened and the airway resistance is lowered. Conversely, during expiration, when the pressure in the thorax becomes positive, the airways are narrowed and resistance is increased. The intra-alveolar pressure is given in centimeters H_2O and the flow in liters per second; the airway resistance is expressed in centimeters H_2O per liter per second. Most airway resistance measurements are made at or near the functional residual capacity (end expiratory) level.

From the preceding discussion it can be seen that to obtain compliance and airway resistance determinations, volume, intra-alveolar pressure, intrathoracic pressure, and instantaneous airflow measurements are required. The methods for measurement of volume for these determinations are no different from those used for the volume and capacity measurements discussed earlier.

8.2.3. Instrumentation for Measuring the Mechanics of Breathing

As shown in previous sections, all the parameters dealing with the mechanics of breathing can be derived from measurement of lung volumes at various levels and conditions of breathing, pressures within the lungs and the thorax with respect to outside air pressure, and instantaneous airflow. The complexity of pulmonary measurements lies not in the variety required but rather in gaining access to the sources of these measurements and in providing suitable conditions to make them meaningful.

The most widely used laboratory instrument for respiratory volume measurements is the *recording spirometer,* an example of which is shown in Figure 8.4. All lung volumes and capacities that can be determined by measuring the amount of gas inspired or expired under a given set of conditions or during a specified time interval can be obtained by use of the spirometer. Included are the timed vital capacity and forced expiratory volume measurements. The only volume and capacity measurements that cannot be obtained with a spirometer are those requiring measurement of the gas that cannot be expelled from the lungs under any conditions. Such measurements include the residual volume, functional residual capacity, and total lung capacity.

The standard spirometer consists of a movable bell inverted over a chamber of water. Inside the bell, above the water line, is the gas that is to be breathed. The bell is counterbalanced by a weight to maintain the gas inside at atmospheric pressure so that its height above the water is proportional to the amount of gas in the bell. A breathing tube connects the mouth of the patient with the gas under the bell. Thus, as the patient breathes into the tube, the bell moves up and down with each inspiration and expiration

Figure 8.4. Spirometer. (Courtesy of Warren E. Collins, Inc., Braintree, MA.)

in proportion to the amount of air breathed in or out. Attached to the bell or the counterbalancing mechanism is a pen that writes on an adjacent drum recorder, called a *kymograph*. As the kymograph rotates, the pen traces the breathing pattern of the patient.

Various bell volumes are available, but 9 and 13.5 liters are most common. A well-designed spirometer offers little resistance to airflow, and the bell has little inertia. Various paper speeds are available for the kymograph, with 32, 160, 300, and 1920 mm/min most common. The compact spirometer shown in Figure 8.4 is a widely used instrument for pulmonary function testing. It is used both in the physician's office and in the hospital ward. Its 9-liter capacity is often considered adequate for recording the largest vital capacities, for extended-period oxygen-uptake determinations, and even for spirography during mild exercise. However, many physicians prefer the larger size (13.5 liters) because of the extra capacity. The principle of operation is similar for both. Easily removable flutter valves and a CO_2 absorbent container permit minimized breathing resistance during tests for maximal respiratory flow rates. This instrument is equally suitable for clinical spirography, for cardiopulmonary function testing, and for metabolism determinations. The instrument directly records basal minute volume, exercise ventilation, or maximum breathing capacity. The ventilation equivalent for oxygen may be calculated directly from the spirogram slope lines for ventilation and oxygen uptake.

In addition to the type of spirometer just described, and illustrated in Figure 8.4, several other types are available. For example, *waterless spirometers,* which are also used clinically, operate on a principle similar to that of the spirometer just described. One type, called the *wedge spirometer,* is shown in Figure 8.5. In this instrument the air to be breathed is held in a chamber enclosed by two parallel metal pans hinged to each other along one edge. The space between the two pans is enclosed by a flexible bellows (like a fireplace bellows) to form the chamber. One of the pans, which contains an inlet tube, is fixed to a stand and the other swings freely with respect to it. As air is introduced into the chamber or withdrawn from it, the moving pan changes its position to compensate for the volume changes. Construction is such that the pan moves in response to very slight changes in volume. A well-designed wedge spirometer imposes an almost undetectable amount of air pressure on the patient's lungs. The instrument provides electrical outputs proportional to both volume and airflow, from which the required determinations can be obtained.

In a similar type of waterless spirometer, the volume of the chamber is varied by means of a lightweight piston that moves freely in a cylinder as air is withdrawn and replaced in breathing. A Silastic rubber seal between the piston and the cylinder wall keeps the chamber airtight. Instruments of this type have characteristics similar to those of the wedge spirometer.

Figure 8.5. Wedge spirometer. (Courtesy of Med. Science Electronics, St. Louis, MO.)

Another group of instruments, sometimes called *electronic spirometers,* measures airflow and, by use of electronic circuitry, calculates the various volumes and capacities. Such a device is shown in Figure 8.6. This instrument provides both a graphic output similar to that of a standard spirometer and a digital readout of the desired parameters. Various types of airflow transducers are used, utilizing such devices as small breath-driven turbines and heated wires that are cooled by the breath.

A *bronchospirometer* is a dual spirometer that measures the volumes and capacities of each lung individually. The air-input device is a double-lumen tube that divides for entry into the airway to each lung and thus provides isolation for differential measurement. The main function of the bronchospirometer is the preoperative evaluation of oxygen consumption of each lung.

The usual output of a spirometer is tne *spirogram.* An example is shown in Figure 8.7. The recording is read from right to left. In this particular example, inspiration moves the pen toward the bottom of the chart and expiration toward the top. Some spirometers, however, provide spirograms with inspiration toward the top.

Figure 8.6. Electronic spirometer with digital readout, printed tape, and computer interface capabilities. (Courtesy of Life Support Equipment Co., Woburn, MA.)

Figure 8.7. Typical spirogram. Read right to left. (See text for explanation.)

In order to produce a spirogram, the patient is instructed to breathe through the mouthpiece of the spirometer. His nose is blocked with a clip so that all breathing is through the mouth. The recorder is first set to a slow speed to measure vital capacity (typically, 32 mm/min). To produce the spirogram shown in the figure, the patient breathed quietly for a short time at rest so as to provide a baseline. He was then instructed to exhale completely and then to inhale as much as he could. This process produced the vital capacity record at the extreme right of the figure. With his lungs at the maximal inspirational level, the patient held his breath a short time while the recorder was shifted to a higher chart speed (e.g., 1920 mm/min). The patient was then instructed to blow out all the air he could as quickly as possible to produce the FEV_1 curve on the record. To calculate the FEV_1, a 1-second interval was measured from the beginning of the maximum slope. Sometimes it is necessary to determine the beginning point by extending the maximum slope to the level of maximum inspiration. This step ensures that the initial friction and inertia of the spirometer have been overcome and compensates for error on the part of the patient in performing the test as instructed.

The spirogram in Figure 8.7 also shows a maximal voluntary ventilation (MVV) record. For this determination, the recorder is set at an intermediate speed. After a short rest, a few cycles of resting respiration were recorded. The patient was then instructed to breathe in and out as rapidly as possible for about 10 seconds, producing the MVV record in the figure.

Most spirometry tests are repeated two or three times, and the maximum values are used to ensure that the patient performed the test to the best of his ability. Although some instruments are calibrated for direct readout, others require that the height of the tracings be converted to liters by use of a calibration factor for the instrument, called the *spirometer factor*. This calibration factor can be obtained from a table or chart.

Although the usual output for a spirometer is the spirogram, other types of output, including digital readouts, are available, particularly from the waterless and electronic types of spirometers. Some instruments even have built-in computational capability to calculate automatically the required volumes and capacities from the basic measurements.

Incorporation of microprocessors (see Chapter 15) has resulted in instruments that not only calculate all required parameters, but also print additional information and compare the measured results with normal data based on the patient's sex, height, and weight. Figure 8.8 shows a microprocessor-based system for measurement of forced vital capacity (FVC), forced expiratory volume (FEV), forced expiratory flow (FEF), and maximal voluntary ventilation (MVV). When used in conjunction with a wedge spirometer, this instrument provides a digital readout of patient data, test results, and a pulmonary volume-flow loop, which involves both

Figure 8.8. Pulmonary function studies system. (Courtesy of Med. Science Electronics, St. Louis, MO.)

compliance and airway resistance. A volume-flow loop is shown on the screen in photograph. Measured results are automatically compared with predicted normal values, based on the sex, height, and weight of the patient. In addition, the instrument is able to correct for ambient temperature and barometric pressure.

8.2.3.1. Measurement of residual volume. From the spirogram and the outputs of some of the other instruments described above, all the lung volumes and capacities can be determined except those that require measurement of the air still remaining in the lungs and airways after maximum expiration. These parameters, which include the residual volume, FRC, and total lung capacity, can be measured through the use of foreign gas mixtures. A gas analyzer is required for these tests. A description of several types of gas analyzers is presented in Section 8.3.1, which is concerned with gas distribution and diffusion.

The *closed-circuit technique* involves rebreathing from a spirometer charged with a known volume and concentration of a marker gas, such as hydrogren or helium. Helium is usually used. After several minutes of breathing, complete mixing of the spirometer and pulmonary gases is assumed, and the residual volume is calculated by a simple proportion of gas volumes and concentrations.

The *open-circuit* or *nitrogen washout method* involves the inspiration of pure oxygen and expiration into an oxygen-purged spirometer. If the patient has been breathing air, the gas remaining in his lungs is 78 percent nitrogen. As he begins to breathe the pure oxygen, it will mix with the gas still in his lungs, and a certain amount of nitrogen will "wash out" with each breath. By measuring the amount of nitrogen in each expired breath, a washout curve is obtained from which the volume of air initially in the lungs can readily be calculated. The preferred breathing level for beginning this measurement is the end expiratory level.

The functional residual capacity (FRC) (from which residual volume can also be calculated by subtracting the expiratory reserve volume) can be measured by using a *body plethysmograph*. This instrument, shown in Figure 8-9, is an airtight box in which the patient is seated. Utilizing Boyle's law (at constant temperature, the volume of gas varies inversely with the pressure), the ratio of the change in lung volume to change in mouth pressure is used to determine the thoracic gas volume. The patient breathes

Figure 8.9. Body plethysmograph. (Courtesy of Warren E. Collins, Inc., Braintree, MA.)

air from within the box through a tube containing an airflow transducer and a shutter to close off the tube for certain portions of the test. Pressure transducers measure the air pressure in the breathing tube on the patient's side of the shutter and inside the box. The amount of air in the box, including that in the patient's lungs, remains constant, since there is no way for air to enter or escape. However, when the patient compresses the air in his lungs during expiration, his total body volume is reduced, thus reducing the pressure in the box. Conversely, when the patient inhales by reducing the pressure in his thoracic region, his body volume increases and increases the box pressure. The FRC is measured with the shutter in the breathing tube closed. With no air allowed to flow, the mouth pressure (sensed by the transducer in the tube) can be assumed to equal the alveolar pressure. The patient is instructed to pant at a slow rate against the closed shutter. As he does so, he alternately expands and compresses the air in his lungs. By measuring the changes in mouth pressure and corresponding changes in intrathoracic volume (Equal and opposite to changes in box volume outside the patient), it is possible to calculate the intrathoracic volume. If the test is performed at the end expiratory level, the intrathoracic volume is equal to the FRC.

8.2.3.2. Intra-alveolar and intra-thoracic pressure measurements. The body plethysmograph can also be used to measure intra-alveolar and intrathoracic pressures. These measurements are important in the determination of both compliance and airway resistance, since inaccessibility of these chambers makes direct measurement impossible. For measurement of intra-alveolar pressures, the shutter in the breathing tube is opened to allow the patient to freely breathe air from within the closed box. Since the patient and the box form a closed system containing a fixed amount of gas, pressure and volume variations in the box are the inverse of the pressure variations in the lungs as the gas within the lungs expands and is compressed due to the positive and negative pressures in the lungs. For calibration, the patient's breathing tube is blocked for a few seconds, during which the patient is asked to the "pant" while mouth pressure is measured. Since mouth pressure and lung pressure are the same when there is no airflow, these data can be used in calibration of the measurement.

For measurement of intrathoracic pressures, a balloon is placed in the patient's esophagus, which is within the thoracic cage. Since the balloon is exposed to the intrathoracic pressure, its pressure, measured with respect to mouth pressure by using some form of differential pressure transducer, represents the difference between pressures.

8.2.3.3. Airway resistance measurements. Airway resistance can be determined by simultaneously measuring the intra-alveolar pressure and

airflow in the body plethysmograph and by dividing the difference between the intra-alveolar pressure and the atmospheric pressure by the flow.

$$R = \frac{P_{ia} - P_A}{f}$$

where R = airway resistance
P_{ia} = intra-alveolar pressure
P_A = *atmospheric pressure*
f = airflow

A variety of instruments can be used to measure airflow. One of the most widely used is the *pneumotachometer,* often called the *pneumotachograph,* shown in Figure 8.10. This device utilizes the principle that air flowing through an orifice produces a pressure difference across the orifice that is a function of the velocity of the air. In the more common pneumotachometer, the orifice consists of a set of capillaries or a metal screen. Since the cross section of the orifice is fixed, the pressure difference can be calibrated to represent flow. Two pressure transducers or a differential pressure transducer can be used to measure the pressure difference.

Another method of measuring airflow is a transducer in which a heated wire is cooled by the flow of air, and the resistance change due to the cooling is measured as representative of airflow. Because the cooling effect is the same regardless of the direction of airflow, this transducer is insensitive to direction, whereas the pneumotachograph described above indicates not only the amount of flow but also the direction.

Ultrasonic airflow-measuring devices utilizing the Doppler effect (see Chapters 6 and 9) have been developed. Since flow is the first derivative or rate of change of volume, some volume-measuring devices also produce a measurement of flow. Also in use is a small breath-driven turbine which operates a miniature electrical generator that produces an output voltage proportional to the air velocity

Figure 8.10. Pneumotachometer. Air inlet and outlet are at left and right. Connections at top are for pressure transducer. Black "knob" is a heating element. (Courtesy of Veterans Administration Hospital, Sepulveda, CA.)

In some applications, the actual flow or volume of respiration is not required, but a measure of *respiration rate* (number of breaths per minute) is needed. Respiration rate can, of course, be obtained from any instrument that records the volume changes during the respiratory cycle. There are, however, other instruments that are difficult to calibrate for volume changes but that well serve the purpose of measuring respiration rate. Such instruments are much simpler and easier to use than the spirometer or other devices intended for volume measurements. These instruments include a mercury plethysmograph of the type described in Chapter 2 and an impedance pneumograph in which impedance changes due to respiration can be measured across the chest.

8.2.3.4. Measurement of closing volume. In measuring the closing *volume,* two techniques can be used. In the *bolus method,* a bolus of a marker gas (usually argon, xenon, or helium) is inspired at the residual volume level. The patient is instructed to inhale air until his or her maximal inspirational level is reached and then to *slowly* expire as much as possible. A person with average lung volume should complete expiration in about 8 to 10 seconds. During expiration, the concentration of the marker gas is monitored at the mouthpiece and plotted against the lung volume level.

In the second method of measuring closing volume, the residual nitrogen in the lungs is used as the marker gas. To perform the measurement, the patient fills his or her lungs with pure oxygen and exhausts all the air possible. The nitrogen concentration of the exhausted air is plotted against lung volume level. At the closing volume level, the nitrogen concentration suddenly begins to increase at a more rapid rate. The *closing volume* is the difference between that level and the residual volume level and is usually expressed as a percentage of the patient's vital capacity.

8.3. GAS EXCHANGE AND DISTRIBUTION

Once air is in the lungs, oxygen and carbon dioxide must be exchanged between the air and the blood in the lungs and between the blood and the cells in the body tissues. In addition, the gases must be transported between the lungs and the tissue by the blood. The physiological processes involved in this overall task were presented briefly in Section 8.1. A number of tests have been devised to determine the effectiveness with which these processes are carried out. Some of these tests and the instrumentation required for their performance are described and discussed in this section. The tests connected with the exchange of gases are treated first, after which measurements pertaining to the transport of oxygen and CO_2 in the blood are covered.

8.3.1. Measurements of Gaseous Exchange and Diffusion

The mixing of gases within the lungs, the ventilation of the alveoli, and the exchange of oxygen and carbon dioxide between the air and blood in the lungs all take place through a process called *diffusion.* Diffusion is the movement of gas molecules from a point of higher pressure to a point of lower pressure to equalize the pressure difference. This process can occur when the gas is unequally distributed in a chamber or wherever a pressure difference exists in the gas on two sides of a membrane permeable to that gas.

Measurements required for determining the amount of diffusion involve the partial pressures of oxygen and carbon dioxide, P_{O_2} and P_{CO_2}, respectively. There are many methods by which these measurements can be obtained, including some chemical analysis methods and measurements of diffusing capacity.

8.3.1.1. Chemical analysis methods. The original gas analyzers developed by Haldane, and modified by Scholander, were of the chemical type. In these devices, a gas sample of approximately 0.5 ml is introduced into a reaction chamber by use of a transfer pipet at the upper end of the reaction chamber capillary. An indicator droplet in this capillary allows the sample to be balanced against a trapped volume of air in the thermobarometer. Absorbing fluids for CO_2 and O_2 can be transferred in from side arms without causing any change in the total volume of the system. The micrometer is adjusted so as to put mercury into the system in place of the gases being absorbed. The volume of the absorbed gases is read from the micrometer barrel calibration.

8.3.1.2. Diffusing capacity using CO infrared analyzer. To determine the efficiency of perfusion of the lungs by blood and the diffusion of gases, the most important tests are those that measure O_2, CO_2, pH, and bicarbonate in arterial blood. In trying to measure the diffusion rate of oxygen from the alveoli into the blood, it is usually assumed that all alveoli have an equal concentration of oxygen. Actually, this condition does not exist because of the unequal distribution of ventilation in the lung; hence, the terms *diffusing capacity* or *transfer factor* (rather than *diffusion*) are used to describe the transfer of oxygen from the alveoli into the pulmonary capillary blood.

Carbon monoxide (CO) resembles oxygen in its solubility and molecular weight and also combines with hemoglobin reversibly. Its affinity for hemoglobin is about 200 to 300 times that of oxygen, however. Carbon monoxide can thus be used as a tracer gas in measuring the diffusing capacity of the lung. It passes from the alveolar gas into the alveolar walls, then into the plasma, from which it enters the red blood cells, where it combines with hemoglobin.

A relationship may be obtained that is a function of both the diffusing capacity of the alveolar membrane and the rate at which CO combines with hemoglobin in the alveolar capillaries. This relationship may be expressed as follows:

$$\frac{1}{TF} = \frac{1}{D_m} + \frac{1}{\theta V_c} \quad \text{mm Hg/ml/min}$$

where TF = diffusing capacity for the lung for CO
   D_m = diffusing capacity for the alveolar membrane
   V_c = volume of blood in the capillaries
   θ = reaction rate of CO with oxyhemoglobin

TF, the *diffusing capacity for the whole lung,* in normal adults ranges from 20 to 38 ml/min/mm Hg. It varies with depth of inspiration, increases during exercise, and decreases with anemia or low hemoglobin.

The principal methods of measuring diffusing capacity involve the inhalation of low concentrations of carbon monoxide. The concentration is less than 0.25 percent and usually ranges from 0.05 to 0.1 percent. The concentration of CO in the alveoli and the rate of its uptake into the blood per minute are measured by either the steady-state method or the single-breath method, both of which are described below. In either method, uptake of carbon monoxide is calculated by measuring the concentration and the volume of the air–CO mixture. Since the concentration of CO fluctuates throughout the respiratory cycle, end-tidal expired air is collected and the CO in the air is measured.

In the single-breath method, the last 75 to 100 ml of the expired air is collected so that enough end-tidal air containing CO is available for the measurement. CO in the alveolar gas is measured. In the steady-state method, the patient rebreathes the gas until equilibrium is reached.

The small amount of CO in the blood is negligible, for it combines with the hemoglobin in the red blood cells and exerts no significant back pressure. By estimating the P_{CO} in the blood by the rebreathing method, the diffusing capacity can be calculated as

$$TF \text{ or diffusing capacity} = \frac{\text{ml CO taken up/min}}{P_{CO} \text{ in alveoli (mm/Hg)}}$$

For this measurement, as well as for all methods requiring carbon monoxide determination, a carbon monoxide analyzer or a gas chromatograph is used. The commonly used carbon monoxide analyzer utilizes an infrared energy source, a beam chopper, sample and reference cells, plus a detector and amplifier. A milliammeter or a digital meter may be used for display.

Two infrared beams are generated, one directed through the sample and the other through the reference. The CO gas mixture flowing through the sample cell absorbs more infrared energy than does the reference gas. The two infrared beams are each measured by a differential infrared detector. The output signal is proportional to the amount of monitored gas in the sample cell. The signal is amplified and presented to the output display meter or to a recorder.

8.3.1.3. Gas chromatograph. The quantities of various gases in the expired air can also be determined by means of a *gas chromatograph*, an instrument in which the gases are separated as the air passes through a column containing various substances that interact with the gases. The reactions cause different gases to pass through the column at different rates so that they leave the column at different times. The quantity of each gas is measured as it emerges. To identify the gases in the expired air other than oxygen, nitrogen, or CO_2, a *mass spectrometer* is used in conjunction with the gas chromatograph. The mass spectrometer identifies the ions according to their mass/charge ratio.

8.3.2. Measurements of Gas Distribution

The distribution of oxygen from the lungs to the tissues and carbon dioxide from the tissues to the lungs takes place in the blood. The process by which each gas is transported, however, is quite different. As mentioned earlier, oxygen is carried by the hemoglobin of the red blood cells. On the other hand, carbon dioxide is carried through chemical processes in which CO_2 and water combine to produce carbonic acid, which is dissolved in the blood. The amount of carbonic acid in the blood, in turn, affects the pH of the blood. In assessing the performance of the blood in its ability to transport respiratory gases, then, measurements of the partial pressures of oxygen (P_{O_2}) and carbon dioxide (P_{CO_2}) in the blood, the percent of oxygenation of the hemoglobin, and the pH of the blood are most useful.

Electrodes for measurement of P_{O_2}, P_{CO_2}, and pH are described in detail in Chapter 4. These electrodes, together with amplification and readouts, provide a fairly simple method for this type of analysis. Measurements both in vitro and in vivo are possible with these electrodes. A blood gas analyzer that utilizes such electrodes and provides a digital output of the pH, P_{CO_2}, and P_{O_2} readings is shown in Figure 8.11. This device provides continuous, automatic calibration as well as checking of critical system components and reagent conditions. It can also measure respiratory gases, and a printed readout option is available. All measured and calculated results are displayed in digital form, along with calibration values.

Figure 8.11. Automated digital blood gas analyzer. (Courtesy of Instrumentation Laboratory, Inc., Lexington, MA.)

Another in vitro method for analyzing both P_{O_2} and P_{CO_2} utilizes the *Van Slyke apparatus.* In this device, a measured quantity of blood is used and the O_2 and CO_2 are extracted by vacuum. The quantity of these two gases is measured manometrically, after which the CO_2 is absorbed. The quantity is measured again, the oxygen is absorbed, and the remaining gas, which is nitrogen, is measured. The amount of O_2 and CO_2 may be calculated from these measurements as a percentage of the total gas.

Another method involving the measurement of pH as part of the blood gas determination is called the *Astrup technique* and utilizes a semilogarithmic paper with a special nomogram. In this method a pH determination is made on a heparinized microsample of blood. Two other pH determinations are made on the same sample after it has been equilibrated with two known CO_2 tensions, obtained from cylinders accompanying the apparatus. These three points are plotted on special graph paper and connected by a straight line. The slope of the line is an index of the buffering capacity of the blood, which is calculated using this nomogram.

When hemoglobin is oxygenated, its light-absorption properties change as a function of the percentage of oxygen saturation. At a wavelength of 6500 Å (angstrom units), the difference in absorption between oxygenated and nonoxygenated blood is greatest, whereas at 8050 Å the absorption is the same. Thus, by measuring the absorption of a sample of blood at both wavelengths on a special photometer, the percentage of oxygenation can be determined.

A similar principle can be used to measure the percentage of oxygenation of the blood in vivo. Here an instrument called an *ear oximeter* is used. The ear oximeter is composed of an ear clip that holds a light source on one side of the earlobe and two sensors on the opposite side, so that the light passing through the earlobe is picked up by both of the sensors. As the blood in the capillaries of the earlobe changes color, these changes are reflected in the amount of light transmitted through the ear at each of the two aforementioned wavelengths. Since each of the sensors receives and filters transmitted light so that its maximum response is at one of the two wavelengths, variations in the percentage of oxygenation can be measured. This method should only be used to measure differences in oxyhemoglobin saturation rather than exact oxygen blood level or exact percentage of oxygenation.

8.4. RESPIRATORY THERAPY EQUIPMENT

When a patient is incapable of adequate ventilation by natural processes, mechanical assistance must be provided so that sufficient oxygen is delivered to the organs and tissues of the body and excessive levels of carbon dioxide are not permitted to accumulate. The procedures and instrumentation involved in providing mechanical assistance in respiration and in supplying hypoxic patients with higher-than-normal concentrations of oxygen or other therapeutic gases or medications constitute a field known as *respiratory therapy*. Until the past few years, this field was known as *inhalation therapy,* but since it covers much more than inhalation, the more encompassing term is preferred. Instruments for respiratory therapy include such devices as inhalators, ventilators, respirators, resuscitators, positive-pressure breathing apparatus, humidifiers, and nebulizers. Many of these instruments, however, have overlapping functions, and the name used for a particular device may vary among manufacturers.

8.4.1. Inhalators

The term *inhalator* generally indicates a device used to supply oxygen or some other therapeutic gas to a patient who is able to breathe spontaneously without assistance. As a rule, inhalators are used when a concentration of oxygen higher than that of air is required. The inhalator consists of a source of the therapeutic gas, equipment for reducing the pressure and controlling the flow of the gas, and a device for administering the gas. Devices for administering oxygen to patients include nasal cannulae and catheters, face masks that cover the nose and mouth, and, in certain settings, such as pediatrics, oxygen tents. The oxygen concentration presented to the patient is controlled by adjusting the flow of gas into the mask.

8.4.2. Ventilators and Respirators

The terms *ventilator* and *respirator* are used interchangeably to describe equipment that may be employed continuously or intermittently to improve ventilation of the lungs and to supply humidity or aerosol medications to the pulmonary tree. Most ventilators in clinical settings use positive pressure during inhalation to inflate the lungs with various gases or mixtures of gases (air, oxygen, carbon dioxide, helium, etc.). Expiration is usually passive, although under certain conditions pressure may be applied during the expiratory phase as well, in order to improve arterial oxygen tension. Only under rare circumstances is negative airway pressure utilized during expiration.

Most respirators in common use are classified as assistor-controllers, and can be operated in any of three different modes. These modes differ in the method by which inspiration is initiated.

1. In the *assist* mode inspiration is triggered by the patient. A pressure sensor responds to the slight negative pressure that occurs each time the patient attempts to inhale and triggers the apparatus to begin inflating the lungs. Thus, the respirator helps the patient inspire when he wants to breathe. A sensitivity adjustment is provided to select the amount of patient effort required to trigger the machine. The assist mode is used for patients who are able to control their breathing but are unable to inhale a sufficient amount of air without assistance or for whom breathing requires too much effort.

2. In the *control* mode breathing is controlled by a timer set to provide the desired respiration rate. Controlled ventilation is required for patients who are unable to breathe on their own. In this mode the respirator has complete control over the patient's respiration and does not respond to any respiratory effort on the part of the patient.

3. In the *assist-control* mode the apparatus is normally triggered by the patient's attempts to breathe, as in the assist mode. However, if the patient fails to breathe within a predetermined time, a timer automatically triggers the device to inflate the lungs. Thus, the patient controls his own breathing as long as he can, but if he should fail to do so, the machine is able to take over for him. This mode is most frequently used in critical care settings.

In addition to the three modes described, many respirators can be triggered manually by means of a control on the panel.

Once inspiration has been triggered, inflation of the lungs continues until one of the following conditions occurs:

1. The delivered gas reaches a predetermined pressure in the proximal or upper airways. A ventilator that operates primarily in this manner is said to be *pressure-cycled*.
2. A predetermined volume of gas has been delivered to the patient. This is the primary mode of operation of *volume-cycled ventilators*.
3. The air or oxygen has been applied for a predetermined period of time. This is the characteristic mode of operation for *time-cycled ventilators*.

The various types of ventilators in clinical use can be categorized by two basic types. The first is a *pressure-cycled,* positive-pressure *assistor-controller*. An example of this type of respirator is shown in Figure 8.12. The device is powered pneumatically from a source of gas and requires no electrical power. Devices in this category may contain an electrically powered compressor or can be used with a separate compressor to permit ventilation with ambient air.

Although a ventilator of the type shown in Figure 8.12 is quite small, it includes all the necessary equipment to control the flow of gas, mix air and oxygen, sense the patient's effort to inspire, terminate the inspiration when the desired pressure is reached, permit adjustment of the sensitivity of the triggering mechanism and the desired pressure level, and even generate a negative pressure to assist expiration on some devices. A special type of valve that incorporates a magnet senses the small negative pressure created by a patient when he attempts to inhale. Timing for operation in the controlled mode is accomplished by filling a chamber with gas and letting it bleed off through an adjustable needle valve. In the prescribed time, the pressure drops to a level at which a spring-loaded valve can operate. One widely used respirator in this category includes three pneumatic timing devices of a somewhat different type to provide time cycling as well as pressure cycling.

A form of volume-controlled respiration is possible with the type of pneumatically-operated respirator that permits time cycling. This flexibility is based on the premise that a given amount of airflow for a specified time duration results in a controlled volume.

The second category of respirator is the *volume-cycled ventilator,* often called a *volume respirator*. This type of device shown in Figure 8.13 uses either a piston or bellows to dispense a precisely controlled volume for each breath. In the critical care setting where patients have pulmonary abnormalities and require predictable volumes and concentrations of gas, this type of ventilator is preferred. It is much larger than the pneumatically-operated units, and most units stand on the floor beside the patient's bed. Volume respirators are electrically operated and provide a much greater degree of control over the ventilation than the pressure-cycled types.

Most devices of this type have adjustable pressure limits and alarms for safety. Also, their provision for adjusting pressure limits and both inspiratory and expiratory times can be used in conjunction with the volume setting to ensure therapeutic pulmonary function in the patient who needs it most.

Volume-cycled ventilators used in critical patient care are always supplied with a spirometer to permit accurate monitoring of the patient's ventilation. Other available features include a heated humidifier and optional capabilities for negative pressure and positive end expiratory pressure (PEEP).

Figure 8.12. Mark 7 respirator, and example of a pressure-cycled, positive-pressure, assistor-controller. (Courtesy of Bird Corporation, Palm Springs, CA.)

Figure 8.13. MA-2 ventilator. (Courtesy of Puritan-Bennet Corporation, Kansas City, MO.)

8.4.3. Humidifiers, Nebulizers, and Aspirators

In order to prevent damage to the patient's lungs, the air or oxygen applied during respiratory therapy must be humidified. Thus, virtually all inhalators, ventilators, and respirators include equipment to humidify the air, either by heat vaporization (steam) or by bubbling an air stream through a jar of water.

When therapy requires that water or some type of medication be suspended in the inspired air as an aerosol, a device called a *nebulizer* is used. In a nebulizer the water or medication is picked up by a high-velocity jet of oxygen (or some other gas) and thrown against one or more baffles or other surfaces to break the substance into controllable-sized droplets or particles, which are then applied to the patient via a respirator.

A more effective (but also more expensive) type of nebulizer is the *ultrasonic nebulizer,* shown in Figure 8.14. This electronic device produces high-intensity sound energy well above the audible range. When applied to water or medication, the ultrasonic energy vibrates the substance with such intensity that a high volume of minute particles is produced. Such equipment usually consists of two parts, a generator that produces a radio-frequency current to drive the ultrasonic transducer, and the nebulizer itself, in which the transducer generates the ultrasound energy and applies it to the water or medication. Unlike the conventional nebulizer, the ultrasonic unit does not depend on the breathing gas for operation. Thus, the therapeutic agent can be administered during oxygen therapy or a mechanical ventilation procedure.

Aspiration and other types of *suction apparatus* are often included as part of a ventilator or inhalator to remove mucus and other fluids from the airways. Where the aspirator is not provided as part of the respiratory therapy equipment, a separate suction device may be utilized.

Figure 8.14. Ultrasonic nebulizer. (Courtesy of the DeVilbiss Company, Medical Products Division, Somerset, PA.)

9

Noninvasive Diagnostic Instrumentation

In the previous chapters many methods of medical measurements have been discussed that involve getting inside the body, or "invading" it. To say the least, such procedures are usually traumatic for the patient and sometimes result in faulty data or detrimental side effects. As these techniques have become more sophisticated, it has been realized that sometimes equally suitable results can be obtained without invasion of the body. As a result, considerable emphasis has been devoted to developing methods of *noninvasive* testing. Some noninvasive methods, like the indirect method of taking blood pressure, have been around for years. Others have just recently been developed, and many new techniques await development of instrumentation that will make them possible.

In presenting material in a broad textbook such as this, it is often difficult to decide where to place certain material. In the case of noninvasive methods, this is certainly true. Does the material pertaining to a given technique belong in the context of the measurement in the body system involved, or should it be treated as a separate topic? A decision was made to use both approaches. For example, probably the best known noninvasive methods involve the use of X rays. While it is true that X rays are noninvasive in the sense that no physical contact or cutting is involved, the body is nevertheless "invaded" by radiation. Therefore, this type of measurement technique is discussed in its own context of ionizing radiation in Chapter 14. Conversely, the newer technique of the use of ultrasound to obtain information similar to that obtained by X-ray techniques is covered in this chapter. An example can be taken from obstetrics. Prior to the extensive use of ultrasonics, expectant mothers were sometimes X-rayed to determine position of the fetus when there was a possibility of problems during delivery which might necessitate a caesarian section. However, the radiation could have effects on both the mother and the fetus. As far as is presently known, using ultrasound to determine pelvic structure and the like has no known effects that could be detrimental. Ultrasonics is considered as one of the main areas of noninvasive testing.

Another example is in cardiology. In Chapter 6 the traumatic procedure of catheterization was discussed. Some of the results can be obtained today by the use of ultrasound methods. In this case the appropriate measurement technique, echocardiography, is discussed in this chapter. For the brain, one of the latest methods of visualization is computerized axial tomography, but since this procedure involves computers, it is discussed in Chapter 15. There are, of course, cross references for all these topics.

All forms of noninvasive testing are based on the fundamental concepts of physics. Throughout the book there are examples of the use of heat, light, sound, electricity, magnetism, and mechanics. This chapter concentrates on two of these areas, the use of heat and temperature measurements and the application of ultrasound to medicine. Each of these topics is discussed from the point of view of its basic principles, after which the measurement techniques, application, and diagnostic methods are explored. Ultrasonic techniques are covered in greater depth, since this material is not usually as available in broader-based textbooks.

9.1. TEMPERATURE MEASUREMENTS

Body temperature is one of the oldest known indicators of the general well-being of a person. Techniques and instruments for the measurement of temperature have been commonplace in the home for years and throughout all kinds of industry, as well as in the hospital. Except for the narrow range required for physiological temperature measurements and the size and shape of the sensing element, instrumentation for measurement of temperature in the human body differs very little from that found in various industrial applications.

Two basic types of temperature measurements can be obtained from the human body: systemic and skin surface measurements. Both provide valuable diagnostic information, although the systemic temperature measurement is much more commonly used.

Systemic temperature is the temperature of the internal regions of the body. This temperature is maintained through a carefully controlled balance between the heat generated by the active tissues of the body, mainly the muscles and the liver, and the heat lost by the body to the environment. Measurement of systemic temperature is accomplished by temperature-sensing devices placed in the mouth, under the armpits, or in the rectum. The normal oral (mouth) temperature of a healthy person is about 37 °C (98.6 °F). The underarm temperature is about 1 degree lower, whereas the rectal temperature is about 1 degree higher than the oral reading. The systemic body temperature can be measured most accurately at the tympanic membrane in the ear, which is believed to approximate the temperature at the "inaccessible" temperature control center in the brain. For some still unknown reason, the body temperature, even in a healthy person, does not remain constant over a 24-hour period but is often 1 to 1½ degrees lower in the early morning than in late afternoon. Although strenuous muscular exercise may cause a temporary rise in body temperature from about 0.5 to 2 °C (about 0.9 to 3.6 °F), the systemic temperature is not affected by the ambient temperature, even if the latter drops to as low as − 18 °C (0 °F) or rises to over 38 °C (100 °F). This balance is upset only when the metabolism of the body cannot produce heat as rapidly as it is lost or when the body cannot rid itself of heat fast enough.

The temperature-control center for the body is located deep within the brain (in the forepart of the hypothalamus) (see Chapter 10). Here the temperature of the blood is monitored and its control functions are coordinated. In warm, ambient temperatures, cooling of the body is aided by production of perspiration due to secretion of the sweat glands and by increased circulation of the blood near the surface. In this manner, the body acts as a radiator. If the external temperature becomes too low, the body conserves heat by reducing blood flow near the surface to the minimum required for maintenance of the cells. At the same time, metabolism is increased. If these measures are insufficient, additional heat is produced by increasing the tone of skeletal muscles and sometimes by involuntary contraction of skeletal muscles (shivering) and of the arrector muscles in the skin (gooseflesh).

In addition to the central "thermostat" for the body, temperature sensors at the surface of the skin permit some degree of local control in the event a certain part of the body is exposed to local heat or cold. Cooling or heating is accomplished by control of the surface blood flow in the region affected.

The only deviation from normal temperature control is a rise in temperature called "fever," experienced with certain types of infection. The onset of fever is caused primarily by a delicate shutdown of the mechanisms for heat elimination. The body temperature increases·as though the "thermostat" in the brain were suddenly turned "up," thus causing additional metabolism because the increased temperature accelerates the chemical reactions of the body. At the beginning of a fever the skin is often pale and dry and shivering usually takes place, for the blood that normally keeps the surface areas warm is shut off, and the skin and muscles react to the coolness. At the conclusion of the fever, as the body temperature is lowered to normal, increased sweating ("breaking of the fever") is often noted as the means by which the additional body heat is eliminated.

Surface or *skin temperature* is also a result of a balance, but here the balance is between the heat supplied by blood circulation in a local area and the cooling of that area by conduction, radiation, convection, and evaporation. Thus, skin temperature is a function of the surface circulation, environmental temperature, air circulation around the area from which the measurement is to be taken, and perspiration. To obtain a meaningful skin temperature measurement, it is usually necessary to have the subject remain with no clothing covering the region of measurement in a fairly cool ambient temperature [approximately 21 °C (70 °F)]. Care must be taken, however, to avoid chilling and the reactions relative to chilling. If a surface measurement is to include the reaction to the cooling of a local region, it should be recognized that the cooling of the skin increases surface circulation, which in turn causes some local warming of adjacent areas. Heat transferred into the site of measurement from adjacent areas of the body must also be accounted for.

9.1.1. Measurement of Systemic Body Temperature

Since the internal or systemic body temperature is a good indicator of the health of a person, measurement of this temperature is considered one of the vital signs of medicine. For this reason, temperature measurement constitutes one of the more important physiological measurements. Although a high degree of accuracy is not always important, methods of temperature measurement must be reliable and easy to perform. In the case of continuous monitoring, the temperature measurement must not cause discomfort to the patient.

Where continuous recording of temperature is not required, the *mercury thermometer* is still the standard method of measurement. Since these devices are inexpensive, easy to use, and sufficiently accurate, they will undoubtedly remain in common use for many years to come. Even so, electronic thermometers, such as that shown in Figure 9.1, are available as

Figure 9.1. Oral temperature measurement using electronic thermometer. (Courtesy of Diagnostic, Inc. Indianopolis, IN.)

replacement for mercury thermometers. With disposable tips, these instruments require much less time for a reading and are much easier to read than the conventional thermometer. Where continuous recording of the temperature is necessary, or where greater accuracy is needed than can be obtained with the mercury thermometer or its electronic counterpart, more sophisticated measuring instruments must be used.

Two types of electronic temperature-sensing devices are found in biomedical applications. They are the *thermocouple,* a junction of two dissimilar metals that produces an output voltage nearly proportional to the temperature at that junction with respect to a reference junction, and the *thermistor,* a semiconductor element whose resistance varies with temperature. Both types are available for medical temperature measurements, although thermistors are used more frequently than thermocouples. This preference is primarily because of the greater sensitivity of the thermistor in the temperature range of interest and the requirement for a reference junction for the thermocouple.

To obtain a voltage proportional to variations in temperature in a thermocouple, the reference junction must be maintained at a known temperature. In practice, the circuit is opened at the reference junction for measurement of the potential. This voltage, called the *contact potential,* ranges from a very few microvolts to a few hundred microvolts per degree centigrade, depending on the two metals used. Generally, the output voltage of a thermocouple is measured directly by using a meter or measured indirectly by comparing the measured voltage with a precisely known voltage obtained by using a potentiometer. Care must be taken to minimize current through the thermocouple circuit, for the current not only causes heating at the junctions but also an additional error due to the *Peltier effect,* wherein one junction is warmed and the other is cooled. (The connections of the leads to the two dissimilar metals constitute a single junction.)

Thermistors are variable resistance devices formed into disks, beads, rods, or other desired shapes. They are manufactured from mixtures of oxides (sometimes sulfates or silicates) of various elements, such as nickel, copper, magnesium, manganese, cobalt, titanium, and aluminum. After the mixture is compressed into shape, it is sintered at a high temperature into a solid mass. The result is a resistor with a large temperature coefficient. Where most metals show an increase of resistance of about 0.3 to 0.5 percent per °C temperature rise, thermistors decrease their resistance by 4 to 6 percent per °C rise.

Unfortunately, the relationship between resistance change and temperature change is nonlinear. The resistance R_{t_1} of a thermistor at a given temperature T_1 can be determined by the following equation:

$$R_{t_1} = R_{t_0} e^{\beta(1/T_1 - 1/T_0)}$$

where R_{t_1} = resistance at temperature T_1

R_{t_0} = resistance at a reference temperature T_0

e = base of the natural logarithms (approximately 2.718)

β = temperature coefficient of the material, usually in the range of about 3000 to 4000

T_1 = temperature at which the measurement is being made, (degrees Kelvin)

T_0 = reference temperature, (degrees Kelvin)

To overcome the nonlinear characteristics of thermistors, the instrumentation in which the resistance is measured often incorporates special linearizing circuits. Some such circuits employ pairs of matched thermistors as part of the linearizing network.

In addition to nonlinearity, the use of thermistors can result in other problems, such as the danger of error due to self-heating, the possibility of hysteresis, and the changing of characteristics because of aging. The effect of self-heating can be reduced by limiting the amount of current used in

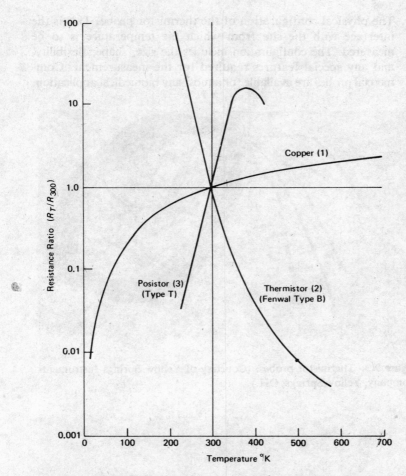

Figure 9.2. Resistance-temperature relationship of copper, thermistor and positor. (From L.A. Geddes and L.E. Baker, *Principles of Applied Biomedical Instrumentation.* John Wiley & Sons, Inc., 1969, by permission.)

measuring the resistance of the thermistor. If the power dissipation of the thermistor can be kept to about a milliwatt, the error should not be excessive, even when temperature differences as small as 0.01 °C are sought.

Semiconductor devices with positive temperature coefficients have been developed but are not commonly used. A comparison of resistance versus temperature curves for copper, a thermistor, and the Posistor (one of the positive coefficient devices) is given in Figure 9.2.

The most important characteristics to consider in selecting a thermistor probe for a specific biomedical application are the following:

1. The physical configuration of the thermistor probe. This is the interface with the site from which the temperature is to be measured. The configuration includes the size, shape, flexibility, and any special features required for the measurement. Commercial probes are available for almost any biomedical application,

Figure 9.3. Thermistor probes. (Courtesy of Yellow Springs Instruments Company, Yellow Springs, OH.)

particularly for measurement of oral and rectal temperatures. Some of these probes are shown in Figure 9.3.

2. The sensitivity of the device. This is its ability to measure accurately small changes in temperature, but it can also be interpreted as the resistance change produced by a given temperature change. Usually, overall sensitivity is a function of both the thermistor probe and the circuitry used to measure the resistance, but the limiting factor is the resistance-temperature characteristic of the thermistor (see Figure 9.2).

3. The absolute temperature range over which the thermistor is designed to operate. This is usually no problem with body temperature measurements, for the temperature range to be measured is so limited, but often, if a general-type temperature measuring instrument is used, the range is so wide that the desired resolution is not attainable.

4. Resistance range of the probe. Thermistor probes are available with resistances from a few hundred ohms to several megohms. A probe should be selected with a suitable resistance range corresponding to the temperature range of interest to match the impedance of the bridge or other type of circuit used to measure the resistance.

Although the resistance of a thermistor can be measured by use of an ohmmeter, most thermistor thermometers use a Wheatstone bridge or similar circuit to obtain a voltage output proportional to temperature variations. Generally, the bridge is balanced at some reference temperature and calibrated to read variations above and below that reference. Either ac or dc excitation can be used for the bridge. If the temperature difference between two measurement sites is desired, thermistors at the two locations are placed in adjacent legs of the bridge.

9.1.2. Skin Temperature Measurements

Although the systemic temperature remains very constant throughout the body, skin temperatures can vary several degrees from one point to another. The range is usually from about 30 to 35 °C (85 to 95 °F). Exposure to ambient temperatures, the covering of fat over capillary areas, and local blood circulation patterns are just a few of the many factors that influence the distribution of temperatures over the surface of the body. Often, skin temperature measurements can be used to detect or locate defects in the circulatory system by showing differences in the pattern from one side of the body to the other.

Skin temperature measurements from specific locations on the body are frequently made by using small, flat thermistor probes taped to the skin (Figure 9.3). The simultaneous readings from a number of these probes provide a means of measuring changes in the spatial characteristics of the circulatory pattern over a time interval or with a given stimulus.

Although the effect is insignificant in most cases, the presence of the thermistor on the skin slightly affects the temperature at that location. Other methods of measuring skin temperature that draw less heat from the point of measurement are available. The most popular of these methods involve the measurement of infrared radiation.

The human skin has been found to be an almost perfect emitter of infrared radiation. That is, it is able to emit infrared energy in proportion to the surface temperature at any location of the body. If a person is allowed to remain in a room at about 21 °C (70 °F) without clothing over the area to be measured, a device sensitive to infrared radiation can accurately read the surface temperature. Such a device, called an *infrared thermometer,* is shown in Figure 9.4. Infrared thermometers in the physiological temperature range are available commercially and can be used to locate breast cancer and other unseen sources of heat. They can also be used to detect areas of poor circulation and other sources of coolness and to measure skin temperature changes that reflect the effects of circulatory changes in the body.

An extension of this method of skin temperature measurement is the *Thermograph,* shown in Figure 9.5(a). This device is an infrared thermometer incorporated into a scanner so that the entire surface of a body, or some portion of the body, is scanned in much the same way that a television camera scans an image, but much slower. While the scanner scans the body, the infrared energy is measured and used to modulate the intensity of a light beam that produces a map of the infrared energy on photographic

Figure 9.4. Infrared thermometer. Barnes model MT-3 noncontact thermometer provides fast, accurate measurements of skin temperature. (Courtesy of Barnes Engineering Company, Stamford, CT.)

Figure 9.5. Thermography: (a) high resolution thermograph; (b) thermogram (see explanation in text). (Courtesy of Barnes Engineering Company, Stamford, CT.)

paper. This presentation is called a *thermogram.* Figure 9.5(b) shows a photograph of two men and a corresponding thermogram. The thermogram shows that each of the two men has an artificial leg. The advantage of this method is that relatively warm and cool areas are immediately evident. By calibrating the instrument against known temperature sources, the picture can be read quantitatively.

A similar device, called *Thermovision,* has a scanner that operates at a rate sufficiently high to permit the image to be shown in real time on an oscilloscope. The raster has about 100 vertical lines per frame, and the horizontal resolution is also about 100 lines, which seems to be adequate for good representation. The intensity of the measured infrared radiation is reproduced

Figure 9.6. Thermovision system: (a) Thermovision 680 Medical, camera and display unit; (b) Thermovision 680 Medical with accessories. (Courtesy of AGA Infrared Systems AB, Sweden.)

(a)

Figure 9.6. *Continued.*

by Z-axis modulation (brightness variation) of the oscilloscope beam. One advantage of this system is that certain portions of the gray scale can be enhanced to bring out specific features of the picture. Also, the image can be changed so that warm spots appear dark instead of light, as they usually do. All these enhancement measures can be performed while the subject is being scanned. A Thermovision system is shown in Figure 9.6.

9.2. PRINCIPLES OF ULTRASONIC MEASUREMENT

Recently, many of the innovations of medicine have taken place because of the use of ultrasound. By definition, *ultrasound* is sonic energy at frequencies above the audible range (greater than 20 kHz). Its use in medical diagnosis dates back to the period following World War II and is a direct outgrowth of the military development of sonar, in which pulsed ultrasound was used in the detection of submarines and other underwater objects by reflection of the ultrasonic waves.

9.2.1. Properties of Ultrasound

Like other forms of sonic energy, ultrasound exists as a sequence of alternate compressions and rarefactions of a suitable medium (air, water, bone, tissue, etc.) and is propagated through that medium at some velocity. Its behavior also depends on the frequency (wavelength) of the sonic energy and the density and mechanical compliance of the medium through which it travels. At the frequencies normally used in diagnostic applications, ultrasound can be focused into a beam and obeys the laws of reflection and refraction.

Whenever a beam of ultrasound passes from one medium to another, a portion of the sonic energy is reflected and the remainder is refracted, as shown in Figure 9.7. The amount of energy reflected depends on the difference in density between the two media and the angle at which the transmitted beam strikes the medium. The greater the difference in media, the greater will be the amount reflected. Also, the nearer the angle of incidence between the beam and the interface is to 90° the greater will be the reflected portion.

Figure 9.7. Reflection and refraction of ultrasound at an interface between media of different densities.

At interfaces of extreme difference in media, such as between tissue and bone or tissues and a gas, almost all the energy will be reflected and practically none will continue through the second medium. For this reason, the propagation path for ultrasound into or through the body must not include bone or any gaseous medium, such as air. In applying ultrasound to the body, an airless contact is usually produced through use of an aqueous gel or a water bag between the transducer and the skin.

Table 9.1 lists the density and other properties of various materials, including several of biological interest. The temperature and ultrasonic frequency are given for most of the measurements. Note that the density of water and most body fluids and tissues is approximately 1.00 g/cm³. Benzene has a density of 0.88, whereas the density of bone is almost twice as great (1.77g/cm³).

Table 9.1. ULTRASONIC CHARACTERISTICS OF MATERIALS[a]

Material	Temperature (°C)	Density (g/cm³)	Velocity (m/sec)	Characteristic Impedance × 10⁶ (kg/m²/sec)	β	f (MHz)	α (per cm)
Water	40	0.992	1529	1.517	1	2	0.00025
Saline, 0.9% normal	40	0.998	1539	1.537			
Castor oil	40	0.941	1411	1.328	1	1.67	0.037
Brain, average	37	1.03	1510	1.56	1	1	0.11
						5	0.44
Cortical gray matter	37	1.03			1	1	0.08
Cortical white matter	37	1.03			1	1	0.14
Muscle, skeletal	37	1.07	1570	1.68	1	1	0.13
Fat	37	0.97	1440	1.40	1	1	0.05
Bone, skull	37	1.77	3360	6.00	0.5	1.7	0.37
						1	1.2
						1.5	2.5
						2	4.0
						2.5	5.9
						3	8.1
						3.5	10.5
Skin				1.63			
Liver		1.08	1510	1.63		2	0.19
Blood		1.01	1550	1.56		2	0.04
Lucite				3.23			
Brain tumor							
Meningioma						5	0.73
Glioblastoma						5	0.38
Metastatic						5	0.50
Kidney		1.04	1560	1.62		2	0.27
Eye							
Aqueous humor		1.00	1500	1.50			
Vitreous humor		1.00	1530	1.53			
Lens		1.14	1630	1.85			
Benzene		0.88	1320	1.17			
Rubber							
Rhoc		1.00	1560	1.56			
Soft		0.95	1050	1.00			
Spleen		1.05	1570	1.65			

Attenuation Constant, $\alpha = cf^{\beta}$

From W. Welkowitz and S. Deutsch, *Biomedical Instruments: Theory and Design,* Academic Press, New Yo 976; by permission.

The velocity of sound propagation through a medium varies with the density of the medium and its elastic properties. It also varies with temperature. As shown in Table 9.1, the velocity through most body fluids and soft tissues is in a fairly narrow range around 1550 m/sec. The velocity in water is just slightly lower (1529 m/sec). Note that the velocity of sound through fat is significantly lower (1440 m/sec) and through bone is much higher (3360 m/sec).

Every material has an *acoustic impedance,* which is a ratio of the acoustic pressure of the applied ultrasound to the resulting particle velocity in the material. Since acoustic impedance is a complex value, consisting of both resistive and reactive components, a simpler term, called *characteristic impedance,* is more often used. The characteristic impedance of a material is the product of its density and the velocity of sound through it. Table 9.1 gives the characteristic impedances of several materials.

Also given in Table 9.1 is an *attenuation constant,* α, for each material. As ultrasound travels through the material, some of the energy is absorbed and the wave is attenuated a certain amount for each centimeter through which it travels. The amount of attenuation is a function of both the frequency of the ultrasound and the characteristics of the material. The attenuation constant, α, is defined by the equation.

$$\frac{\text{amplitude at point X}}{\text{amplitude at } X + 1 \text{ unit distance}} = \beta$$

As shown in Table 9.1,

$\alpha \text{ (per cm)} = cf_\beta$

where c = proportionality constant
f = ultrasound frequency
β = exponential term determined by the properties of the material

This formula shows that attenuation increases with some power of the frequency, which means that the higher the frequency, the less distance it can penetrate into the body with a given amount of ultrasonic energy. For this reason, lower ultrasound frequencies are used for deeper penetration. However, lower frequencies are incapable of reflecting small objects. As a rule, a solid object surrounded by water or saline must be at least a quarter-wave thick in order to cause a usable reflection. Thus, for finer resolution, higher frequencies must be used. Ultrasound frequencies of 1 to 15 MHz are usually used for diagnostic purposes. At 2 MHz, distinct echoes can be recorded from interfaces 1 mm apart. Higher-frequency ultrasound is also more subject to scattering than ultrasound at lower frequencies. However, the high-frequency ultrasound beam can be focused for greater resolution at a given depth.

Another useful way of assessing the attenuation of ultrasound as it penetrates the body is the *half-value layer* of the medium given in Table 9.2. The half-value layer is the depth of penetration at which the ultrasound energy is attenuated to half the applied amount.

Table 9.2. ULTRASOUND ABSORPTION

Type of Tissue	Frequency (MHz)	Half-Value Layer (cm)
Blood	1.0	35.0
Bone	0.8	0.23
Fat	0.8	3.3
Muscle	0.8	2.1

(From Feigenbaum, Echocardiography, 2nd Edition, Lea and Febiger, 1976 by permission.)

A well-known characteristic of ultrasound frequently utilized in biomedical instrumentation is the *Doppler effect,* in which the frequency of the reflected ultrasonic energy is increased or decreased by a moving interface. The amount of frequency shift can be expressed in the formula:

$$\Delta f = \frac{2V}{\lambda}$$

where f = shift in frequency of the reflected wave
  V = velocity of the interface
  λ = wavelength of the transmitted ultrasound

The frequency increases when the interface moves toward the transducer and decreases when it moves away. With an ultrasound frequency of 3 MHz, the shift is about 40 Hz for each cm/sec of interface velocity.

A useful way to understand this in general terms is to consider what happens if an automobile with its horn sounding passes by on the street. The pitch or perceived frequency of the sound seems higher as the car is approaching but seems lower as it goes away. This is an example of the Doppler frequency shift. When ultrasound is reflected from a moving object, the measured frequency shift is proportional to velocity.

9.2.2. Basic Modes of Transmission

Ultrasound can be transmitted in various forms. Following are the modes of transmission most commonly used in diagnostic medical applications:

1. *Pulsed ultrasound:* In this mode, ultrasound is transmitted in short bursts at a repetition rate ranging from 1 to 12 kHz.

Returning echoes are displayed as a function of time after transmission, which is proportional to the distance from the source to the interface. Movement of interfaces with respect to time can also be displayed. The burst duration is generally about 1 μsec. Pulsed ultrasound is used in most imaging applications.

2. *Continuous Doppler:* Here a continuous ultrasonic signal is transmitted while returning echoes are picked up by a separate receiving transducer. Frequency shifts due to moving interfaces are detected and recorded and the average velocity of the targets is usually determined as a function of time. This mode always requires two transducer crystals, one for transmission and one for receiving, whereas any of the pulsed modes can use either one or two crystals. Continuous Doppler ultrasound is used in blood flow measurements (see Chapter 6) and in certain other applications in which the average velocity is measured without regard to the distance of the sources.

3. *Pulsed Doppler:* As in pulsed ultrasound, short bursts of ultrasonic energy are transmitted and the returning echoes are received. However, in this mode frequency shifts due to movement of the reflected interfaces can be measured in order to determine their velocities. Thus, both the velocity and distance of a moving target can be measured. In a typical application, three cycles of 3-MHz ultrasound are transmitted per pulse at a pulse rate of 4 to 12 kHz.

4. *Range-gated pulsed Doppler:* This mode is a refinement of pulsed-Doppler ultrasound, in which a gating circuit permits measurement of the velocity of targets at a specific distance from the transducer. The velocity of these targets can be measured as a function of time. With range-gated pulsed Doppler ultrasound, the velocity of blood can be measured, not only as a function of time, but also as a function of the distance from the vessel wall.

In any of the above-described modes, the most effective frequency of the ultrasound depends upon the depth of penetration desired and the required resolution.

9.2.3. Ultrasonic Imaging

The most widely used applications of ultrasound in diagnostic medicine involve the noninvasive imaging of internal organs or structures of the body. Such imaging can provide valuable information regarding the size, location, displacement, or velocity of a given structure without the necessity of surgery or the use of potentially harmful radiation. Tumors and other regions of an organ that differ in density from surrounding tissues can be detected. In many instances, ultrasonic techniques have replaced more risky or more traumatic procedures in clinical diagnosis.

Imaging systems generally utilize the pulsed ultrasound or pulsed Doppler mode. Instrumentation must include an electrical signal source capable of driving the transmitter, which consists of a piezoelectric crystal. The same crystal can be used for receiving echoes or a second crystal may be used.

After amplification, the received information is displayed in one of several display modes. There is some confusion in the literature in the definition of some of these modes. For example, some authors consider the M-scan used in echocardiography (Section 9.3.2) as a form of the B-scan mode rather than a separate mode. While it is true that these two modes are very similar, differences in the information presented make it necessary to distinguish between the two in order to properly interpret the display. Also, some authors have adopted terminology from military sonar displays which is not appropriate to imaging in medical applications. The following definitions are those most generally found in the literature and are used consistently in this text:

1. *A-scan display [Figure 9.8(a)]:* This is the simplest form of display. Each transmitted pulse triggers the sweep of an oscilloscope. That pulse (often attenuated) and the returning echoes are displayed as vertical deflections on the trace. The sweep is calibrated in units of distance, and may provide several ranges in order to accurately determine the distance of the interfaces of interest. Often, the amplifier gain is varied with the sweep to compensate for the lower amplitude of more distant echoes. In most cases the transducer is kept stationary so that any movement of echoes along the trace will be the result of moving targets. An example of an A-scan display is that of the echoencephalogram.

2. *M-scan display:* As in the A-scan mode, each transmitted pulse triggers the oscilloscope sweep; however, the received pulses are used to brighten the trace rather than control the vertical deflection, as shown in Figure 9.8(b). The quiescent brightness level is set below the visibility threshold so that only the echoes, which appear as dots with brightness proportional to the intensity of each echo, can be seen. For the M-scan, the transducer is held stationary so that the movement of the dots along the sweep represent movement of received targets. If photographic paper is slowly moved past the face of the oscilloscope so that each

Figure 9.8. Ultrasound Display Principles. (a) Typical A-scan. Echoes cause vertical deflection of oscilloscope pattern. (b) Corresponding display in which echoes control brightness of oscilloscope beam. This principle is used in both B- and M- scan displays.

Figure 9.9 M-scan of moving and stationary target with corresponding A-scan.

trace lies immediately adjacent to the one preceding it, the dot representing each target will trace a line on the paper as shown in Figure 9.9. A stationary target will trace a straight line, whereas a moving target will trace the pattern of its movement with respect to time. A light-pen recorder in which the intensity of the light source can be controlled may be used instead of an oscilloscope to produce a chart record of the movement of echoes with respect to time. An example of an M-scan recording is the echocardiogram shown in Figure 9.12.

3. *B-scan display:* While the M-scan is used to display the movement of targets with respect to time, the B-scan presents a two-dimensional image of a stationary organ or body structure. As in the M-scan, the brightness of the oscilloscope or light-pen beam is controlled by returning echoes; however, in the B-scan the transducer is moved with respect to the body while the vertical deflection of the oscilloscope or movement of the chart paper is made to correspond to the movement of the transducer. The movement may be linear, circular, or a combination of the two, but where it is anything other than linear, the sweep must be made to compensate for the variations in order to provide a true two-dimensional display of the segment being scanned. Examples of B-scan displays are shown in Figure 9.15.

9.3. ULTRASONIC DIAGNOSIS

The applications of ultrasonic methods to medicine are many and varied. The techniques are used in cardiology, for abdominal imaging, in brain studies, in eye analysis, and in obstetrics and gynecology. The records obtained have various names, which usually include the words "echo" or "sono." For example the *echocardiogram,* analogous to the electrocardiogram, is a record of ultrasonic measurements in the heart. The *echoencephalogram* is a record obtained from the brain. A general term used, especially with eye analysis, is the *ultrasonogram.* Examples of these will be presented later in this section. Multiple names have been coined for the instruments used, including many trade titles. Typical designations are *ultrasonograph, ultrasonoscope,* and *sonofluoroscope.* The latter is used essentially for moving structures, whereas some of the devices are used for static images.

Before discussing some of the components and specific medical fields, perhaps a general overview and illustration will give the reader a perspective. Figure 9.10 is a *phased-array ultrasonograph,* which represents a class of instruments that has recently appeared. It is virtually an entire medical ultrasound laboratory in one mobile instrument.

Figure 9.10. Phased array ultrasonograph. (Courtesy of Varian Associates, Medical Group, Palo Alto, CA.)

The V-3000 uses a large video display. The displayed scan image represents the area of the sector swept, up to the selected maximum depth, which may be 7, 15, or 21 cm. The image on the screen remains the same size regardless of the depth chosen. A calibrated scale appropriate to the chosen depth appears on the edges of the image and allows accurate measurement of the anatomy scanned.

The video monitor facilitates easy viewing and simultaneously presents ancillary information along with the diagnostic image. Orthogonal calibration marks appear on the edges of the image. Keyboard-entered patient identification, date, and time are displayed above the image along with the frame number and ECG trigger time relative to the R wave. A nonfade ECG trace is shown below the scan image. When the instrument is used in the A or M modes, a brightened ray indicates the spatial orientation chosen for the particular one-dimensional study being done.

Two separate sets of gain controls give maximum flexibility in optimizing the image for a specific examination. In addition to an overall gain control, a set of seven slide controls allows independent adjustment of gain for each depth interval, corresponding to one-seventh of the selected total penetration depth. Other controls are available which adjust gray scale and suppress noise.

M-mode and A-mode are available on the V-3000 in addition to the two-dimensional imaging capability. In a pure two-dimensional imaging application, the V-3000 operates at a scanning speed of 30 frames per second. For an M-mode or A-mode study, the frame rate is halved to 15 frames per second, with every other pulse used to accumulate data for the M- or A-mode. In M- or A-mode scanning, a brightened line is superimposed on the main display indicating the single ray along which the data are obtained. In the case of A-mode, these data are displayed directly along the brightened ray; for the M-mode, it appears on the optional slow oscilloscope. When a footswitch is depressed, the M-mode information is printed out on a strip-chart recorder.

For cardiac applications, an optional ECG amplifier is available. The trace appears on all displays, including the strip-chart recorder. ECG-triggered photographs may be made by positioning a cursor at the desired time position on the ECG trace.

The V-3000 includes computer-directed self-diagnosis, activated by a front-panel control. These diagnostic routines test the various circuit boards and show the results on the main display.

Phased-array sector scanning describes a technique in which the ultrasonic beam is electronically swept through an arc to produce sharp, high-resolution images in real time while the small transducer is held stationary in any desired position. Scanning is accomplished by pulsing individual crystals in the transducer at slightly different times under the control of a microcomputer. Because the emitted (and received) ultrasonic beam is swept electronically, a wide-angle image is instantly produced wherever the transducer is placed, allowing thorough and rapid imaging with no constraints on transducer positioning.

The video recorder cart is an essential element of the V-3000 system. It includes all the necessary components to do dynamic recording and allows off-line detailed study of these recordings. During an examination, video recordings can be activated by a foot switch. The cart contains a video tape recorder with slow- and stop-motion capabilities, a viewing monitor, and a camera directed at an internal live video monitor optimized for photography.

The video recorder cart is a complete video playback system, and is easily disconnected from the diagnostic module. It can be moved to remote locations for video-tape viewing and photographic record making. The off-line photographic capabilities, combined with the stop action of the video tape recorder, give a physician the opportunity to reanalyze difficult cases, freeze motion, and produce records when it was inconvenient to do so during the actual examination.

This ultrasonograph can be used in a wide variety of medical applications. The wide image plane and ability to scan between the ribs allow cardiac imaging from the precordial, apical, subxiphoid, and suprasternal positions. This versatility permits visualization of all four chambers and all four valves of the heart, plus the great arteries and the great veins.

The high-speed, high-resolution gray-scale imaging capabilities allow the physician to make rapid and thorough "fluoroscopic" examinations, free of distortion caused by involuntary motion. The small and unconstrained transducer permits thorough examination despite patient position or movement and is especially useful when imaging anatomy under the ribs, in the pelvis, or in the presence of sutures.

The small transducer is easily positioned to obtain, without patient discomfort, high-resolution images through any plane in the female pelvis. The continuous change in the real-time image, as this plane is swept through the pelvis, permits the visualization of very small structures such as the ovaries and tubes, or, in the case of the gravid uterus, the fetus as early as the 4-week stage.

9.3.1. Ultrasonic Transducers

Whatever the application, the basic ultrasonic system consists of a generator for the electric signal, a transducer, the necessary amplifiers, and other electronic processing devices and the display unit. It is the transducer that converts the electric signals into the mechanical vibrations and thus the acoustic waves which form the basis of the technique. Transducers are produced in a variety of configurations for the various applications, and with varying frequency capabilities. The acoustic wave from the transducer enters the body through the skin surface and is then propagated in a predetermined beam pattern (wide or narrow depending on requirements) toward the structure to be examined. When the ultrasonic waves strike an acoustic interface such as the boundary of an organ, some energy is reflected. This reflected energy is picked up on the transducer and is amplified, processed, and finally displayed on an oscilloscope.

Figure 9.11 shows a Dapco echocardiology transducer. These are available in a variety of internal focal arrangements. In transducers of this type, the length of the focal zone is determined by the distance from the transducer to the cardiac structures of interest. The choice of frequency depends on the amount of tissue attenuation encountered. Transducers are available at frequencies of 1.6, 2.25, 3.5, and 5.0 MHz and with crystal diameters of 6, 13, and 20 mm for each frequency.

Figure 9.11. Echocardiology transducer. (Courtesy of Dapco Industries, Ridgefield, CT.)

The size of a transducer generally refers to the size of the active element (diameter in millimeters). The size is determined by the area to be examined. In the case of general abdominal B-scanning, there are few anatomical restrictions. However, a larger-diameter transducer provides ease of mechanical scanning and optimum focus at the required longer focal zones. Smaller transducers are best suited for investigations in anatomic areas of irregular shapes, reduced skin surface, and investigations necessitating improved resolution with minimal penetration (i.e., eye, neck, chest, and limbs). In echocardiography, the smaller active-element diameters are used to facilitate ease of placement and maneuverability within the intercostal space. The 13-mm active-element diameter transducer is most commonly used for investigations on the average adult. When investigating an extremely large and/or obese patient or when placement is not critical, a 20-mm diameter can be used: On the other hand, a 6-mm diameter is recommended for pediatric and neonatal echocardiography.

The type of tissue and the amount of tissue attenuation encountered during a diagnostic examination determines the frequency to be used. A frequency of 2.25 MHz is the most commonly used for general-purpose ultrasonography. Transducers of higher frequency, such as 3.5 or 5.0 MHz, are utilized when tissue penetration is easily accomplished and improved resolution at short distances is required. In view of the small size and shorter examination depth in children, a higher frequency is usually used to ensure good resolution. The 5.0-MHz transducer is recommended for the majority of pediatric echocardiography, reserving the 3.5 MHz for investigations of the older and larger children.

When tissue penetration becomes a concern, as with most obese patients, a low-frequency (i.e., 2.25 or 1.6 MHz) transducer should be employed, which can provide more information than can be obtained with a transducer of a higher frequency.

Echocardiology transducers are available nonfocused or in a choice of focal configurations. Generally, a focused transducer is preferred for echocardiography. The sound beams generated in a focused transducer have a reduced width to provide optimal lateral resolution and sensitivity at given depths. In selecting a focal length, two factors must be considered: the distance from the transducer to the structure to be investigated and the transducer's diameter. The focal zone of a transducer refers to the distance (in centimeters) the sound beam travels in water to a standard test object. The focal zones are commonly referred to as short (5.0 cm), medium (7.5 cm), and long (10.0 cm) in water. If echocardiography is to be performed on a small child, the distance from the transducer to the cardiac structure usually falls within 5.0 cm; therefore, a short focal length should be utilized.

Size of the transducer also affects the choice of focal lengths. For instance, a 20-mm active-element diameter can be focused best at the longer focal lengths, whereas a 13-mm or smaller diameter can accommodate all three with optimum results.

A variation of the standard echocardiology transducer is the cardiac suprasternal notch transducer. This type of transducer is designed with a small active-element diameter and is commonly utilized at a frequency of 3.5 or 5.0 MHz. When these transducers are positioned in the region of the suprasternal notch, simultaneous measurement of the aortic arch, right pulmonary artery, and left atrium can be easily obtained. The cardiac suprasternal notch transducer is extremely useful in diagnosing and monitoring a variety of heart diseases and defects, including mitral insufficiency, patent ductus arteriosus, ventricular septal defects, and hypertensive cardiovascular heart disease.

The transducers are available also as general scanners, standard medical transducers which can be utilized for A-mode or M-mode application, biopsy transducers for tissue biopsy under direct vision, plus special types for thyroid examination and ophthalmic ultrasonography. There are also microprobe needle transducers.

9.3.2. Echocardiography

One use of ultrasound in the cardiovascular system has already been discussed in Section 6.3. This is the Doppler technique in blood flow measurement. Pulsed Doppler ultrasound can be used to measure the velocity gradient across a blood vessel as well as the velocity of the heart wall or specific valves in the heart. Some additional applications will be discussed later in the chapter. The major application in cardiovascular diagnosis, however, is the *echocardiogram,* which utilizes an M-scan technique. In the echocardiogram movements of the valves and other structures of the heart are displayed as a function of time and usually in conjunction with an electrocardiogram.

Over the past several years, echocardiology has been extremely useful in diagnosing many cardiac abnormalities, among them are calcific aortic stenosis, pulmonary valve stenosis, mitral valve stenosis, left atrial myxoma, mitral valve prolapse, and rheumatic heart disease.

In selecting a transducer for an echocardiographic investigation, the following factors must be considered for optimum results:

1. The type of investigation to be performed.
2. Physical size of the patient.
3. The anatomic area involved.
4. The type of tissue to be encountered.
5. The depth of the structure(s) to be studied.

Figure 9.12 is a typical echocardiogram. Figure 9.13 is a sketch showing placement of the transducer. For this particular echocardiogram the transducer was placed so that the beam crossed the chest wall into the right ventricle, through the septum, into the left ventricle, and ultimately through the left atrium. The aorta and mitral valve are also imaged.

With ultrasound it is possible to distinguish between different soft tissues and to measure the motion of structures of the heart. This fact has made it a valuable method of analysis in cardiology. One important factor is that there is virtually no interference by echoes from other body structures, since the heart is surrounded by the lungs, which are literally air bags. This helps greatly in the interpretation. The heart has a number of acoustic interfaces, such as the atrial and ventricular walls, the septum, and the various valves. The position and movements of each interface can be measured by the reflected ultrasound. The echoes from these walls and valves are predictable since the components of the heart move in a known manner.

A good example of this technique is shown in Figure 9.12. This type of echocardiogram is useful in interpreting the movements of the mitral valve with respect to time. The mobility of the valve is measured by the displacement of the echo per unit time during diastole. If the mobility is reduced, as in the case of mitral stenosis (narrowing of the left ventricular orifice), its severity compared with other existing conditions can determine the appropriate action to take, including the possible use of surgery.

Another use of echocardiography is in the detection of fluids. When the pericardium (the sac surrounding the heart) is inflamed (a condition known as pericarditis), there is sometimes an escape of fluid. The presence of this fluid can be detected in the echocardiogram.

Figure 9.12. Echocardiogram. (Courtesy of Dept. of Cardiology, Cedars-Sinai Hospital, Los Angeles, CA.)

270

Figure 9.13. Typical transducer placement to obtain echocardiogram.

Fast scanning speeds are required to prevent blurring of the image due to heart movements. To give a thorough dynamic analysis, many simultaneous recordings can be taken in different positions so as to give cross-sectional images at various points along the length of the heart. As techniques and interpretations continue to advance, the medical profession believes that the potential of this diagnostic method will continue to increase.

9.3.3. Echoencephalography

A well-established clinical application of ultrasonic imaging using the A-scan mode of display is the echoencephalogram, which is used in determining the location of the midline of the brain. An ultrasonic transducer is held against the side of the head to measure the distance to the midline of the brain. The midline echoes from both sides of the head are simultaneously displayed on the oscilloscope, one side producing upward deflection of the beam and the other producing downward deflection.

In the normal brain these two deflections line up, indicating equal distance from the midline to each side of the head. Nonalignment of these deflections indicates the possibility of a tumor or some other disorder that might cause the midline of the brain to shift from its normal position. The instrument for this measurement produces ultrasound energy at a frequency of from 1 to 10 MHz. The pulse rate is 1000 per second.

9.3.4. Ophthalmic Scans

Another important application involves diagnostic scanning of the eye. Figure 9.14 shows an ophthalmic B-scan with camera. The transducer is shown at the bottom of the picture. The transducer is placed directly over

Figure 9.14. Ophthalmic B-scan with camera. (Courtesy of Storz Instrument Co., St. Louis, MO.).

Figure 9.15. Typical ultrasonograms of the eye. (a) Phthisis bulbi (wasting away of the eye) in a 13-year-old child. (b) Papilledema. (c) Retinitis proliferans with detachment of the retina associated with this condition. (d) Intraocular foreign body. (Courtesy of Storz Instrument Co., St. Louis, MO.)

the eye of the patient. The result is a series of ultrasonograms of the type shown in Figure 9.15. Ultrasonic techniques are the only means of identifying intraocular pathology in the presence of opaque media.

9.3.5. Some Other Types of Ultrasonic Imaging

Ultrasonic techniques utilizing the B-scan mode are used for visualizing various organs and structures of the body, including the breasts, kidneys, and the organs and soft tissues of the abdomen. In obstetrics and gynecology, ultrasonic imaging permits visualization of very small structures, such as the ovaries and tubes, and permits examination of a fetus as early as the 4-week stage. Diagnostic ultrasonic equipment used for intracranial and abdominal visualization generally utilizes frequencies from 1 to 2 MHz, whereas for examination of the eye, breast, and body surfaces, frequencies in the range 4 or 5 to 15 MHz are used to obtain better resolution.

9.3.6. Other Applications

Ultrasonic tomography techniques, in which information from scans taken from many different vantage points are combined mathematically, provide increased detail in the visualization of certain parts of the body. The principle involved is very similar to that of computerized axial tomography utilizing X-ray information, which is described in detail in Chapter 15. However, because of the limited penetrating range, particularly at higher frequencies, and the requirement that no gaseous regions or bone lie in the ultrasonic path, the uses in which ultrasonic tomography is practical are limited. Where these techniques can be used, however, they provide a way of obtaining detailed cross sections without radiation exposure.

9.3.7. The Noninvasive Vascular Laboratory

In Section 9.3.2 the diagnosis of the heart and the use of ultrasound in cardiology were discussed. In Section 6.3.2, measurement of blood flow by ultrasonic methods was described. Also, in the introductory paragraphs of Section 9.3, the phased-array ultrasonograph was presented as an example of a medical ultrasound laboratory. To expand on these ideas and to help complete the picture on the status of the use of ultrasound in cardiology it is appropriate to introduce the *noninvasive vascular laboratory*. Although defined in many ways and by various manufacturers of the necessary equipment, this type of laboratory, in general, involves the scanning of the vascular portion of the cardiovascular system, and, as in inferred by the name, all methods are noninvasive. Also, the procedures can be performed with outpatients as well as those in the hospital. Some major hospitals have set up

Figure 9.16. Dopscan Ultrasonic Doppler arterial scanning system.
(Courtesy of Carolina Medical Electronics, King, NC.)

subdepartments within their cardiology departments for many of these
relatively new procedures.

A typical noninvasive vascular system is illustrated in Figure 9.16. The
ultrasonic Doppler arterial scanning system utilizes the Doppler effect
described in Sections 9.2.1 and 9.2.2. It is primarily used for the diagnosing
of potential stroke conditions using Doppler ultrasound scanning of the
carotid and other arteries in the neck area, and can be used in conjunction
with X-ray angiography or as an alternative to it. The system is used for
patients who are suspected of reduced cerebral circulation or who have
arterial bruits (noises) caused by turbulence in the flow of blood through a
constriction. It enables blood vessel mappings to be made, including photographic records, chart recordings of pulsatile directional blood flow, and
magnetic tape recordings of arterial flow sounds along with comments by
the operator. It is extremely useful for patients who are considered to be
risk candidates in X-ray angiography.

In a normal procedure, the patient relaxes in a reclining position on
an examination table while the carotid arterial system is transcutaneously
scanned with a focused ultrasonic beam. The small, smooth probe is attached

to an X-Y position-sensing arm. As the technician moves the probe in a prescribed scanning pattern over the skin, the probe's position is plotted on the screen of a storage oscilloscope whenever it senses blood flow. Repeated passes over the carotid bifurcation and adjacent arteries gradually construct on the oscilloscope a representation of the vessels scanned. Simultaneously, blood flow velocity is displayed on a monitor scope and the sounds characteristic of ultrasonically detected blood flow are available by means of a loudspeaker or headphones. All information is permanently recorded.

When the screening is complete, the vascular map is photographed, and this, along with the pulsatile flow tracings, the sound recordings, and the operator's comments provide permanent graphic and aural records for subsequent clinical evaluation.

Although the image obtained does not have as much intimate detail as one obtained by angiography, it is quite adequate in most cases. For example, it is quite easy to detect the narrowing of a major artery (arterial stenosis).

This system is also useful in investigating blood flow in the ophthalmic region and some of the pathways around the vertebrae and the base of the skull. It can be used on other major superficial vessels such as femoral, brachial, and popliteal arteries.

Figure 9.17. Directional Doppler. (Courtesy of Parks Electronic Laboratory, Beaverton, OR.)

Another useful device for the noninvasive vascular laboratory is illustrated in Figure 9.17. This instrument is a single-frequency directional Doppler blood flow detector. A dual-frequency model is also available. The single-frequency model employs either 5 or 10 MHz, whereas the dual-frequency type has both frequencies available in the same machine. The 10-MHz ultr .sound is better for the small arteries around the eye, whereas the lower frequency gives better results for the deep vessels of the thigh and the iliacs.

Examining the face of the instrument in the photograph, the directional aspects can be observed on the two meters showing blood flow away from and toward the probe. The probe is shown at the bottom of the picture and is plugged in when used. It should be noted that stereo headphones can be plugged into the stereo output. This procedure is useful in small-vessel studies because the stereo effect lets the operator know if the ultrasonic beam is intercepting more than one vessel. This device can be used for venous flow as well as arterial. An external speaker-amplifier is available if the instrument is to be used in teaching.

10

The Nervous System

The task of controlling the various functions of the body and coordinating them into an integrated living organism is not simple. Consequently, the nervous system, which is responsible for this task, is the most complex of all systems in the body. It is also one of the most interesting. Composed of the brain, numerous sensing devices, and a high-speed communication network that links all parts of the body, the nervous system not only influences all the other systems but is also responsible for the behavior of the organism. In this broad sense, *behavior* includes the ability to learn, remember, acquire a personality, and interact with its society and the environment. It is through the nervous system that the organism achieves autonomy and acquires the various traits that characterize it as an individual.

A complete study of the nervous system, with all its ramifications, would be far beyond the scope of this book. However, an overall view can be given that provides the reader with a physiological background for measurements within the nervous system, as well as some understanding of

the effect of the nervous system on measurements from other systems of the
body. To make this presentation more useful in the study of biomedical instrumentation, many of the concepts and theories are greatly simplified.
This simplification is not intended to detract from the reader's understanding of the concepts and theories, but it should facilitate visualization of an
extremely complex system and provide a better perspective for further
detailed study, if required. The simplification requires, however, that caution must be used in attempting to extrapolate or generalize from the information presented.

10.1. THE ANATOMY OF THE NERVOUS SYSTEM

The basic unit of the nervous system is the *neuron*. A neuron is a
single cell with a *cell body,* sometimes called the *soma,* one or more "input"
fibers called *dendrites,* and a long transmitting fiber called the *axon*.
Often the axon branches near its ending into two or more terminals. Examples of three different types of neurons are shown in Figure 10.1.

The portion of the axon immediately adjacent to the cell body is called
the *axon hillock*. This is the point at which action potentials are usually
generated. Branches that leave the main axon are often called *collaterals*.
Certain types of neurons have axons or dendrites coated with a fatty insulating substance called myelin. The coating is called a *myelin sheath* and
the fiber is said to be *myelinated*. In some cases, the myelin sheath is interrupted at rather regular intervals by the *nodes of Ranvier,* which help speed
the transmission of information along the nerves. Outside of the central
nervous system, the myelin sheath is surrounded by another insulating layer,
sometimes called the *neurilemma*. This layer, thinner than the myelin sheath
and continuous over the nodes of Ranvier, is made up of thin cells, called
Schwann cells.

As can be seen from Figure 10.1, some neurons have long dendrites,
whereas others have short ones. Axons of various lengths can also be found
throughout the nervous system. In appearance, it is difficult to tell a dendrite from an axon. The main difference is in the function of the fiber and
the direction in which it carries information with respect to the cell body.

Both axons and dendrites are called *nerve fibers,* and a bundle of individual nerve fibers is called a *nerve*. Nerves that carry sensory information
from the various parts of the body *to the brain* are called *afferent nerves,*
whereas those that carry signals *from the brain* to operate various muscles
are called *efferent nerves*.

The *brain* is an enlarged collection of cell bodies and fibers located inside the skull, where it is well protected from light as well as from physical,
chemical, or temperature shock. At its lower end, the brain connects with

Figure 10.1. Schematic drawings: Three different types of neurons. (From W.F. Evans, *Anatomy and Physiology, The Basic Principles.* Englewood Cliffs, N.J., Prentice-Hall, Inc., 1971, by permission.)

the *spinal cord,* which also consists of many cell bodies and fiber bundles. Together the brain and spinal cord comprise one of the main divisions of the nervous system, the *central nervous system* (CNS). In addition to a large number of neurons of many varieties, the central nervous system also contains a number of large fatty cell bodies called *glial cells.* About half the brain is composed of glial cells. At one time it was believed that the main function of glial cells was structural and that they physically supported the neurons in the brain. Later it was postulated, however, that the glial cells play a vital role in ridding the brain of foreign substances and seem to have some function in connection with memory.

Cell bodies and small fibers in fresh brain are gray in color and are called *gray matter,* whereas the myelin coating of larger fibers has a white appearance, so that a collection of these fibers is referred to as *white matter.*

Collections of neuronal cell bodies within the central nervous system are called *nuclei,* while similar collections outside the central nervous system are called *ganglia.*

The central nervous system is generally considered to be *bilaterally symmetrical,* which means that most structures are anatomically duplicated on both sides. Even so, some functions of the central nervous system in humans seem to be located nonsymmetrically. Several of the functions of the central nervous system are *crossed over,* so that neural structures on the left side of the brain are functionally related to the right side of the body, and vice versa.

Nerve fibers outside the central nervous system are called *peripheral nerves.* This name applies even to fibers from neurons whose cell bodies are contained within the central nervous system. Throughout most of their length, many peripheral nerves are mixed, in that they contain both afferent and efferent fibers. Afferent peripheral nerves that bring sensory information into the central nervous system are called *sensory nerves,* whereas efferent nerves that control the motor functions of muscles are called *motor nerves.* Peripheral nerves leave the spinal cord at different levels, and the nerves that *innervate* a given level of body structures come from a given level of the spinal cord.

The interconnections between neurons are called *synapses.* The word "synapse" can be used as both a noun and a verb. Thus, the connection is called a *synapse,* and the act of connecting is called *synapsing.* All synapses occur at or near cell bodies. As explained in Section 10.2, mammalian neurons that synapse do not touch each other but do come into close proximity, so that the axon (output) of one nerve can activate the dendrite or cell body (input) of another by producing a chemical that stimulates the membrane of a dendrite or cell body. In some cases, the chemical is produced by one axon, near another axon, to inhibit the second axon from activating a neuron with which it can normally communicate. This action is explained more fully below. Because of the chemical method of transmission across a synapse from axon to dendrite or cell body, the communication can take place in one direction only.

The peripheral nervous system actually consists of several subsystems. The system of afferent nerves that carry sensory information from the sensors on the skin to the brain is called the *somatic sensory nervous system. Visual pathways* carry sensory information from the eyes to the brain, whereas the *auditory nervous system* carries information from the auditory sensors in the ears to the brain.

Another major division of the peripheral nervous system is the *autonomic nervous system,* which is involved with emotional responses and controls smooth muscle in various parts of the body, heart muscle, and the secretion of a number of glands. The autonomic nervous system is composed of two main subsystems that appear to be somewhat antagonistic to each other, although not completely. These are the *sympathetic nervous system,* which speeds up the heart, causes secretion of some glands, and inhibits other body functions, and the *parasympathetic nervous system,* which tends to slow the heart and controls contraction and secretion of the stomach. In general, the sympathetic nervous system tends to mobilize the body for emergencies, whereas the parasympathetic nervous system tends to conserve and store bodily resources.

A very general look at the anatomy of the brain should be helpful in understanding the functions of the nervous system. Figure 10.2 shows a side view of the brain and spinal cord, and Figure 10.3 is a cutaway showing some of the major structures.

The part of the brain that connects to the spinal cord and extends up into the center of the brain is called the *brainstem.* The essential parts of the brainstem are the *medulla* (sometimes called the *medulla oblongata*), which is the lowest section of the brainstem itself, the *pons* located just above the medulla and protruding somewhat in front of the brainstem, and the upper part of the brainstem called the *midbrain.* Above and slightly forward

Figure 10.2. The brain and spinal cord. (From W.F. Evans, *Anatomy and Physiology, The Basic Principles,* Englewood Cliffs, N.J., Prentice-Hall, Inc., 1971, by permission.)

Figure 10.3. Cutaway section of the human brain. (From W.F. Evans, *Anatomy and Physiology, The Basic Principles,* Englewood Cliffs, N.J., Prentice-Hall, Inc., 1971, by permission.)

of the midbrain are the *thalamus* and *hypothalamus.* Behind the brainstem is the *cerebellum.* Almost completely surrounding the midbrain, thalamus, and hypothalamus are the structures of the *cerebrum.* The outer surface of the cerebrum is called the *cerebral cortex.* The *corpus callosum* is the interconnection between the left and right hemispheres of the brain. Structurally, the two hemispheres appear to be identical, but as indicated earlier, they seem to differ functionally in man. Just forward of the hypothalamus is the *hypophysis* or *pituitary gland,* which produces hormones that control a number of important hormonal functions of the body. Not shown in the figures, but surrounding the thalamus, is the *reticular activating system.* The specific functions of each of these major portions of the brain, as far as they have been discovered to date, are discussed in Section 10.3.

10.2. NEURONAL COMMUNICATION

As discussed in detail in Chapter 3, neurons are among the special group of cells that are capable of being excited and that, when excited, generate action potentials. In neurons, these action potentials are of very short duration and are often called *neuronal spikes* or *spike discharges.* Information is usually transmitted in the form of *spike discharge patterns.*

These patterns, which are simply the sequences of spikes that are transmitted down a particular neuronal pathway, are shown in Figures 10.4 and 10.5. The form of a given neuronal pattern depends on the firing patterns of other neurons that communicate with the neuron generating the pattern and the refractory period of that neuron (see Chapter 3). When an action potential is initiated in the neuron, usually at the cell body or axon hillock, it is propagated down the axon to the axon terminals where it can be transmitted to other neurons.

Figure 10.4. Spike discharge pattern from a single neuron in the red nucleus of a cat. The red nucleus is involved with motor functions. (Courtesy of Neuropsychology Research Laboratory, Veterans Administration Hospital, Sepulveda, CA.)

Figure 10.5. Spike discharge patterns from a single thalamic cell in a cat: (a) Random quiet pattern; (b) Burst pattern. (Courtesy of Neuropsychology Research Laboratory, Veterans Administration Hospital, Sepulveda, CA.)

(a)

(b)

Given sufficient excitation energy, most neurons can be triggered at almost any point along the dendrites, cell body, or axon and generate action potentials that can move in both directions from the point of initiation. The process does not normally happen, however, because in their natural function, neurons synapse only in a certain way; that is, the axon of one neuron excites the dendrites or cell body of another. The result is a one-way communication path only. If an action potential should somehow be artificially generated in the axon and caused to travel up the neuron to the dendrites, the spike cannot be transmitted the wrong way across the gap to the axon of another neuron. Thus, the one-way transmission between neurons determines the direction of communication.

It was believed for many years that transmission through a synapse was electrical and that an action potential was generated at the input of a neuron due to ionic currents or fields set up by the action potentials in the adjacent axons of other neurons. More recent research, however, has disclosed that in mammals, and in most synapses of other organisms, the transmission times across synapses are too slow for electrical transmission. This has led to the presently accepted chemical theory, which states that the arrival of an action potential at an axon terminal releases a chemical—Probably *acetylcholine* in most cases—that excites the adjacent membrane of the receiving neuron. Because of the close proximity of the transmitting axon terminal to the receiving membrane, the time of transmission is still quite short. The possibility that some of the chemical may still be present after the refractory period is eliminated by the presence of *acetylcholine esterase,* another chemical that breaks down the acetylcholine as soon as it is produced, but not before it has been able to initiate its intended action potential in the nearby membrane. This chemical theory of transmission is diagrammed in Figure 10.6.

Actually, the situation is not quite as simple as has been described. There are really two kinds of communication across a synapse, excitatory and inhibitory. The same chemical appears to be used in both. In general, several axons from different neurons are in communication with the "input" of any given neuron. Some act to excite the membrane of the receiver, while others tend to prevent it from being excited. Whether the neuron fires or not depends on the net effect of all the axons interacting with it.

The effects of the various neurons acting on a receiving neuron are reflected in changes in the graded potentials of the receiving neuron. *Graded potentials* are variations around the average value of the resting potential. When this graded potential reaches a certain threshold, the neuron fires and an action potential develops. Regardless of the graded potential before firing, the action potentials of a given neuron are always the same and always travel at the same rate. An excitatory graded potential is called an

1 Action potential arrives at axon terminal.

Presynaptic axon terminal

Postsynaptic dendrite membrane

2 Chemical transmitter is released from axon terminal and quickly fills gap.

3 Arrival of chemical transmitter causes potential change in postsynaptic dendrite membrane.

4 Antagonistic chemical in gap breaks down transmitter during refractory period of membrane.

5 Unless inhibited, membrane potential change leads to generation of action potential in postsynaptic neuron.

Figure 10.6. Sequence of events during chemical transmission across a synapse.

excitatory postsynaptic potential (EPSP), and an inhibitory graded potential is called an *inhibitory postsynaptic potential* (IPSP).

There are several theories as to how inhibitory action takes place. One possibility is that the inhibitory axon somehow causes a graded potential (IPSP) in the receiving neuron which is more negative than the normal resting potential, thus requiring a greater amount of excitation to cause it to fire. Another possibility is that the inhibiting axon acts, not on the receiving neuron but on the excitatory transmitting axon. In this case, the inhibiting axon might set up a premature action potential in the transmitting axon, so that the necessary combination of chemical discharges cannot occur in synchronism as it would without the inhibition. Whatever method is actually used, the end result is that certain action potentials which would otherwise be transmitted through the synapse are prevented from doing so when inhibitory signals are present. Synapses, then, behave much like multiple-input AND and NOR logic gates and, by their widely varied patterns of excitatory and inhibitory "connections," provide a means of switching and interconnecting parts of the nervous system with a complexity far greater than anything yet conceived by man.

10.3. THE ORGANIZATION OF THE BRAIN

Knowledge of the actual function of various parts of the brain is still quite sparse. Experiments in which portions of an animal's brain have been removed (oblated) show that there is a tremendous amount of redundancy in the brain. There is also a great amount of adaptivity in that if a portion of a brain believed responsible for a given function is removed from an infant animal, the animal somehow still seems able to develop that function to some extent. This result has led to the idea of the "law of mass action," in which it is theorized that the impairment caused by damage to some portion of the brain is not so much a function of *what* portions have been damaged but, rather, *how much* was damaged. In other words, when one region of the brain is damaged, another region seems to take over the function of the damaged part. Also, while tests show that a particular region of the brain seems to be related to some specific function, there are also indications of some relationship of that function to other parts of the brain. Thus, when, in the following paragraphs, certain functions are indicated for certain parts of the brain, it must be realized that these parts only seem to play a predominant role in those functions and that other parts of the brain are undoubtedly also involved.

In the brainstem, the *medulla* seems to be associated with control of some of the basic functions responsible for life, such as breathing, heart rate, and kidney functions. For this purpose, the medulla seems to contain a number of timing mechanisms, as well as important neuronal connections.

The *pons* is primarily an interconnecting area. In it are a large number of both ascending and descending fiber tracts, as well as many nuclei. Some of these nuclei seem to play a role in salivation, feeding, and facial expression. In addition, the pons contains relays for the auditory system, spinal motor neurons, and some respiratory nuclei.

The cerebellum acts as a physiological microcomputer which intercepts various sensory and motor nerves to smooth out what would otherwise be "jerky" muscle motions. The cerebellum also plays a vital role in man's ability to maintain his balance.

The *thalamus* manipulates nearly all sensory information on its way to the cerebrum. It contains main relay points for the visual, auditory, and somatic sensory systems.

The *reticular activation system* (RAS), which surrounds the thalamus, is a nonspecific sensory portion of the brain. It receives excitation from all the sensory inputs and seems to be aroused by any one of them, but it does not seem to distinguish which type of sensory input is active. When aroused, the RAS alerts the cerebral cortex, making it sensitive to incoming information. It is the RAS that keeps a person awake and alert and causes him to pay attention to a sensory input. Most information reaching the RAS is relayed through the thalamus.

The *hypothalamus* is apparently the center for emotions in the brain. It controls the neural regulation of endocrine gland functions via the pituitary gland and contains nuclei responsible for eating, drinking, sexual behavior, sleeping, temperature regulation, and emotional behavior generally. The hypothalamus exercises primary control over the autonomic nervous system, particularly the sympathetic nervous system.

The *basal ganglia* seem to be involved in motor activity and have indirect connections with the motor neurons.

The main subdivision of the *cerebrum* is the *cerebral cortex,* which contains some 9 billion of the 12 billion neurons found in the human brain. The cortex is actually a rather thin layer of neurons at the periphery of the brain, which contains many fissures or inward folds to provide a greater amount of surface area. Some of the deeper fissures, also called *sulci,* are used as landmarks to divide the cortex into certain lobes. Several of the more prominent ones are shown in Figure 10.7, along with the location of the important lobes.

Figure 10.7. The cerebral cortex. (From W.F. Evans, *Anatomy and Physiology, The Basic Principles,* Englewood Cliffs, N.J., Prentice-Hall, Inc., 1971, by permission.)

All sensory inputs eventually reach the cortex, where certain regions seem to relate specifically to certain modalities of sensory information. Other regions of the cortex seem to be specifically related to motor functions. For example, all somatic sensory (heat, cold, pressure, touch, etc.) inputs lead to a region of the cortical surface just behind the central sulcus, encompassing the forward part of the *parietal lobe.* Somatic sensory inputs from each part of the body lead to a specific part of this region, with the inputs from the legs and feet nearest the top, the torso next, followed by the arms, hands, fingers, face, tongue, pharynx, and, finally, the intra-abdominal regions at the bottom. The amount of surface allotted to each part of the body is in proportion to the number of sensory nerves it contains rather than its actual physical size. A pictorial representation of the layout of these areas, called a *homunculus,* is depicted as a rather grotesque human figure, upside down, with enlarged fingers, face, lips, and tongue.

Just forward of the central sulcus is the *frontal lobe,* in which are found the primary motor neurons that lead to the various muscles of the body. The motor neurons are also distributed on the surface of the cortex in a manner similar to the sensory neurons. The location of the various motor functions can also be represented by a homunculus, also upside down but proportioned according to the degree of muscular control provided for each part of the body.

Figure 10.8 shows both the sensory and motor homunculi, which represent the spatial distribution of the sensory and motor functions on the cortical surface. In each case, the figure shows only one-half of the brain in cross section through the indicated region.

The forward part of the brain, sometimes called the *prefrontal lobe,* contains neurons for some special motor control functions, including the control of eye movements.

The *occipital lobe* is at the very back of the head, over the cerebellum. The occipital lobe contains the visual cortex, in which the patterns obtained from the retina are mapped in a geographic representation.

Auditory sensory input can be traced to the *temporal lobes* of the cortex, located just above the ears. Neurons responding to different frequencies of sound input are spread across the region, with the higher frequencies located toward the front and low frequencies to the rear.

Smell and taste do not have specific locations in the cerebral cortex, although an olfactory bulb near the center of the brain is involved in the perception of smell.

The cerebral cortex has many areas that are neither sensory nor motor. In man, this accounts for the largest portion of the cortex. These *association areas* are believed by many scientists to be involved with integrating or associating the various inputs to produce the appropriate output responses and transmit them to the motor neurons for control of the body.

Figure 10.8. Human sensory and motor homunculi. (From W. F. Evans, *Anatomy and Physiology, The Basic Principles*, Englewood Cliffs, N.J., Prentice-Hall, Inc., 1971, by permission.)

10.4. NEURONAL RECEPTORS

Certain special types of neurons are sensitive to energy in some form other than the usual chemical discharge from axons of other neurons. Those in the retina of the eye, for example, are sensitive to light, while others, such as the pressure sensors at the surface of the body, are sensitive to pressure or touch. Actually, any of these sensors can respond to any type of stimulation if the energy level is sufficiently high, but the response is greatest to the form of energy for which the sensor is intended. In each case, the energy sensed from the environment produces patterns of action potentials that are transmitted to the appropriate region of the cerebral cortex. Coding is accomplished either by having a characteristic of the sensed energy determine which neurons are activated or by altering the pattern in which spikes are produced in a given neuron. In some cases, both of these methods are employed.

The *somatic sensory system* consists of receptors located on the skin that respond to pain, pressure, light, touch, heat, or coolness—each receptor responding to one of these modalities. The intensity of the sensory input is coded by the frequency of spike discharges on a given neuron, plus the number of neurons involved. There is considerable feedback to provide extremely accurate localization of the source of certain types of inputs, especially fine touch.

In the *visual system,* light sensors, both rods and cones, are located at the retina of the eye. Some processing of the sensed information occurs at the retina, from which it is transmitted via the optic nerve, through the thalamus, to the occipital cortex. The crossover in the visual system is interesting. Instead of all the information sensed by the left eye going to the right brain, as one might expect, information from the left half of each retina (which views the right visual field) is transmitted to the left side of the brain. Thus, the demarcation is according to the field of vision and not according to which eye generates the signals. The rods, which are more sensitive to dim light, are not sensitive to color, whereas the less-sensitive cones carry the color information. There is still a certain amount of speculation as to the exact manner in which color information is coded, but it is fairly well agreed that the color information is sensed as some combination of primary colors, each of which is carried by its own set of sensors and neurons.

In the *auditory system,* the frequency of sound seems to be coded in two different ways. After passing through the acoustical system into the inner ear, the sound excites the basilar membrane, a rather stiff membrane coiled in a fluid-filled chamber. The sound vibrations are actually carried to the membrane by the fluid. At lower frequencies, the entire membrane seems to vibrate as a unit, and the sound frequency is coded into a spike discharge frequency by the hair-cell sensory neurons located along the membrane. Above a certain crossover point (about 4000 Hz), however, the situation is different, and the frequencies seem to distribute themselves along the basilar membrane. Thus, for higher frequencies, the frequency is coded according to which sensors are activated, whereas for lower frequencies, the coding is by spike discharge frequency. Auditory information from both ears is transmitted to the temporal lobes on both sides of the cerebral cortex. Timing devices are provided so that if a sound strikes both ears a fraction of a millisecond apart, the ear receiving it first inhibits the response from the other ear. This gives the hearing a sense of direction.

This same directional characteristic also applies to smell and taste. That is, an odor reaching one nostril a fraction of a millisecond before it reaches the other causes inhibition that provides a sense of direction for the odor. Coding for taste and smell is not well understood, although intensity is somehow coded into firing rates of neurons as well as the number of neurons activated.

10.5.   THE SOMATIC NERVOUS SYSTEM AND SPINAL REFLEXES

The somatic sensory nervous system carries sensory information from all parts of the body to corresponding sites in the cerebral cortex, whereas motor neurons carry control information to the muscles of the body. The sensory and motor neurons are not necessarily single uninterrupted channels that go all the way from the cortex to the big toe, for example. They may have a number of synapses along the way to permit inhibition as well as excitation. There are, of course, exceptions in which some of the motor control functions are carried out by extremely long axons. In this system countless feedback loops control the action of the muscles. The muscles themselves contain stretch and position receptors that permit precise control over their operation.

Many of the routine muscular movements of the body are not controlled by the brain at all but occur as reflexes of the spinal cord. The spinal cord has many nuclei of neurons that give almost automatic response to input stimuli. Actually, only the more complicated responses are controlled by the brain. In a simplified form, this process could be comparable to a large central computer (the brain) connected to a number of small satellite computers in the spinal cord. Each of the small computers handles the data processing and controls the functions of the system within which it operates. Whenever one of the small computers is faced with a situation beyond its limited capability, the data are sent to the central computer for processing. Thus, the spinal reflexes seem to handle all responses except those beyond their capability.

10.6. THE AUTONOMIC NERVOUS SYSTEM

The autonomic nervous system differs from the somatic and motor nervous systems in that its control is essentially involuntary. It was once thought that the autonomic system is completely involuntary, but recent experimentation indicates that it is possible for a person to learn to control portions of this system to some extent.

The major divisions of the autonomic nervous system are the *sympathetic* and *parasympathetic systems.* The sympathetic nervous system receives its primary control from the hypothalamus and is essentially a function of emotional response. It is the sympathetic nervous system that is responsible for the "fight-or-flight" reaction to danger and for such responses as fear and anger. When one or more of the sensory inputs to the brain indicate danger, the body is immediately mobilized for action. The heart rate, respiration, red blood cell production, and blood pressure all increase. Normal functions of the body, such as salivation, digestion, and sexual functions, are all inhibited to conserve energy to meet the situation. Blood flow patterns in the body are altered to favor those functions required for the emergency, and adrenalin, which is the chemical that apparently activates synapses in the sympathetic nervous system, is released throughout the body to maintain the emergency status. Other indications of activation of the sympathetic nervous system are dilation of the pupils of the eyes and perspiration at the palms of the hands, which lowers the skin resistance.

The sympathetic nervous system is designed for "global" action, with short neurons leaving the spine at all levels to innervate the motor systems affected by these nerves. In contrast, the parasympathetic system is responsible for more specific action. Although not completely antagonistic to the sympathetic system, the parasympathetic nervous system causes dilation of the arteries, inhibition or slowing of the heart, contractions and secretions of the stomach, constriction of the pupils of the eyes, and so on. Where the sympathetic system is primarily involved in mobilizing the body to meet emergencies, the parasympathetic system is concerned with the vegetating functions of the body, such as digestion, sexual activity, and waste elimination.

10.7. MEASUREMENTS FROM THE NERVOUS SYSTEM

Direct measurements of the electrical activity of the nervous system are few. However, the effects of the nervous system on other systems of the body are manifested in most physiological measurements. It is possible, in many cases to stimulate sensor neurons with their specific type of stimulus and measure the responses in various nerves or, in some cases, in individual neurons either in the peripheral or central nervous system. It is also possible to stimulate individual neurons or nerves electrically and to measure either the muscle movement that results from the stimulation or the neuronal spikes that occur in various parts of the system due to the stimulation.

When measuring responses to electrical stimulation, care must be taken to see that the stimulation does not create a wider response than that which would occur if the neuron were stimulated naturally. For example, if electrical stimulation is used, it is very easy to activate other neurons in the vicinity of the intended neuron inadvertently, thus causing responses that are not really related to the desired response.

10.7.1. Neuronal Firing Measurements

Several methods of measuring the neuronal spikes associated with nerve firings have been developed. They differ basically in the vantage point from which the measurement is taken. A *gross* nerve firing measurement is obtained when a relatively large (greater than 0.1 mm in diameter) electrode is placed in the vicinity of a nerve or a large number of neurons. The result is a summation of the action potentials from all the neurons in the vicinity of the electrode. For a more localized measurement, the action potentials of a single neuron can be observed either *extracellularly,* with a microelectrode located just outside the cell membrane, or *intracellularly,* with a microelectrode actually penetrating the cell. Figure 10.9 shows an example of a gross neuronal measurement; Figure 10.10 is an example of an extracellular measurement of a single neuron; and Figure 10.11 shows an intracellular measurement of a single neuron.

Figure 10.9. Gross measurement of multiple unit neuronal discharge. (Full width covers time span of 500 msec. Maximum peak-to-peak amplitude is approximately 145 microvolts.) (Courtesy of Neuropsychology Research Laboratory, Veterans Administration Hospital, Sepulveda, CA.)

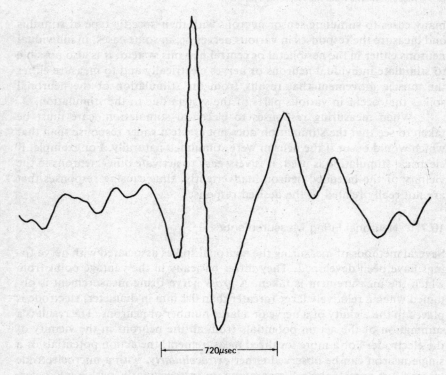

|← 720μsec →|

Figure 10.10. Extracellular measurement of unit discharge from red nucleus of a cat. Peak-to-peak height is approximately 180 microvolts.

Figure 10.11. Intracellular measurement of antidromic spike from abducens nucleus of a cat. (Part of motor control system for the eye.) Spike height is about 61 millivolts. Each horizontal division equals 0.5 millisecond. (Courtesy of Brain Research Institute, UCLA.)

Because of the difficulty of penetrating an individual cell without damaging it and holding an electrode in that position for any length of time, the use of intracellular measurements is limited to certain specialized cell preparations, usually involving only the largest type of cells. Yet, although action potential spikes can be measured readily with extracellular electrodes, the actual value of resting and action potentials and the measurement of graded potentials require the use of intracellular techniques. Any form of single neuron measurement is much more difficult to obtain than gross measurements. In practice, the microelectrode is inserted into the general area and then moved about slightly until a firing pattern indicative of a single neuron can be observed. Even though this is done, identification of the neuron from which the measurement originates is difficult.

Electrodes and microelectrodes used in the measurement of gross and single neuronal firings are described in detail in Chapter 4. Single neuron measurements require microelectrodes with tips of about 10 μm in diameter for extracellular measurements and as small as 1 μm for intracellular measurements. A fine needle or wire electrode is used for gross neuronal measurements. When the measurement is made between a single electrode and a "distant" indifferent electrode, the measurement is defined as *unipolar*. When the measurement is obtained between two electrodes spaced close together along a single axon or a nerve, the measurement is called *bipolar*.

Neuronal firing measurements range from a few hundred microvolts for extracellular single-neuron measurements to around 100 mV for intracellular measurements. For most of these measurements, especially those less than 1 mV, differential amplication is required to reduce the effect of electrical interference. The amplifier must have a very high input impedance to avoid loading the high impedance of the microelectrodes and the electrode interface. Because of the short duration of neuronal spikes, the amplifier must have a frequency response from below 1 Hz to several thousand hertz.

Ordinary pen recorders are generally unsuitable for recording or display of neuronal firings because of the high upper-frequency requirement. As a rule, an oscilloscope with a camera for photographing the spike patterns or a high-speed light-galvanometer or an electrostatic recorder is used for these measurements.

Another measurement involving neuronal firings is that of nerve conduction time or velocity. Here a given nerve is stimulated while potentials are measured from another nerve or from a muscle actuated by the stimulated nerve. The time difference between the stimulus and the resultant firing is measured on an oscilloscope. Some commercial electromyograph (EMG) instruments, such as those described in Section 10.7.3., have provisions for performing nerve conduction velocity measurement.

10.7.2. Electroencephalogram (EEG) Measurements

Electroencephalography was introduced in Chapter 3 as the measurement of the electrical activity of the brain. Since clinical EEG measurements are obtained from electrodes placed on the surface of the scalp, these waveforms represent a very gross type of summation of potentials that originate from an extremely large number of neurons in the vicinity of the electrodes.

Originally it was thought that the EEG potentials represent a summation of the action potentials of the neurons in the brain. Later theories, however, indicate that the electrical patterns obtained from the scalp are actually the result of the graded potentials on the dendrites of neurons in the cerebral cortex and other parts of the brain, as they are influenced by the firing of other neurons that impinge on these dendrites. There are still many unanswered questions regarding the neurological source of the observed EEG patterns.

EEG potentials have random-appearing waveforms with peak-to-peak amplitudes ranging from less than 10 μV to over 100 μV. Required bandwidth for adequately handling the EEG signal is from below 1 Hz to over 100 Hz.

Electrodes for measurement of the EEG are described in Chapter 4. For clinical measurements, surface or subdermal needle electrodes are used. The ground reference electrode is often a metal clip on the earlobe. As discussed in Chapter 4, a suitable electrolyte paste or jelly is used in conjunction with the electrodes to enhance coupling of the ionic potentials to the input of the measuring device. To reduce interference and minimize the effect of electrode movement, the resistance of the path through the scalp between electrodes must be kept as low as possible. Generally, this resistance ranges from a few thousand ohms to nearly 100 kΩ depending on the type of electrodes used.

Placement of electrodes on the scalp is commonly dictated by the requirements of the measurement to be made. In clinical practice, a standard pattern, called the *10-20 electrode placement system,* is generally used. This system, devised by a committee of the International Federation of Societies for Electroencephalography, is so named because electrode spacing is based on intervals of 10 and 20 percent of the distance between specified points on the scalp. The 10-20 EEG electrode configuration is illustrated in Figure 10.12.

In addition to the electrodes, the measurement of the electroencephalogram requires a readout or recording device and sufficient amplification to drive the readout device from the microvolt-level signals obtained from the electrodes. Most clinical electroencephalographs provide the capability of simultaneously recording EEG signals from several regions of the brain.

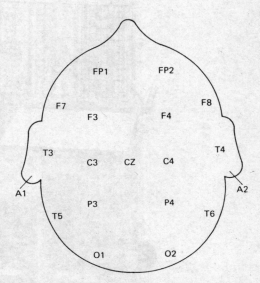

Figure 10.12. 10—20 EEG electrode configuration.

For each signal, a complete channel of instrumentation is required. Thus, Electroencephalographs having as many as 16 channels are available. A clinical instrument with eight channels and a portable unit are shown in Figure 10.13.

Because of the low-level input signals, the electroencephalograph must have high-quality differential amplifiers with good common-mode rejection. The differential preamplifier is generally followed by a power amplifier to drive the pen mechanism for each channel. In nearly all clinical instruments, the amplifiers are ac-coupled with low-frequency cutoff below 1 Hz and a bandwidth extending to somewhere between 50 and 100 Hz. Stable dc amplifiers can be used, but possible variations in the dc electrode potentials are often bothersome. Most modern electroencephalographs include adjustable upper- and lower-frequency limits to allow the operator to select a bandwidth suitable for the conditions of the measurement. In addition, some instruments include a fixed 60-Hz rejection filter to reduce powerline interference.

To reduce the effect of electrode resistance changes, the input impedance of the EEG amplifier should be as high as possible. For this reason, most modern electroencephalographs have input impedances greater than 10 MΩ.

Perhaps the most distinguishing feature of an electroencephalograph is the rather elaborate lead selector panel, which in most cases permits any two electrodes to be connected to any channel of the instrument. Either a bank of rotary switches or a panel of pushbuttons is used. The switch panel also permits one of several calibration signals to be applied to any desired channel for calibration of the entire instrument. The calibration

Figure 10.13. Electroencephalographs: (a) Grass model 16. (Courtesy of Grass Instrument Company, Quincy, Mass.); (b) Beckman portable model. (Courtesy of Beckman Instruments, Schiller, Park, IL.)

Figure 10.14. Averaging of EEG evoked potentials: (a) raw EEG of single response; (b) average of 8 responses; (c) average of 64 responses. (Courtesy of Dr. Norman S. Namerow, The Center for Health Sciences, Department of Neurology, UCLA, whose research was supported by M.S. Grant #516-C-3.)

signal is usually an offset of a known number of microvolts, which, because of capacitive coupling, results in a step followed by an exponential return to baseline.

The readout in a clinical electroencephalograph is a multichannel pen recorder with a pen for each channel. The standard chart speed is 30 mm/sec, but most electroencephalographs also provide a speed of 60 mm/sec for improved detail of higher-frequency signals. Some have a third speed of 15 mm/sec to conserve paper during setup time. An oscilloscope readout for the EEG is also possible, but it does not provide a permanent record. In some cases, particularly in research applications, the oscilloscope is used in conjunction with the pen recorder to edit the signal until a particular feature or characteristic of the waveform is observed. In this way, only the portions of interest are recorded. Many electroencephalographs also have provisions for interfacing with an analog tape recorder to permit recording and play-back of the EEG signal.

In some research applications, the EEG signals are separated into their conventional frequency bands by means of bandpass filters and the output signals of the individual filters are recorded separately (see Chapter 3). In some cases, they are displayed as biofeedback to the subject whose EEG is being measured (see Chapter 11). In other situations, the entire EEG signal is digitized for computer analysis and through Fourier analysis is converted into a frequency spectrum.

A special form of electroencephalography is the recording of *evoked potentials* from various parts of the nervous system. In this technique the EEG response to some form of sensory stimulus, such as a flash of a light or an audible click, is measured. To distinguish the response to the stimulus from ongoing EEG activity, the EEG signals are time-locked to the stimulus pulses and averaged, so that the evoked response is reinforced with each presentation of the stimulus, while any activity not synchronized to the stimulus is averaged out. Figure 10.14 shows a raw EEG record containing an evoked response from a single presentation of the stimulus and the effect of averaging 8 and 64 presentations, respectively.

10.7.3. Electromyographic (EMG) Measurements

Like neurons, skeletal muscle fibers generate action potentials when excited by motor neurons via the motor end plates. They do not, however, transmit the action potentials to any other muscle fibers or to any neurons. The action potential of an individual muscle fiber is of about the same magnitude as that of a neuron (see Chapter 3) and is not necessarily related to the strength of contraction of the fiber. The measurement of these action potentials, either directly from the muscle or from the surface of the body, constitutes the electromyogram, as discussed in Chapter 3.

Although action potentials from individual muscle fibers can be recorded under special conditions, it is the electrical activity of the entire muscle that is of primary interest. In this case, the signal is a summation of all the action potentials within the range of the electrodes, each weighted by its distance from the electrodes. Since the overall strength of muscular contraction depends on the number of fibers energized and the time of contraction, there is a correlation between the overall amount of EMG activity for the whole muscle and the strength of muscular contraction. In fact, under certain conditions of isometric contraction, the voltage-time integral of the EMG signal has a linear relationship to the isometric voluntary tension in a muscle. There are also characteristic EMG patterns associated with special conditions, such as fatigue and tremor.

The EMG potentials from a muscle or group of muscles produce a noiselike waveform that varies in amplitude with the amount of muscular activity. Peak amplitudes vary from 50 μV to about 1 mV, depending on the location of the measuring electrodes with respect to the muscle and the activity of the muscle. A frequency response from about 10 Hz to well over 3000 Hz is required for faithful reproduction.

Surface, needle, and fine-wire electrodes are all used for different types of EMG measurement. Surface electrodes are generally used where gross indications are suitable, but where localized measurement of specific muscles is required, needle or wire electrodes that penetrate the skin and contact the muscle to be measured are needed. As in neuronal firing measurements, both unipolar and bipolar measurements of EMG are used.

The amplifier for EMG measurements, like that for ECG and EEG, must have high gain, high input impedance and a differential input with good common-mode rejection. However, the EMG amplifier must accommodate the higher frequency band. In many commercial electromyographs, the upper-frequency response can be varied by use of switchable lowpass filters.

Unlike ECG or EEG equipment, the typical electromyograph has an oscilloscope readout instead of a graphic pen recorder. The reason is the higher frequency response required. Sometimes a storage cathode-ray tube is provided for retention of data, or an oscilloscope camera is used to obtain a permanent visual record of data from the oscilloscope screen. A typical commercial electromyograph is shown in Figure 10.15.

Most electromyographs include an audio amplifier and loudspeaker in addition to the oscilloscope display to permit the operator to hear the "crackling" sounds of the EMG. This audio presentation is especially helpful in the placement of needle or wire electrodes into a muscle. A trained operator is able to tell from the sound not only that his electrodes are making good contact with a muscle but also which of several adjacent muscles he has contacted.

Figure 10.15. Electromyograph. (Courtesy of Hewlett-Packard Company, Waltham, MA.)

Another feature often found in modern electromyographs is a built-in stimulator for nerve conduction time or nerve velocity measurements. By stimulating a given nerve location and measuring the EMG downstream, a latency can be determined from the time difference displayed on the oscilloscope.

The EMG signal can be quantified in several ways. The simplest method is measurement of the amplitude alone. In this case, the maximum amplitude achieved for a given type of muscle activity is recorded. Unfortunately, the amplitude is only a rough indication of the amount of muscle activity and is dependent on the location of the measuring electrodes with respect to the muscle.

Another method of quantifying EMG is a count of the number of spikes, or, in some cases, zero crossings, that occur over a given time interval. A modification of this method is a count of the number of times a given amplitude threshold is exceeded. Although these counts vary with the amount of muscle activity, they do not provide an accurate means of quantification, for the measured waveform is a summation of a large number of action potentials that cannot be distinguished individually.

The most meaningful method of quantifying the EMG utilizes the time integral of the EMG waveform. With this technique, the integrated value of the EMG over a given time interval, such as 0.1 second, is measured and recorded or plotted. As indicated above, this time integral has a linear relationship to the tension of a muscle under certain conditions of isometric contraction, as well as a relationship to the activity of a muscle under isotonic contraction. As with the amplitude measurement, the integrated EMG is greatly affected by electrode placement, but with a given electrode location, these values provide a good indication of muscle activity.

In another technique that is sometimes used in research, the EMG signal is rectified and filtered to produce a voltage that follows the envelope or contour of the EMG. This envelope, which is related to the activity of the muscle, has a much lower frequency content and can be recorded on a pen recorder, frequently in conjunction with some measurement of the movement of a limb or the force of the muscle activity.

11

Instrumentation for Sensory Measurements and the Study of Behavior

The most obvious difference between inanimate and animate objects is that the latter move, respond to their environment, and show changes in their body functions. These properties of animate objects, in a general sense, are called *behavior*. In animals and men the behavior is controlled by the nervous system. The specialized field of medicine in which the nervous system is studied and its diseases are treated is called *neurology*. The *behavior* of organisms, on the other hand, is studied within the various fields of *psychology*. The *experimental psychologist* studies the behavior of animals and men by observing them in experimental situations. The way in which physical stimuli are perceived by men is studied in a specialty called *psychophysics*. The interaction between environmental stimuli and physiological functions of the body is studied in the field of *psychophysiology*. *Clinical psychologists,* as well as *psychiatrists* (who have medical training), deal with the study and treatment of abnormal (pathological) behavior. Behavior is considered abnormal if it interferes substantially with the well-being of the individual and with his interaction with society.

For the treatment of disorders involving the various senses, especially those related to communication, a number of specialized fields have evolved. The *audiologist* determines deficiencies in the acuity of hearing, which often can be improved by the prescription of hearing aids. The *speech pathologist* treats disorders of speech, which may be due to damage to the structures involved in the formation of sounds or may have a neurological cause. The *ophthalmologist* is a physician who specializes in disorders of the eye, whereas the *optometrist* has no medical training and treats only those visual disorders that can be corrected by the prescription of eyeglasses. For the measurement of the acuity of the senses, as well as for the study of behavior, large numbers of instruments have been developed, which can be highly specialized.

The results of behavioral studies seldom show a simple cause-and-effect relationship but are usually in the form of statistical evidence. This peculiarity requires large numbers of experiments in order to obtain results that are statistically significant. As a result, especially in animal experiments, automated systems are frequently used to control the experiment automatically and record the results. The diversity of the field, on the other hand, has resulted in commercially available instruments that are often in the form of modules and building blocks which can be assembled by the experimenter into specialized systems to suit the requirments of a particular experiment.

One obvious way to study behavior is to measure the electrical signals in the brain and the nervous system that control the behavior, as discussed in Chapter 10. However, because the voltages recorded on an electroencephalograph are the result of many processes that occur simultaneously in the brain, only events that involve larger areas of the brain, such as epileptic seizures, can be readily identified on the EEG recording. For this reason, mental disorders generally cannot be diagnosed from the electroencephalogram, although the EEG is usually used to rule out certain organic disorders of the brain (e.g., tumors), which can show symptoms similar to those of nonorganic types of mental illness. The instrumentation used to measure the EEG is described in Chapter 10.

11.1. PSYCHOPHYSIOLOGICAL MEASUREMENTS

As stated in Chapter 10, many body functions, including blood pressure, heart rate, perspiration, and salivation, are controlled by the autonomic nervous system. This part of the nervous system normally cannot be controlled voluntarily but is influenced by external stimuli and emotional states of the individual. By observing and recording these body functions, insight into emotional changes that cannot be measured directly can be obtained. A practical application of this principle is the *polygraph* (colloquially called the "lie detector"), a device for simultaneously recording several body functions that are likely to show changes when questions asked by the interrogator cause anxiety in the tested person.

For the measurement of blood pressure, heart rate, and respiration rate in psychophysiological studies, the same instruments are used as are utilized for medical applications (see Sections 6.1 and 6.2, and Chapter 8, respectively). For measuring variations in perspiration, a special technique has been developed. In response to an external stimulus, such as touching a sharp point, the resistance of the skin shows a characteristic decrease, called the *galvanic skin response* (GSR). The baseline value of the skin resistance, in this context, is called the *basal skin resistance* (BSR). The GSR is believed to be caused by the activity of the sweat glands. It does not depend on the overt appearance of perspiration, however, and the actual mechanism of the response is not completely understood. The GSR is measured most readily at the palms of the hands, where the body has the highest concentration of sweat glands. An active electrode, positioned at the center of the palm, can be used together with a neutral electrode, either at the wrist or at the back of the hand. In some devices clips are simply attached to two fingers. Frequently, in order to increase the stability of the measurement, nonpolarizing electrodes, such as silver-silver chloride surface electrodes (see Chapter 4), are used with an electrode jelly that has about the same salinity as the perspiration. In order to minimize the polarization at the electrodes, the current density is kept below $10\ \mu A/cm^2$.

Figure 11.1 shows a block diagram of a device that allows the simultaneous measurement, or recording, of both the BSR and the GSR. Here a current generator sends a constant dc current through the electrodes. The voltage drop across the basal skin resistance, typically on the order of several kilohms to several hundred kilohms, is measured with an amplifier and a meter that can be calibrated directly in BSR values. A second meter, coupled through an *RC* network with a time constant of about 3 to 5 seconds, measures the GSR as a change of the skin resistance of from several hundred ohms to several kilohms. The output of this amplifier can be recorded on a suitable graphic recorder. A measurement of the absolute magnitude of the GSR is not very meaningful. The change of the magnitude of the GSR, depending on the experimental conditions and its *latency* (the time delay between stimulus and response), can be used to study emotional changes. A polygraph for recording physiological functions, including GSR is shown in Figure 11.2.

Instead of the change of the skin resistance, the change of the *skin potential* has been used occasionally. This is actually a potential difference of between 50 and 70 mV that can be measured between nonpolarizing electrodes on the palm and the forearm and that also shows a response to emotional changes.

Figure 11.1. Block diagram of a device to measure and record basal skin resistance (BSR) and the galvanic skin response (GSR.)

Figure 11.2. Polygraph for the recording of four body functions. The sensors (right and bottom, clockwise) are for respiration (2 channels) galvanic skin response (GSR) and blood pressure changes. (Courtesy of Stoelting Co., Chicago, IL.)

Although the activity of the autonomic nervous system cannot be controlled directly, it can be influenced in an indirect way by two mechanisms known as *conditioning* and *feedback*.

Certain physiological responses are normally elicited by certain external stimuli. The view of food, for instance, stimulates the production of saliva and causes "one's mouth to water." As discovered by Pavlov in his famous experiments with dogs, a previously neutral stimulus can be made to elicit the same response as the view of food if it is presented several times just before the natural stimulus. This process of making the autonomic nervous system respond to previously neutral stimuli is called *Pavlovian* (or *classical*) *conditioning*.

Experiments of this type require the continuous recording of one or more of the autonomic responses. Pavlov, for example, measured the flow rate of saliva. Sometimes the autonomic responses can be influenced by simply informing the subject when a change in the response occurs. This, again, requires that the response be measured and that certain characteristics of it be signaled to the subject in a suitable way. This principle is called *biological feedback* or *biofeedback*. Although this technique had been known for some time, it received renewed interest during the early 1970s for possible therapeutic uses in controlling variables like heart rate, blood pressure, and the occurrence of certain patterns in the electroencephalogram. Biofeedback is described in more detail in Section 11.5.

11.2. INSTRUMENTS FOR TESTING MOTOR RESPONSES

Motor responses, or responses of the skeletal muscles, are under voluntary control but often require a learning process for the proper interaction between several muscles in order to perform the response correctly. Numerous devices have been described in the literature, or are available commercially, to measure motor responses and to study the influence of factors like fatigue, stress or the effects of drugs. Some of these devices are very simple. Manual dexterity tests, for instance, consist of a number of small objects that the subject is required to assemble in a certain way, while the time required for completion of the task is measured. In related instruments called *steadiness testers* a metal stylus must be moved through channels of various shapes without touching the metal walls. An error closes the contact between wall and stylus and advances an electromechanical counter. The *pursuit rotor* uses a similar principle. A light spot moves with adjustable speed along a circular, or star-shaped, pattern on the top surface of the tester. The subject has the task of pursuing the spot with a hook-shaped probe that contains a photoelectric sensor. An indicator and timer automatically measure the percentage of time during which the subject is "on target" during a certain test interval.

The performance of certain muscles or muscle groups can be measured with various *dynamometers,* which measure the force that is exerted either mechanically or with an electric transducer.

11.3. INSTRUMENTATION FOR SENSORY MEASUREMENTS

The human senses provide the information inputs required by man to orient himself in his environment and to protect himself from danger. Many methods and instruments have been developed to measure the performance of the sense organs, study their functioning, and detect impairments. Some of the senses do not require very sophisticated equipment. The temperature senses, for instance, can be studied with several metal objects, or water containers, which are maintained at certain temperatures. Some of the original work on touch perception, early in this century, was performed by stimulating the skin with bristles of horsehair that had been calibrated to exert a known pressure. The same method is still in use today except that nylon has replaced the horsehair. More complicated devices are necessary for studying optical perception. An example would be a measurement in which a spot of controllable brightness and size is viewed against a background whose brightness can also be varied. Variations in the size and brightness of the spot and the brightness of the background are all independently controlled. Another special device for studies of visual perception is the *tachistoscope.* Here a display of an illuminated card is presented to the viewer by means of a semitransparent mirror or by a slide projector. A second display is then presented for an adjustable short time interval, which may be followed by either a repeat of the original card or by a third display. The change of displays is achieved by switching the illumination or by means of electromechanical shutters. By varying the presentation time for the second display and by using displays of various complexity, the perception and recognition of objects can be studied. The purpose of the presentation of the third display is to mask optical afterimages, which might prolong the actual presentation time of the second display.

Acuity of hearing can be measured with the help of an instrument called an *audiometer.* Here the sound intensity in an earphone is gradually increased until the sound is perceived by the subject. The hearing in the other ear during this measurement is often masked by presenting a neutral stimulus (white noise) to this ear. Normally, the threshold of hearing is determined at a number of frequencies. This process is automated in the *Békésy audiometer* (named after George von Békésy, its inventor), shown in Figure

11.3. In order to perform a measurement, the subject first presses a control button, thus starting a reversible motor, which drives a volume control potentiometer and increases the amplitude of the stimulus signal until it is perceived by the subject. The subject then releases the button, opening the switch, and the motor reverses. By alternately closing and opening the switch, the subject maintains the volume at a level at which the tone can just be heard. A pen, connected to the volume-control mechanism, draws a line on a moving paper. At the same time the paper-drive mechanism, which is linked to the instrument's frequency control, slowly changes the frequency of the tone. Within about 15 minutes a recording, called an *audiogram*, is obtained. The audiogram is often calibrated, not in absolute values of the perception threshold but in relative values referred to the acuity of normal subjects (which is stored in the instrument in a mechanical cam, not shown in Figure 11.3). The resultant curve corresponds directly to the hearing loss as a function of frequency. Figure 11.4 shows a somewhat simplified version of the original Békésy audiometer, which changes the frequency of the stimulus in steps instead of continuously.

Figure 11.3. Békésy audiometer diagram.

Figure 11.4. Bekesy audiometer. (Courtesy of Grason-Stadler. Subsidiary of General Radio Company, Concord, MA.)

Hearing acuity in infants or uncooperative subjects can be tested with the help of a conditioning method. A light electrical shock can cause a change in the galvanic skin resistance. An audible tone, when paired with the shock, can be made to elicit the same response. Once this conditioning has been completed, the skin reflex can be used to determine whether the subject can hear the same tone presented at a lower volume. This technique, however, is not always completely reliable. A better method is to measure the evoked EEG response when a tone with a certain intensity is presented. This requires the repeated presentation of the tone and an averaging technique to extract the evoked response from the ongoing activity (see Section 10.7.2).

11.4. INSTRUMENTATION FOR THE EXPERIMENTAL ANALYSIS OF BEHAVIOR

In order to describe and analyze behavior accurately, data must be recorded in terms other than the subjective report of an observer. Especially for a mathematical analysis, numerical values must be assigned to some aspects of behavior. For behavior involving motor responses and motor skills, special testing devices have been developed to obtain a numerical rating—for example, the pursuit rotor just described. Other tests required the completion of some manual or mental task in which the time required for completion is measured. Sometimes the number of errors is also used to compare the performance of individuals.

Many basic behavioral experiments are performed with animals (rats, pigeons, monkeys) as subjects. These experiments are made in a neutral environment provided by a soundproof enclosure, often called a "Skinner box" (after B.F. Skinner, who pioneered the method), in which the animal is isolated from uncontrolled environmental stimuli. Each experiment must be designed in such a way that the behavior is well defined and can be measured automatically. For example, such events as pressing a bar or pecking on a key, or the presence of an animal in one part of the cage or jumping over a barrier could be measured. In specially instrumented cages, the activity of animals can be quantified.

Behavior emitted by organisms to interact with and modify their environment is called *instrumental* or *operant behavior*. Such behavior, which is controlled by the central nervous system rather than by the autonomic nervous system, can also be conditioned but in a way that differs from classical conditioning. Operant behavior that is positively reinforced (rewarded) tends to occur more frequently in the future; behavior that is negatively reinforced decreases in frequency. In animal experiments, positive reinforcement is usually administered in the form of food or water given to animals that had been deprived of these commodities. This reinforcement can be administered easily by automatic dispensing devices. Negative reinforcement is in the form of harmless, but painful, electric shocks administered through isolated grid bars that serve as the floor of the cage. With suitable reinforcement, the animal can be conditioned to "emit certain behavior," such as the pressing of a bar, in response to a certain stimulus. From changes in the behavior that can occur under the influences of drugs, or when the stimulus is modified, valuable insight into the mechanisms of behavior can be obtained.

Figure 11.5 shows a setup as it might be used for the simpler types of such experiments, using rats as subjects. The Skinner box is equipped with a response bar and a stimulus light. Positive reinforcement is administered by an automatic dispenser for food pellets. An electric-shock generator is connected to the grid floor of the cage through a scrambler switch that makes it impossible for the animal to escape the shock by clinging to bars that are of the same electrical potential. An automatic programmer turns on the stimulus at certain time intervals and controls the reinforcements according to the animal's response, following a prescribed schedule (called the *contingency*). In many experiments, these schedules can be very complex.

Figure 11.5. Skinner Box. (Courtesy of BRS-Foringer, Beltsville, MD.)

Elaborate modular control systems, either with relays or based on solid-state logic, are therefore available for programming stimulus contingencies and measuring response parameters. Simple behavior is often recorded on a *cumulative-event recorder*. In this device a paper strip is moved with a constant speed (4 in./hour). Each time the bar is pressed by the animal, a solenoid or stepping motor is energized and moves a pen a small distance over the paper perpendicular to the direction of paper movement. The pen is reset, either when it has traveled the full width of the paper or by a timing motor after a certain time interval (for example, every 10 minutes). The position of the pen at any time represents the total number of events (bar presses) that have occurred since the last resetting of the pen. Reinforcement is indicated by a diagonal movement of the pen. This recording method, despite its simplicity, is very informative. The slope of the curve corresponds to the response rate. When reset after fixed time intervals, the pen excursion directly represents a form of time histogram (see Figure 11.6).

Insight into behavior mechanisms obtained in animal experiments has been extrapolated to human behavior. Part of human behavior can be explained as having been conditioned by reinforcements administered by society and the environment. In a form of treatment called *behavior therapy,* behavioral and emotional problems are treated according to the principles of operant conditioning, sometimes using special equipment.

Perhaps the best-known example of a behavior-therapy method using electronic equipment is the treatment of bed wetting with the *Mowrer sheet* (named after the psychologists who first used it). This method uses a moisture sensor placed beneath the bed sheet, which activates an acoustical alarm and turns on a light to awaken the subject when the presence of moisture is first detected.

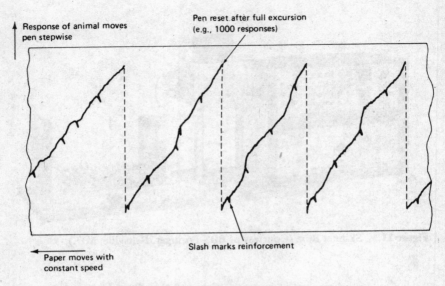

Figure 11.6. Graph from a cumulative event recorder.

11.5. BIOFEEDBACK INSTRUMENTATION

In general engineering terms, feedback is used to control a process. If this concept is applied to biological processes within the body, it is known as *biological feedback* or *biofeedback*. A variable produced by the process is measured and compared with a reference value and, based on the difference, action is taken to bring the variable to the reference value.

As stated in Chapter 10, the body functions that are controlled by the autonomic nervous system are not normally subject to voluntary control. In fact, most of these body functions are not consciously perceived. However, it has been found that if these functions are measured by some suitable method, and, if information pertaining to their magnitude can be conveyed to the subject, a certain degree of voluntary control can be exercised over some of the body functions hitherto believed uncontrollable. Biofeedback is not completely understood and there appears to be a certain overlap with Pavlovian and operant conditioning, but it is presently being used in clinical treatments.

Many different physiological processes have been evaluated for possible control by biofeedback methods, including EEG, EMG, heart rate, and blood pressure. For example, it had been observed that the duration or prevalence of certain brainwave patterns in the EEG, especially the alpha waves (see Chapter 3), could be influenced by biofeedback methods. It had also been observed that the alpha pattern is more prevalent in the EEGs of subjects when they are meditating or simply if their eyes are kept closed.

For a while "alpha feedback" was promoted in counterculture circles as a way of achieving a "drugless high," and a certain cult developed around the method. Among serious researchers this method is now very controversial. More promising are attempts to control the onset of seizures in certain forms of epilepsy by making the subject aware of certain EEG patterns that precede such seizures.

EMG voltages can be measured relatively easily and their presence or magnitude can be signaled to the subject. EMG feedback is used in two different ways. In *relaxation training* the patient is taught to maintain a low EMG-activity level, corresponding to relaxation of the muscles. In the rehabilitation of paralytic patients after traumatic injury or other nerve damage, on the other hand, EMG signals can be measured before muscle activity is detected by other means and can be used to train such patients in the use of paralyzed muscles. It might be mentioned that EMG feedback has also been used in the treatment of *bruxism*, the nocturnal grinding of the teeth.

Heart rate can be measured fairly easily. Blood pressure, on the other hand, is a fairly elusive variable. While it has been shown that both of these variables can be controlled to a certain degree by biofeedback methods, clinical applications for the treatment of hypertension have had disappointing results. There have been a number of experiments in the use of biofeedback for secondary effects. For example, by observing bioelectric data some patients have been able to control glandular secretions, such as insulin in the case of diabetics.

Biofeedback instrumentation includes a transducer and amplifiers to measure the body variable that is to be controlled by the biofeedback process. The magnitude of the measured variable, or, more commonly, changes in the magnitude, are converted into some suitable visual or auditory cue that is presented to the subject. Sometimes it is necessary to provide additional signal processing between the measurement and feedback part of the instrumentation. This is especially true when the variable to be controlled is subject to substantial fluctuations and only a statistical characteristic (e.g., the mean over a certain trial time) is to be controlled.

Some applications of biofeedback that have been demonstrated successfully include a group of medical students who were able to slow their heart rates by an average of 9 beats per minute, a group who were able to equate their own EEGs to their relaxation habits and some patients who have been able to control migraine headaches. Biofeedback has been represented by some to be the purest form of "self-control." The instrumentation is really an adaptation of many instruments discussed throughout this book. The success of biofeedback depends on interpretation of data and the training of the subjects so that they can use the results effectively.

12

Biotelemetry

There are many instances in which it is necessary to monitor physiological events from a distance. Typical applications include the following:

1. Radio-frequency transmissions for monitoring astronauts in space.
2. Patient monitoring where freedom of movement is desired, such as in obtaining an exercise electrocardiogram. In this instance, the requirement of trailing wires is both cumbersome and dangerous.
3. Patient monitoring in an ambulance and in other locations away from the hospital.
4. Collection of medical data from a home or office.
5. Research on unrestrained, unanesthetized animals in their natural habitat.

6. Use of telephone links for transmission of electrocardiograms or other medical data.
7. Special internal techniques, such as tracing acidity or pressure through the gastrointestinal tract.
8. Isolation of an electrically susceptible patient (see Chapter 16) from power-line-operated ECG equipment to protect him from accidental shock.

These applications have indicated the need for systems that can adapt existing methods of measuring physiological variables to a method of transmission of resulting data. This is the branch of biomedical instrumentation known as biomedical telemetry or biotelemetry.

12.1. INTRODUCTION TO BIOTELEMETRY

Literally, *biotelemetry* is the measurement of biological parameters over a distance. The means of transmitting the data from the point of generation to the point of reception can take many forms. Perhaps the simplest application of the principle of biotelemetry is the stethoscope, whereby heartbeats are amplified acoustically and transmitted through a hollow tube system to be picked up by the ear of the physician for interpretation (see Chapter 6).

Historically, Einthoven, the originator of the electrocardiogram, as a means of analysis of the electrical activity of the heart, transmitted electrocardiograms from a hospital to his laboratory many miles away as early as 1903. The rather crude immersion electrodes (see Figure 4.4), were connected to a remote galvanometer directly by telephone lines. The telephone lines in this instance were merely used as conductors for the current produced by the biopotentials.

The use of wires in the transmission of the biodata by Einthoven suited his purpose; however, a major advantage of modern telemetry is the elimination of the use of wires. Certain applications of biotelemetry utilize telephone systems, but essentially these are situations in which "hard-wire" connections are extended by the telephone lines. However, this chapter is concerned primarily with the use of telemetry by which the biological data are put in suitable form to be radiated by an electromagnetic field (radio transmission). This involves some type of modulation of a radio-frequency carrier and is often referred to as *radio telemetry.*

The purpose of this chapter is merely to outline the elements of the subject and to present an example of its application. For a comprehensive treatment, the reader is referred to the Bibliography.

12.2. PHYSIOLOGICAL PARAMETERS ADAPTABLE TO BIOTELEMETRY

Although there had been examples of biotelemetry in the 1940s, they did not receive much attention until the advent of the NASA space programs. For example, in the 1963 report of the Mercury program, the following types of data were obtained by telemetry:

1. Temperature by rectal or oral thermistor.
2. Respiration by impedance pneumograph.
3. Electrocardiograms by surface electrodes.
4. Indirect blood pressure by contact microphone and cuff.

As the field progressed, it became apparent that literally any quantity that could be measured was adaptable to biotelemetry. Just as with hardwire systems, measurements can be applied to two categories:

1. Bioelectrical variables, such as ECG, EMG, and EEG.
2. Physiological variables that require transducers, such as blood pressure, gastrointestinal pressure, blood flow, and temperatures.

With the first category, a signal is obtained directly in electrical form, whereas the second category requires a type of excitation, for the physiological parameters are eventually measured as variations of resistance, inductance, or capacitance. The differential signals obtained from these variations can be calibrated to represent pressure, flow, temperature, and so on, since some physical relationships exist.

In a typical system, the appropriate analog signal (voltage, current, etc.) is converted into a form or code capable of being transmitted. After being transmitted, the signal is decoded at the receiving end and converted back into its original form. The necessary amount of amplification must also be included. Sometimes it is desirable to store the data for future use. Before discussing these aspects, however, a discussion of the applications for these systems is necessary.

Currently, the most widespread use of biotelemetry for bioelectric potentials is in the transmission of the electrocardiogram. Instrumentation at the transmitting end is simple because only electrodes and amplification are needed to prepare the signal for transmission.

One example of ECG telemetry is the transmission of electrocardiograms from an ambulance or site of an emergency to a hospital, where a cardiologist can immediately interpret the ECG, instruct the trained rescue team in their emergency resuscitation procedures, and arrange for any special treatment that may be necessary upon arrival of the patient at the hospital. In this application, the telemetry to the hospital is supplemented by two-way voice communication. (See Section 12.5.3 for further details.)

The use of telemetry for ECG signals is not confined to emergency applications. It is used for exercise electrocardiograms in the hospitals so that the patient can run up and down steps, unencumbered by wires. Also, there have been cases in which individuals with heart conditions wear ECG telemetry units at home and on the job and relay ECG data periodically to the hospital for checking. Other applications include the monitoring of athletes running a race in an effort to improve their performance. ECG telemetry units are also common in human performance laboratories on some college campuses.

The actual equipment worn by the subject is quite comfortable and usually does not impede movement. In addition to the electrodes that are taped into place, the patient or subject wears a belt around the waist with a pocket for the transmitter. A typical transmitter is about the size of a package of king-size cigarettes. The wire antenna can be either incorporated into the belt or hung loosely. Clothing generally has convenient openings to allow for lead wires from the electrodes to come through to the transmitter. Power for the transmitter is from a battery, usually a mercury cell, with a useful life of about 30 hours.

Cardiovascular research performed with experimental animals necessitates some changes in technique. First, the electrodes used are often of the needle type, especially for long-term studies. Second, the animal is likely to interfere with the equipment. For this reason, miniature transmitters have been designed that can be surgically implanted subcutaneously. However, doing so is not always necessary. Many researchers have designed special jackets or harnesses for animals that have been quite successful. Some of the aspects of the particular problem are discussed later.

Telemetry is also being used for transmission of the electroencephalogram. Most applications have been involved with experimental animals for research purposes. One example is in the space biology program in the Brain Research Institute at the University of California, Los Angeles, where chimpanzees have had the necessary EEG electrodes implanted in the brain. The leads from these electrodes are brought to a small transmitter installed on the animal's head, and the EEG is transmitted. Other groups have developed special helmets with surface electrodes for this application. Similar helmets have been used for the collection of EEGs of football players during a game.

Telemetry of EEG signals has also been used in studies of mentally disturbed children. The child wears a specially designed "football helmet" or "spaceman's helmet" with built-in electrodes so that the EEG can be monitored without traumatic difficulties during play. In one clinic the children are left to play with other children in a normal nursery school environment. They are monitored continuously while data are recorded.

One advantage of monitoring by telemetry is to circumvent a problem that often hampers medical diagnosis. Patients frequently experience pains, aches, or other symptoms that give trouble for days, only to have them disappear just before or during a medical examination. Many insidious symptoms behave in this way. With telemetry and long-term monitoring, the cause of these symptoms may be detected when they occur or, if recorded on magnetic tape, can be analyzed later.

One problem often encountered in long-term monitoring by telemetry is that of handling the large amount of data generated. If the time to detect symptoms is very long, it becomes quite a task to record all the information. In many applications, data can be recorded on tape for later playback. A number of types of tape recorders can play back information at a higher speed than that at which data are recorded. Thus, an hour's worth of data can be played back in ½ minute. These rapid-playback techniques can be used effectively only if the observer is looking for something specific. That is, a certain voltage amplitude or a certain frequency can be sensed by a discriminator circuit and used to activate a signal, either a light or sound. The observer can then stop the machine and record the vital segment of the data on paper. He does not have to record the whole sequence, only that part of most interest.

The third type of bioelectric signal that can be telemetered is the electromyogram. This device is particularly useful for studies of muscle damage and partial paralysis problems and also in human performance studies.

Telemetry can also be used in transmitting stimulus signals to a patient or subject. For example, it is well known that an electrical impulse can trigger the firing of nerves (see Chapter 10). It has been demonstrated that if an electrode is surgically implanted and connected to dead nerve endings, an electrical impulse can sometimes cause the nerves to function as they once did. If a miniature receiver is implanted subcutaneously, the electrical signal can be generated remotely. This point brings up the possibility of using telemetry techniques therapeutically. One example is the use of telemetry in the treatment of "dropfoot," which is one of the most common disabilities resulting from stroke. This condition is essentially an inability of the patient to lift his foot, which results in a shuffling, toe-dragging gait.

A method for correcting "dropfoot" by transmitting a signal to an implanted electronic stimulator has been used successfully at Rancho Los Amigos Hospital in Los Angeles. An external transmitter worn by the patient delivers a pulse-modulated carrier signal of 450 kHz to an implanted receiver that demodulates the signal and delivers the resulting signal (a pulse train with a pulse duration of 300 μsec and a frequency that can be varied between 20 and 50 pulses per second) to the peroneal nerve. This nerve, when stimulated, causes muscles in the lower forepart of the leg to contract, thus raising the foot. Stimulation is automatically cycled during gait by a heel switch that turns the transmitter on and off so as to approximate the normal phasic activity of these muscles during gait.

By using suitable transducers, telemetry can be employed for the measurement of a wide variety of physiological variables. In some cases, the transducer circuit is designed as a separate "plug-in" module to fit into the transmitter, thus allowing one transmitter design to be used for different types of measurements. Also, many variables can be measured and transmitted simultaneously by multiplexing techniques.

The transducers and associated circuits are essentially the same as those discussed in earlier chapters. Sometimes they must be modified as to shape, size, and electrical characteristics, but the basic principles of transduction are identical with their hard-wire system counterparts. Not all types of transducers lend themselves to telemetry, however, and usually, in a typical application, a study of adaptable types is necessary.

One important application of telemetry is in the field of blood pressure and heart rate research in unanesthetized animals. The transducers are surgically implanted with leads brought out through the animal's skin. A male plug is attached postoperatively and later connected to the female socket contained in the transmitter unit.

Blood flow has also been studied extensively by telemetry. Both Doppler-type and electromagnetic-type transducers can be employed.

The use of thermistors to measure temperature is also easily adaptable to telemetry. In addition to constant monitoring of skin temperature or systemic body temperature, the thermistor system has found use in obstetrics and gynecology. Long-term studies of natural birth control by monitoring vaginal temperature have incorporated telemetry units.

A final application, discussed below in more detail, is the use of "radio pills" to monitor stomach pressure or pH. In this application, a pill that contains a sensor plus a miniature transmitter is swallowed and the data are picked up by a receiver and recorded.

It is interesting to note that biotelemetry studies have been performed on dogs, cats, rabbits, monkeys, baboons, chimpanzees, deer, turtles, snakes, alligators, caimans, giraffes, dolphins, llamas, horses, seals, and elks, as well as on humans.

12.3.   THE COMPONENTS OF A BIOTELEMETRY SYSTEM

With the many commercial biotelemetry systems available today, it would be impossible to discuss all the ramifications of each. This section is designed to give the reader an insight into the typical simple system. More complicated systems can be built on this base. In putting together a telemetry system, it should be realized that although parts of it are unique for medical purposes, most of the electronic circuits for oscillators, amplifiers, power supplies, and so on are usually adaptions of circuits in regular use in radio communications.

One of the earliest biotelemetry units was the *endoradiosonde,* developed by Mackay and Jacobson and described in various papers by these two investigators since 1957. The pressure-sensing endoradiosonde is a "radio pill" less than 1 cm³ in volume so that it can be swallowed by the patient. As it travels through the gastrointestinal tract, it measures the various pressures it encounters. Similar devices have also been built to sense temperature, pH, enzyme activity, and oxygen tension values by the use of different sensors or transducers. Pressure is sensed by a variable inductance, whereas temperature is sensed by a temperature-sensitive transducer.

One version of the circuit is shown in Figure 12.1. Basically, it is a transistorized Hartley oscillator having a constant amplitude of oscillation and a variable frequency to communicate information. The ferrite core of the coil is attached to a diaphragm, which causes it to move in and out as a function of pressure and, therefore, varies the value of inductance in the coil. This change in inductance produces a corresponding change in the frequency of oscillations. Inward motion of the ferrite core produces a decrease in frequency. Thus, changes in pressure modulate the frequency. An emitter resistor was used in earlier models, and the radio-frequency voltage across it was transmitted by a combined shield and antenna. In later models the oscillator resonator coil also acts as an antenna. The transmitted frequencies, ranging from about 100 kHz to about 100 MHz, can be picked up on any simple receiver.

Figure 12.1. Circuit of pressure-sensitive endoradiosonde. (From R. S. Mackay, *Biomedical Telemetry*. New York, John Wiley & Sons, Inc., 1968, by permission.)

To illustrate the basic principles involved in telemetry, a simple system will be described. Most applications involve more circuitry. The stages of a typical biotelemetry system can be broken down into functional blocks, as shown in Figure 12.2 for the transmitter and in Figure 12.3 for the receiver. Physiological signals are obtained from the subject by means of appropriate transducers. The signal is then passed through a stage of amplification and processing circuits that include generation of a subcarrier and a modulation stage for transmission.

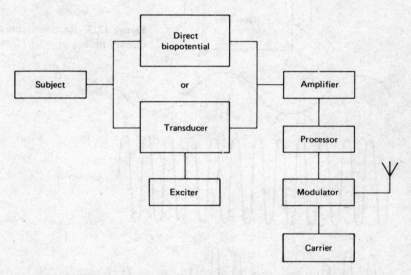

Figure 12.2. Block diagram of a biotelemetry transmitter.

The receiver (Figure 12.3) consists of a tuner to select the transmitting frequency, a demodulator to separate the signal from the carrier wave, and a means of displaying or recording the signal. The signal can also be stored in the modulated state by the use of a tape recorder, as shown in the block diagram. Some comments on these various stages are provided later.

Since most biotelemetry systems involve the use of radio transmission, a brief discussion of some basic concepts of radio should be helpful to the reader with limited background in this field. A *radio-frequency* (RF) *carrier* is a high-frequency sinusoidal signal which, when applied to an appropriate transmitting antenna, is propagated in the form of electromagnetic waves. The distance the transmitted signal can be received is called the *range* of the system. Information to be transmitted is impressed upon the carrier by a process known as *modulation*. Various methods of modulation are desribed below. The circuitry which generates the carrier and modulates it constitutes the *transmitter*. Equipment capable of receiving the transmitted signal and

Figure 12.3. Receiver-storage-display units.

Figure 12.4. Types of modulation.

demodulating it to recover the information comprise the *receiver.* By tuning the receiver to the frequency of the desired RF carrier, that signal can be selected while others are rejected. The range of the system depends upon a number of factors, including the power and frequency of the transmitter, relative locations of the transmitting and receiving antennas, and the sensitivity of the receiver.

The simplest form of using a transmitter is to simply turn it on and off to correspond to some code. Such a system does not lend itself to the transmission of physiological data, but is useful for remote control applications. This is called *continuous wave* (CW) transmission, and does not involve modulation.

The two basic systems of modulation are *amplitude modulation* (AM) and *frequency modulation* (FM). These two methods are illustrated in Figure 12.4.

In an amplitude-modulated system, the *amplitude* of the carrier is caused to vary with the information being transmitted. Standard radio broadcast (AM) stations utilize this method of modulation, as does the video (picture) signal for television. Amplitude-modulated systems are susceptible to natural and man-made electrical interference, since the interference generally appears as variations in the amplitude of the received signal.

In a frequency modulation (FM) system, the *frequency* of the carrier is caused to vary with the modulated signal. An FM system is much less susceptible to interference, because variations in the amplitude of the received signal caused by interference can be removed at the receiver before demodulation takes place. Because of this reduced interference, FM transmission is often used for telemetry. FM broadcast stations and television sound also utilize this method of modulation.

In biotelemetry systems, the physiological signal is sometimes used to modulate a low-frequency carrier, called a *subcarrier,* often in the audio-frequency range. The RF carrier of the transmitter is then modulated by the subcarrier. If several physiological signals are to be transmitted simultaneously, each signal is placed on a subcarrier of a different frequency and all of the subcarriers are combined to simultaneously modulate the RF carrier. This process of transmitting many *channels* of data on a single RF carrier is called *frequency multiplexing,* and is much more efficient and less expensive than employing a separate transmitter for each channel. At the receiver, a multiplexed RF carrier is first demodulated to recover each of the separate subcarriers, which must then be demodulated to retrieve the original physiological signals. Either frequency or amplitude modulation can be used for impressing data on the subcarriers, and this may or may not be the same modulation method that is used to place the subcarriers on the

RF carrier. In describing this type of system, a designation is given in which the method of modulating the subcarriers is followed by the method of modulating the RF carrier. For example, a system in which the subcarriers are frequency-modulated and the RF carrier is amplitude-modulated is designated as FM/AM. An FM/FM designation means that both the subcarriers and the RF carrier are frequency modulated. Both FM/AM and FM/FM systems have been used in biotelemetry, the latter more extensively.

In addition to the basic modulation schemes already described, there are many other techniques. Factors that affect the choice of a modulation system may include size, as in an implantable unit (to be described later), or complexity, as in multichannel units, and also considerations of noise. transmission, and other operational problems.

The common denominator for most of the other approaches is a technique known as *pulse modulation,* in which the transmission carrier is generated in a series of short bursts or pulses. If the *amplitude* of the pulses is used to represent the transmitted information, the method is called *pulse amplitude modulation* (PAM), whereas if the *width* (duration) of each pulse is varied according to the information, a *pulse width modulation* (PWM) system results. In a related method called *pulse position modulation* (PPM), the timing of a very narrow pulse is varied with respect to a reference pulse. All three of these pulse modulation methods have certain advantages and are used under certain circumstances. Sometimes other designations have been used to describe the same process; for example, *pulse duration modulation* (PDM) is the same as pulse width modulation. Other designations are *pulse code modulation* (PCM) and *pulse interval modulation* (PIM). Most pulse-modulated telemetry systems use a subcarrier as well as the RF carrier to achieve better stability and greater accuracy. Direct modulation of the RF as in an AM or FM system makes the transmitter more sensitive to nearby electrical equipment and other transmitters. The double designation defined above can be used with all these systems such as PIM/FM, PWM/FM, and so on.

Pulse interval modulation (PIM) and a related modulation system, *pulse interval ratio modulation* (PIRM), are illustrated in Figure 12.5. Either coding system can use direct *pulsatile transmission* (PULSE) or frequency-modulated transmission (FM) (Figure 12.4), in which the frequency is shifted during the time duration defining each pulse. The FM method consumes much more energy than pulse modulation but has greater range. The pulsatile method radiates RF for only 3 to 5 percent of the time. High-quality RF tuners with special modifications are required to capture pulsatile signals. The pulse mode is shown in Figure 12.5(a).

Both systems use the principle of time-duration encoding. The leading edge of a pulse of radio frequency energy with pulsatile transmission (PULSE) or radio frequency shift (FM) defines the beginning and end of time duration.

Figure 12.5. Pulse modulation

Such denoted times, or ratios of times, are designed to be proportional to voltage and hence to the magnitude of the parameters to be measured (ECG, pressure, etc.). These time durations are very short, usually in the tens of microseconds. Thus, sampling frequency, and hence frequency response, can be very high.

In PIM, Figure 12.5(b), the length of the interval between successive pulses, t_1, is proportional to the signal input. This system is best suited to biopotential or accelerometer usage, but may be used for temperature as well. In PIRM, Figure 12.5(c), the ratio of two successive intervals in each sequential pair of pulses is proportional to a function of the signal input. This system is more complex than PIM but is less dependent on battery voltage. It is best suited for applications such as temperature and pressure.

As in amplitude and frequency modulation systems, multiplexing of several channels of physiological data can be accomplished in a pulse modulation system. However, instead of frequency multiplexing, *time multiplexing* is used. In a time-multiplexing scheme, each of the physiological signals is sampled briefly and used to control either the amplitude, width, or position of one pulse, depending on the type of pulse modulation used. The pulses representing the various channels of data are transmitted sequentially. Thus, in a six-channel system, every sixth data pulse represents a given channel. In order to identify the data pulses, an identifiable reference pulse is included in each set. If the sampling rate is several times the highest frequency component of each data signal, no loss of information results from the sampling process.

A full discussion of all possible methods is beyond the scope of this book, but the reader is referred to the Bibliography for further information. However, some typical examples are presented below.

Figure 12.6. Transducer circuit.

A system for monitoring blood pressure is used to illustrate the FM/FM method of transmission. The transducer used in this case is the flush-diaphragm type of strain-gage transducer. Electrically, it can be represented by the bridge circuit of Figure 12.6. Resistors R_1 and R_3 decrease, whereas R_2 and R_4 increase in value as blood pressure increases. Resistor R_b is simply for balancing or zeroing. The transducer is connected in the transmitter circuit as shown in Figure 12.7.

Either direct current or alternating current can be used as excitation for strain-gage bridges. When dc is used, the amplifier following the bridge must be a dc amplifier, with its associated problems of stability and drift. When ac is used, the bridge acts as a modulator. A demodulator and filter are required in order to recover the signal.

Figure 12.7. One type of exciter-transmitter unit for blood pressure telemetry.

The exciter unit, which in this example consists of a Colpitts transistor oscillator plus an *RC*-coupled common-emitter amplifier stage, excites the bridge with a constant ac voltage at a frequency of approximately 5 kHz. The exciter unit is coupled to the bridge inductively. The bridge is initially balanced both resistively and capacitively so that any changes in the resistance of the arms of the bridge due to changes in pressure on the transducer will result in changes of the output voltage.

This output voltage is inductively coupled to another common-emitter amplifier stage and *RC*-coupled to a further stage of amplification. However, whereas the previous stages are class A amplifiers and do not change the waveshape of the input voltage, the latter stage is a class C amplifier, which means that the transistor is biased beyond cutoff and the resulting output wave is rectified to obtain a signal representative of the pressure variation.

This rectified wave is put through a resistance–capacitance filter, and the resulting voltage controls the frequency of a unijunction (double-base) transistor oscillator. This is the FM subcarrier oscillator that is used to modulate the main carrier.

The system can be arranged so that there is a fairly linear relationship between the subcarrier oscillator frequency and the physiological parameter to be measured. For example, in the system for blood pressure illustrated in Figure 12.7, a frequency range of 1 to 2 kHz represents the range of 0 to 300 mm Hg (0 to 40 kPa) pressure. The transducer action can be traced very easily. The subcarrier is used to frequency-modulate the main transmitter carrier. This carrier is transmitted at low power on a frequency band specially designated for biotelemetry.

The same exciter-transmitter circuit could be used with small modifications if the blood pressure transducer were replaced by another type or by a thermistor or any other electrical resistance device. Also, the exciter-bridge combination could be replaced by a direct biopotential signal input, such as an electrocardiogram signal.

It should be noted that, with the transmission of radio-frequency energy, legal problems might be encountered. Many systems use very low power and the signals can be picked up only a few feet away. Such systems are not likely to present problems. However, systems that transmit over longer distances are subject to licensing procedures and the use of certain allocated frequencies or frequency bands. Regulations vary from country to country, and in some European countries they are more strict than in the United States.

The regulations that are of concern to persons operating in the United States are contained in the Federal Communications Commission (FCC) regulations for low-power transmission. In case of doubt, this material should be referred to in order to ensure compliance (see the Bibliography).

Returning to the system under discussion, the signal transmitted at low power on the FM transmitter is picked up by the receiver, which must be tuned to the correct frequency. The audio subcarrier is removed from the RF carrier and then demodulated to reproduce a signal that can be transformed back to the amplitude and frequency of the original data waveform. This signal can then be displayed or recorded on a chart. If it is desirable to store the data on tape for later use, the original data waveform or the modulated subcarrier signal is put on the tape. In the latter case, when playback is desired, the subcarrier signal is passed through the FM subcarrier demodulator.

There are systems that convert an analog signal, such as ECG, into digital form prior to modulation. The digital form is useful when used in conjunction with computers, a topic covered in Chapter 15.

An example of another type of telemetry system is shown in Figures 12.8 and 12.9. This is a pulse-width modulation (PWM) system capable of simultaneously transmitting four channels of physiological data. The transmitted signal is a composite of a positive synchronizing pulse and a series of negative signal pulses. The data to be telemetered cause the signal pulses to move back and forth in time with respect to the synchronizing pulse X and result in four varying time intervals (t_1, t_2, t_3, t_4). The position of each pulse with respect to its neighbors carries the data.

Figure 12.8. Biolink PWM transmitting system. (Courtesy of BIOCOM, Inc., Culver City, CA.)

Figure 12.9. Biolink PWM receiving system. (Courtesy of BIOCOM, Inc., Culver City, CA.)

Referring to the block diagram of the transmitting system in Figure 12.8, it can be seen that the sync generator begins the action. Its pulse turns the first channel one-shot multivibrator *ON*. How long it remains on depends on the level of the data being fed into it at that instant of time. Its return to the *OFF* position triggers the next channel, and so on down the line. The resultant square waves are thus width-modulated by the data.

After reception, the composite signal must be separated and re-formed to be properly demodulated. The sync-signal separator and amplifiers perform this function, as shown in Figure 12.9. Each channel consists of a flip-flop and an integrating network. The signal pulses are fed through a suitable diode network to all channels. The sync pulse is fed to the first channel only.

In operation, the sync pulse turns the first flip-flop *ON*. The first signal pulse comes in and would turn any *ON* flip-flops *OFF*. Since channel 1 is the only unit that is *ON*, it is turned *OFF*. When it returns to the *OFF* position, it automatically triggers the channel 2 flip-flop *ON*. Subsequent signal pulses are used to turn off (or gate) each corresponding flip-flop after it has been turned on. This situation is shown in Figure 12.10. The resulting square wave out of each flip-flop varies in width corresponding to the original square wave in the transmitter. Simple integration yields the original data.

Figure 12.10. Forming the PWM composite signal. (Courtesy of BIOCOM, Inc., Culver City, CA.)

12.4. IMPLANTABLE UNITS

It was mentioned previously that sometimes it is desirable to implant the telemetry transmitter or receiver subcutaneously. The implanted transmitter is especially useful in animal studies, where the equipment must be protected from the animal. The implanted receiver has been used with patients for stimulation of nerves, as described in Section 12.1.

Although the protective aspect is an advantage, many disadvantages often outweigh this factor, and careful thought should be given before embarking on an implantation. The surgery involved is not too complicated, but there is always risk whenever surgical techniques are used. Also, once a unit is implanted, it is no longer available for servicing, and the life of the unit depends on how long the battery can supply the necessary current.

This section is primarily concerned with completely implanted systems, but there are occasions when a partial implant is feasible. A good example is a system used for the monitoring of the electroencephalogram where the electrodes have been implanted into the brain and the telemetry unit is mounted within and on top of the skull. This type of unit needs a protective helmet.

The use of implantable units also restricts the distance of transmission of the signal. Because the body fluids and the skin greatly attenuate the signal and because the unit must be small to be implanted, and therefore has little power, the range of signal is quite restricted, often to just a few feet. This disadvantage has been overcome by picking up the signal with a nearby antenna and retransmitting it. However, most applications involve monitoring over relatively short distances, and retransmission is not necessary.

Another problem has been the encapsulation of the unit. The outer case and any wiring must be impervious to body fluids and moisture. However, with the plastic potting compounds and plastic materials available today, this condition is easily satisfied. Silicon encapsulation is commonly used.

The power source is of great importance. Mercury and silver-oxide primary batteries have been used extensively and, more recently, lithium batteries have found many applications. Implantable telemetry batteries vary in physical size and electrical capacity, depending on the application. For field work with free-roaming animals, the power requirements are quite different from those needed in a closed laboratory cage. The size of the animal is also a factor. Requirements range from an electrical capacity of 20 mA-hr with a weight of 0.28 gram and a volume of 0.05 cm³ to 1000 mA-hr, with weights of the order of 12 grams and 3.2 cm³. Also, if power is not needed continuously, radio-frequency switches can be used to turn the system on and off on command.

In simple terms the complete implantable telemetry transmitter system consists of the transducer(s), the leads from the transducer(s) to the transmitter, the transmitter unit itself, and the power source. The latter can be encapsulated within the transmitter or may be a separate unit connected by suitable leads to the transmitter. The transducers are implanted surgically in the position required for a particular measurement, such as in the aorta or other artery for blood pressure. Figure 6.28 shows a typical pressure transducer implantation in a dog. The transmitters and power units have to be placed in a suitable body cavity close to the under surface of the skin and situated so that they give no physical or psychological disturbance to the animal. It is extremely important that all units and wires are adequately sealed since leakage of body fluids into equipment or the chemical effects of man-made materials on body tissues can cause malfunction or infection, respectively. Discussion of these materials is beyond the scope of this chapter, but this is an important topic in the general field of biomedical engineering. An antenna loop is also part of the transmitter.

Some implantable units presently in use are used as illustrations of the foregoing discussions of implantable systems. A basic unit is shown in Figure 12.11. This is a single-channel blood pressure transmitter. The module at the top contains the signal conditioning circuitry and RF transmitter. The second module contains a 200-mA-hour lithium power source and a 1.7-MHz RF switch for turning the system on and off remotely. The pressure transducer, shown in the lower left corner, is the same type described in Section 6.2.4.5.

Figure 12.11 Single channel implantable transmitter for blood pressure. (Courtesy of Konigsberg Instruments Inc., Pasadena, CA.)

Figure 12.12. Cut-away single channel temperature transmitter. (Courtesy of Konigsberg Instruments Inc., Pasadena, CA.)

Figure 12.12 is a cutaway view of a single-channel temperature transmitter. A 1.35-V battery is contained inside the antenna loop at the top. Inside, one of the three hybrid packages is shown open. Figure 12.13 shows an array of all parts of the complete system. The top unit in the figure is the TD6 Telemetry Demodulator. It has six main channels and is designed to work with the 88 to 108-MHz receiver shown immediately below it. The receiver is modified to accept both continuous FM and pulsed-RF-mode telemetry signals. An inductive power control wand for turning the implant on and off is shown on the bottom right side. Below the wand there is an external

Figure 12.13. Complete implantable telemetry system. (Courtesy of Konigsberg Instruments Inc., Pasadena, CA.)

recharging transmitter. In use, the coil of the recharging unit must be placed from 1 to 2.5 cm axially from the implanted pickup coil, which is part of the battery system. This pickup coil is shown in the figure adjacent to the recharger coil, and the battery unit to which it is connected is suitably encapsulated. The implantable transmitter and transducer systems that are implanted are shown on the bottom left side of the picture.

A cutaway view of an inductively-powered multichannel telemetry system is shown in Figure 12.14. Sensor leads and compensation components are shown on the right. Power and antenna leads are shown on the left. In the center, one of three hybrid packets is shown open. It contains six sensor-input amplifiers, an eight-channel multiplexer, an analog-to-PWM converter, and a 10-kHz clock and binary counter.

Finally, there are systems with only partial implantations. Referring again to Figure 6.28, a pressure transducer is shown implanted in the aorta of a dog. In that particular system, the lead from the transducer was brought out through the dog's back and connected to a telemetry transducer external to the body of the dog. This type of preparation is achieved by having the dog wear a jacket. Prior to surgery, dogs are trained to wear the jackets continuously so that they get used to them. After the surgical implantation of the transducer and after the chest wall is healed, the jacket is put back on the dog. It is made of strong nylon mesh so that it is comfortable, permits air circulation, but cannot easily be bitten into by the dog. The lead

Figure 12.14. Cut-away multi-channel telemetry system. (Courtesy of Konigsberg Instruments Inc., Pasadena, CA.)

that comes out of the dog's back from the transducer is plugged into an external telemetry transmitter which is kept in a pocket of the jacket. The transmitter can be removed when not in use. Another pocket, on the opposite side of the jacket, is available for other equipment. For example, in an experiment concerned with the effect of the hormone, norepinephrine, on blood pressure, a small chemical pump was placed in the other pocket to inject norepinephrine into the blood stream at various rates. The effect on the blood pressure of the dog was observed and recorded by the use of the telemetry system. By using telemetry the dog is isolated, so that outside effects, such as fear of people, will not be present during the experiment. The telemetry transmitter is about the size of a pack of cigarettes. This type of semi-implantation, with implanted transducer and external transmitter, was used extensively during the early development stages of biotelemetry in animal research. The system is the same as that shown in Figure 12.2. A photograph of a dog wearing a jacket with the telemetry transmitter in the pocket is shown in Figure 12.15.

Figure 12.15. Jacket for partially implanted telemetry system.

12.5 APPLICATIONS OF TELEMETRY IN PATIENT CARE

There are a limited number of situations in which telemetry is practical in the diagnosis and treatment of hospital patients. Most involve measurement of the electrocardiogram. Some common applications are described below.

12.5.1. Telemetry of ECGs from Extended Coronary Care patients

Cardiac patients must often be observed for rhythm disturbances for a period of time following intensive coronary care. Such patients are generally allowed a certain amount of mobility. To make monitoring possible, some

Figure 12.16. ECG telemetry transmitter: (a) Hewlett-Packard Type 78100A in hospital use (Courtesy of Hewlett-Packard Company, Waltham, MA). (b) Electrode placement for telemetered ECG.

hospitals have extended coronary-care units equipped with patient-monitoring systems that include telemetry. In this arrangement, each patient has ECG electrodes taped securely to his chest. The electrodes are connected to a small transmitter unit that also contains the signal-conditioning equipment. The transmitter unit is fastened to a special belt worn around the patient's waist. Figure 12.16 shows typical units. Batteries for powering the signal-conditioning equipment and transmitter are also included in the transmitter package. These batteries must be replaced periodically. Some systems include provisions for easy testing of the transmitter batteries. In other cases, the batteries must be replaced at some predetermined interval.

A telemetry receiver for each monitored patient is usually included as part of the monitoring system. The output of each receiver is connected to one of the ECG channels of the patient monitor. A potential problem in the use of telemetry with free-roaming patients concerns being able to locate a patient in case his alarm should sound. Telemetry equipment has no provision for indicating the location of a transmitter. The area in which the patients are allowed to move must be limited. There may also be a problem if patients are able to venture beyond the range of the telemetry transmitter. Most modern hospitals are constructed in such a way that radio waves cannot pass through the walls. Thus, unless special antennas are provided in hallways, reception may be confined to the ward itself or to a very small portion of the hospital. If a patient wanders beyond the range of the system, his ECG can no longer be monitored and the purpose of the telemetry is defeated.

12.5.2 Telemetry for ECG Measurements During Exercise

For certain cardiac abnormalities, such as ischemic coronary artery disease, diagnostic procedures require measurement of the electrocardiogram while the patient is exercising, usually on a treadmill or a set of steps. Although such measurements can be made with direct-wire connections from the patient to nearby instrumentation, the connecting cables are frequently in the way and may interfere with the performance of the patient. For this reason, telemetry is often used in conjunction with exercise ECG measurements. The transmitter unit used for this purpose is similar to that described earlier for extended coronary care and is normally worn on the belt. Care must be taken to ensure that the electrodes and all wires are securely fastened to the patient, to prevent their swinging during the movement of the patient. In most ECG telemetry systems movement of the wiring with respect to the body results in artifacts on the ECG tracing. However, with proper equipment and with the wiring skillfully tied down, excellent results can be obtained. If other physiological variables in addition to the ECG are to be measured from the exercising patient, suitable transducers and signal-conditioning equipment must be included in the transmitter unit, along with the provision for multiplexing to accommodate the additional channels. In general, the receiver and other equipment used for conditioning and displaying the signals received from the exercising patient are located very near the patient. Thus, the transmitter can operate with low power. The receiver must be able to retrieve the ECG and any other information transmitted, in addition to providing appropriate signals to the remainder of the instrumentation system.

12.5.3. Telemetry for Emergency Patient Monitoring

In many areas ambulances and emergency rescue teams are equipped with telemetry equipment to allow electrocardiograms and other physiological data to be transmitted to a nearby hospital for interpretation. Two-way voice transmission is normally used in conjunction with the telemetry to facilitate identification of the telemetered information and to provide instructions for treatment. Through the use of such equipment, ECGs can be interpreted and treatment begun before the patient arrives at the hospital.

Telemetry of this type requires a much more powerful transmitter than the two applications previously described. Often the data must be transmitted many miles and sometimes from a moving vehicle. To be effective, the system must be capable of providing reliable reception and reproduction of the transmitted signals regardless of conditions. In some cases, an emergency rescue squad can transmit physiological information from a portable transmitter to a receiver in their vehicle. The vehicle, which contains a more powerful transmitter and better antenna system, is able to retransmit the data to the hospital. This process of *retransmission* is necessary in cases where the emergency team might be working in some location from which they are unable to maintain direct communication with the hospital.

One type of system in use is illustrated in Figure 12.17. Figure 12.17(a) shows the portable telemetry unit itself, and 12.17(b) is an action photograph of the unit being used by a paramedic team. The coronary observation display console on the receiving end of the system in the hospital is illustrated in Figure 12.17(c).

The portable unit carried in the ambulance or paramedic vehicle has a nominal output of 12 W RF. It weighs less than 8.6 kg (19 lb) and can be carried by a handle or using a shoulder strap. It can transmit on any of 10 different channels. These are the eight approved MED frequencies and two EMS or public safety dispatch channels. The Federal Communications Commission (FCC) has set up rules and regulations concerning the use of "Special Emergency Radio Service" (see the Bibliography) in which the *MED frequencies* are defined. Table 12.1 shows these frequencies. To cover the band, the mobile telemetry transmitters are usually capable of operating in the range 450 to 470 MHz.

Figure 12.17 Emergency medical care system. (a) Portable transmitter unit. (b) Transmitter unit in use. (c) Hospital console. (Courtesy of Motorola Communications and Electronics Inc., Schaumburg, IL.)

Table 12.1. EMERGENCY MEDICAL SYSTEMS UHF FREQUENCIES (MHz)[a]

Channel Name	Primary Use	Base and Mobile	Mobile Only
Dispatch 1	Dispatch only	462.950	467.950
Dispatch 2	Dispatch only	462.975	467.975
Med 1	Medical voice and telemetry	463.000	468.000
Med 2	Medical voice and telemetry	463.025	468.025
Med 3	Medical voice and telemetry	463.050	468.050
Med 4	Medical voice and telemetry·	463.075	468.075
Med 5	Medical voice and telemetry	463.100	468.100
Med 6	Medical voice and telemetry	463.125	468.125
Med 7	Medical voice and telemetry	463.150	468.150
Med 8	Medical voice and telemetry	463.175	468.175

[a]From FCC Rules and Regulations.

In a typical paramedic operation, after a call is received concerning a person with a possible heart attack, the unit proceeds to the location. The paramedics check the general appearance of the patient, his or her level of consciousness, skin temperature and color, pulse rate and rhythm, respiration rate and depth, and blood pressure. If someone is with the patient, they also try to ascertain weight, medical allergies, and other patient information, because of the possibility of having to administer drugs. If any action is indicated that is within their capabilities, they take it. For example, defibrillation would be performed on the spot if needed. If not, the usual course is to relay the ECG to a hospital. They may be connected with an individual hospital, but they have the capability of communicating with many, using the several frequencies available. In a metropolitan area the MED frequencies are designated to hospitals or groups of hospitals. Channels are 25 kHz apart. The paramedic operator has no need to tune since each frequency is independent and the control is by a single switch with the 10 channels marked on it. Since voice communication is also available, the ECG is usually relayed to the hospital, an interpretation made by a cardiologist, and action taken within minutes. The regulations are such that the receiving unit in the hospital must have the capability of operating on at least four of the eight MED channels.

Emergency medical care has become an important part of the overall health delivery system. Its importance cannot be overemphasized. In November 1976 the IEEE issued a special volume of its transactions (see the Bibliography) on emergency medical services communications, which is an excellent reference that not only gives the history and development of the field, but presents a view of the problem nationally, regionally, urban and rural. It covers equipment and philosophies and even some of the political aspects.

12.5.4. Telephone Links

Although it cannot be considered to be radio telemetry, the use of the telephone system to transmit biological data is becoming quite common. One
application involves the transmission of ECGs from heart patients and
(particularly) pacemaker recipients. In this case the patient has a transmitter
uilit that can be coupled to an ordinary telephone. The transmitted signal
is received by telephone in the doctor's office or in the hospital. Tests can
be scheduled at regular intervals for diagnosing the status and potential
problems indicated by the ECGs.

13

Instrumentation
for the Clinical
Laboratory

Every living organism has within itself a complete and very complicated chemical factory. In higher animals, food and water enter the system through the mouth, which is the beginning of the digestive tract. In the stomach the food is chemically broken down into basic components by the digestive juices. From there it is transported into the intestine, where the nutrients and the excess water are extracted. The extracted nutrients are then further broken down in numerous steps. Some are stored for later use, whereas others are used for the building of new body cells or are metabolized to obtain energy. All life functions, such as the contraction of muscles or the transmission of information through the nervous system, require energy for their operation. This energy is obtained from the nutrients by a series of oxidation processes which consume oxygen and leave carbon dioxide as a waste product. The exchange of oxygen and carbon dioxide with the air takes place in the lungs (see Chapter 8). Many of the chemical processes are performed in the liver, which in an organ specialized for this purpose. Certain soluble waste products are eliminated through the kidneys and the urinary tract. To make all this activity possible, the organism requires an efficient mechanism to transport the various chemical substances between the locations where they are introduced into the organism, are modified, or are excreted.

13.1. THE BLOOD

In very primitive animals, especially in those living in an ocean environment, like the sea anemone, the exchange of nutrients and metabolic wastes between cells and the environment takes place directly through the cell membrane. This simple method is insufficient, however, for larger animals, particularly those that live on land. For these animals, including man, nature has provided a special transport system to exchange chemical products between the specialized cells of the various organs—namely, the blood circulation. The circulatory system of an adult male human contains about 5 liters of blood. Blood consists of a fluid, called the *plasma,* in which are suspended three different types of *formed elements* or *blood cells.* One cubic millimeter of blood (about ⅙ drop) contains approximately the following numbers of cells:

Red blood cells (RBC) or erythrocytes	4.5–5.5 million
White blood cells (WBC) or leucocytes	6000–10,000
Blood platelets or thrombocytes	200,000–800,000

Red blood cells are round disks, indented in the center, with a diameter of about 8 μm. A red blood cell has no cell nucleus, but it has a membrane and is filled with a solution containing an iron-containing protein, *hemoglobin.* Red blood cells transport oxygen by chemically binding the oxygen molecules to the hemoglobin. Depending on the oxygen content, the hemoglobin changes its color, which accounts for the difference in color between oxygen-rich arterial blood (bright red) and oxygen-depleted venous blood (dark red).

White blood cells are of several different types, with an average diameter of about 10 μm. Each contains a nucleus and, like the amoeba, has the ability to change its shape. White blood cells attack intruding bacteria, incorporate them, and then digest them.

Blood platelets are masses of protoplasm 2 to 4 μm in diameter. They are colorless and have no nucleus. Blood platelets are involved in the mechanism of blood clotting.

By spinning blood in a centrifuge, the blood cells can be sedimented. The blood plasma with the blood cells removed is a slightly viscous, yellowish liquid that contains large amounts of dissolved protein. One of the proteins, *fibrinogen,* participates in the process of blood clotting and forms thin fibers called *fibrin*. The plasma from which the fibrinogen has been removed by precipitation is called *blood serum*.

The mechanism of blood clotting serves the purpose of preventing blood loss in case of injury. This mechanism can, on the other hand, cause undesirable or even dangerous blood clots if foreign bodies, like catheters or extracorporeal devices, are introduced into the bloodstream. Blood clotting can be inhibited by the injection of *heparin,* a natural anticoagulant extracted from the liver and lungs of cattle.

Many diseases cause characteristic variations in the composition of blood. These variations can be a characteristic change in the number, size, or shape of certain blood cells (in anemia, for instance, the RBC count is reduced). Other diseases cause changes in the chemical composition of the blood serum (or some other body fluid, like the urine). In diabetes mellitus, for instance, the glucose concentration in the blood (and the urine) is characteristically elevated. A count of the blood cells, an inspection of their size and shape, or a chemical analysis of the blood serum can, therefore, provide important information for the diagnosis of such diseases. Similarly, other body fluids, smears, and small samples of live tissue, obtained by a *biopsy,* are studied through the techniques of *bacteriology, serology,* and *histology* to obtain clues for the diagnosis of diseases.

The purpose of *bacteriological tests* is to determine the type of bacteria that have invaded the body, in order to diagnose a disease and prescribe the proper treatment. For such a test, a sample containing the bacteria (e.g., a smear from a strep throat) is innoculated to the surface of various growth media (nutrients) in test tubes or flat petri dishes. These cultures are then incubated at body temperature to accelerate the growth of the bacteria. When the bacteria have grown into colonies, they can be identified by the color and shape of the colony, by their preference for certain growth media, or by a microscopic inspection, which may make use of the fact that certain stains show a selectivity for certain bacteria groups.

Serological tests serve the same purpose as bacteriological tests but are based on the fact that the organism, when invaded by an infectious disease, develops antibodies in the blood, which defend the body against the infection. These antibodies are selective to certain strains of organisms, and their action can be observed in vitro by various methods. In some methods, for example, agglutination (collecting in clumps) becomes visible under a microscope when a test serum containing the antigen of the organism is added. Because the tests are based not on the organism itself but on the antigen developed by the organism, serological tests are not limited to bacteria but can be used for virus infections and infections by other microorganisms.

Histological tests involve the microscopical study of tissue samples, which are sliced into very thin sections by means of a precision slicer called a *microtome*. The tissue slices are often stained with certain chemicals to enhance the features of interest.

Blood counts and chemical blood tests are often ordered routinely on admission of a patient to a hospital and may be repeated daily to monitor the process of an illness. These tests, therefore, must be performed in very large numbers, even in the smaller hospital. The physician in private practice often has samples analyzed by commercial laboratories specializing in this service. Automated methods of performing the tests have found widespread acceptance, and special instruments have been developed for this purpose.

13.2. TESTS ON BLOOD CELLS

When whole blood is centrifuged, the blood cells sediment and form a packed column at the bottom of the test tube. Most of this column consists of the red blood cells, with the other cells forming a thin, *buffy layer* on top of the red cells. The volume of the packed red cells is called the *hematocrit*. It is expressed as a percentage of the total blood volume. If the number of (red) blood cells per cubic millimeter of blood is known, this number and the hematocrit can be used to calculate the *mean cell volume* (MCV). As stated above, the active component in the red blood cells is the hemoglobin, the concentration of which is expressed in grams/100 ml. From the hemoglobin, the hematocrit and the blood cell count, the *mean cell hemoglobin* (MCH) (in *picograms*) and the *mean cell hemoglobin concentration* (MCHC) (in percent) can be calculated.

The hematocrit can be determined by aspirating a blood sample into a capillary tube and closing one end of the tube with a plastic sealing material. The tube is then spun for 3 to 5 minutes in a special high-speed centrifuge to separate the blood cells from the plasma. Because the capillary tube has a uniform diameter, the blood and cell volumes can be compared by measuring the lengths of the columns. This is usually done with a simple nomogram, as shown in Figure 13.1. When lined up with the length of the blood column the nomogram allows the direct reading of the hematocrit.

The red blood cells have a much higher electrical resistivity than the blood plasma in which they are suspended, and so the resistivity of the blood shows a high correlation with the hematocrit. This factor provides an alternative method of determining the hematocrit that is obviously more adaptable to automation than the centrifugal sedimentation method.

The *hemoglobin concentration* can be determined by lysing the red blood cells (destroying their membranes) to release the hemoglobin and chemically converting the hemoglobin into another colored compound (acid hematin or cyanmethemoglobin). Unlike that of the hemoglobin, the color concentration of these components does not depend on the oxygenation of the blood. Following the reaction, the concentration of the new component can be determined by colorimetry, as described in Section 13.3.

Figure 13.1. Hematocrit determination: (a) blood sample drawn in capillary and sealed with plastic putty; (b) capillary after centrifuging, placed on nomogram to read hematocrit (reading 43%).

Figure 13.2. Blood cell counter, conductivity (Coulter) method. (Explanation in text.)

Manual blood cell counts are performed by using a microscope. Here the blood is first diluted 1:100 or 1:200 for counting red blood cells (RBC) and 1:10 or 1:20 for white blood cell count (WBC). For counting WBC, a diluent is used that dissolves the RBCs, whereas for counting RBCs, an isotonic diluent preserves these cells. The diluted blood is then brought into a counting chamber 0.1 mm deep, which is divided by marking lines into a number of squares. When magnified about 500 times, the cells in a certain number of squares can be counted. This rather time-consuming method is still used quite frequently when a *differential count* is required for which the WBCs are counted, according to their distribution, into a number of different subgroups. An automated differential blood cell analyzer uses differential staining methods to discriminate between the various types of white blood cells.

Today simple RBC and WBC counts are normally performed by automatic or semiautomatic blood cell counters. The most commonly used devices of this kind are based on the conductivity (Coulter) method, which makes use of the fact that blood cells have a much lower electrical conductivity than the solution in which they are suspended. Such a counter (Figure 13.2) contains a beaker with the diluted blood into which a closed glass tube with a very small orifice (1) is placed. The conductance between the solution in the glass tube and the solution in the beaker is measured with two electrodes (2). This conductance is mainly determined by the diameter of the orifice, in which the current density reaches its maximum. The glass tube is connected to a suction pump through a U-tube filled with mercury (5). The negative pressure generated by the pump causes a flow of the solution from the beaker through the orifice into the glass tube. Each time a blood cell is swept through the orifice, it temporarily blocks part of the electrical current path and causes a drop in the conductance measured between the electrodes (2). The result is a pulse at the output of the conductance meter, the amplitude of which is proportional to the volume of the cell. A threshold circuit lets only those pulses pass that exceed a certain amplitude. The pulses that pass this circuit are fed to a pulse counter through a pulse gate. The gate opens when the mercury column reaches a first contact (3) and closes when it reaches the second contact (4), thus counting the number of cells contained in a given volume of the solution passing through the orifice. A count is completed in less than 20 seconds. With counts of up to 100,000, the result is statistically accurate. Great care must be taken, however, to keep the aperture from clogging. Counters based on this principle are available with varying degrees of automation. The most advanced device of this type (shown in Figure 13.3) accepts a new blood sample every 20 seconds, performs the dilutions automatically, and determines not only the WBC and RBC counts but also the hematocrit and the hemoglobin concentration. From these measurements, the mean cell volume, the mean cell

Figure 13.3. Coulter Counter® Model S. Sr. (Courtesy of Coulter Electronics Hialeah, FL.)

Figure 13.4. Blood cell counter, dark field method. (Explanation in text.)

hematocrit, and the mean cell hematocrit concentration are calculated and all results are printed out on a preprinted report form.

A second type of blood cell counter uses the principle of the dark-field microscope (Figure 13.4). The diluted blood flows through a thin cuvette (4). The cuvette is illuminated by a cone-shaped light beam obtained from a lamp (1) through a ring aperture (3) and an optical system (2). The cuvette is imaged on the cathode of a phototube (7) by means of a lens (5) and an aperture (6). Normally no light reaches the phototube until a blood cell passes through the cuvette and reflects a flash of light on the phototube.

13.3. CHEMICAL TESTS

Blood serum is a complex fluid that contains numerous substances in solution. The determination of the concentration of these substances is performed by specialized chemical techniques. Although there are usually several different methods by which any particular analysis can be performed, most tests used are based on a chemical color reaction followed by a colorimetric determination of the concentration. This principle makes use of the fact that many chemical compounds in solution appear colored, with the saturation of the color depending on the concentration of the compound. For instance, a solution that appears yellow when being held against a white background actually absorbs the blue component of the white light and lets only the remainder—namely, yellow light—through. The way in which this light absorption can be used to determine the concentration of the substance is shown in Figure 13.5.

In Figure 13.5(a) it is assumed that a solution of concentration C is placed in a cuvette with a length of the light path, L. Light of an appropriate color or wavelength is obtained from a lamp through filter F. The light that enters the cuvette has a certain intensity, I_0. With part of the light being absorbed in the solution, the light leaving the cuvette has a lower intensity I_1. One way of expressing this relation is to give the *transmittance, T,* of the solution in the cuvette as the percentage of light that is transmitted:

$$T = \frac{I_1}{I_0} \times 100\%$$

If a second cuvette with the same solution were brought into the light path behind the first cuvette, only a similar portion of the light entering this cuvette would be transmitted. The light intensity I_2 behind the second cuvette is

$$I_2 = TI_1$$

or

$$I_2 = T^2 I_0$$

Figure 13.5. Principle of colorimeter analysis.
(Explanation in text.)

The light transmitted through successive cuvettes decreases in the same manner (multiplicatively). For this reason, it is advantageous to express transmittance as a logarithmic measure (in the same way as expressing electronic gains and losses in decibels). This measure is the *absorbance* or optical *density, A.*

$$A = -\log \frac{I_1}{I_0}$$

or

$$A = \log \frac{1}{T}$$

The total absorbance of the two cuvettes in Figure 13.5(a) is, therefore, the sum of the individual absorbances.

The amount of the light absorbed depends only on the number of molecules of the absorbing substance that can interact with the light. If, instead of two cuvettes, each with path length L, one cuvette with path length $2L$, were used [Figure 13.5(b)], the absorbance would be the same. The absorbance is also the same if the cuvette has a path length L, but the concentration of the solution were doubled [Figure 13.5(c)]. This relation can be expressed by the equation:

$$A = aCL \qquad \text{(Beer's law)}$$

where L = path length of the cuvette

C = concentration of the absorbing substance

a = *absorbtivity,* a factor that depends on the absorbing substance and the optical wavelength at which the measurement is performed.

The absorbtivity can be obtained by measuring the absorption of a solution with known concentration, called a *standard.* If A_s is the absorption of the standard, A_u the absorption of an unknown solution, and C_s the concentration of the standard, then the concentration of the unknown is

$$C_u = C_s \frac{A_u}{A_s}$$

Corrections may have to be applied for light losses due to reflections at the cuvette or absorption by the solvent. Figure 13.6 shows the principle of a *colorimeter* or *filter-photometer* used for measuring transmittance and absorbance of solutions. A filter F selects a suitable wavelength range from the light of a lamp. This light falls on two photoelectric (selenium) cells: a reference cell C_R and a sample cell C_S. Without a sample, the output of both cells is the same. When a sample is placed in the light path for the sample cell, its output is reduced and the output of C_R has to be divided by a potentiometer P until a galvanometer (G) shows a balance. The potentiometer can be calibrated in transmittance or absorbance units over a range of 1 to 100 percent transmittance, corresponding to 2 to 0 absorbance units.

Figure 13.6. Colorimeter (filter-photometer).

Other colorimeters, instead of using the potentiometric method, use a meter calibrated directly in transmittance units (a linear scale) and in absorbance. Figure 13.7 shows such a device; the instrument allows measurement at different colors with a built-in filter wheel. If a standard with a known concentration of a certain substance is used as a reference, the scale can be calibrated directly in concentration units for this substance.

Figure 13.7. Unimeter—modern colorimeter system permits the physician to perform blood analysis in the office. The colorimeter with built-in incubator is at the far left, with a centrifuge by its side and packages with pre-measured reagent kits. Test values are read on exchangeable scales shown lying in front of the colorimeter. (Courtesy of Biodynamics/bmc, Indianapolis, IN.)

In order to use the colorimeter to determine the concentration of a substance in a sample, a suitable method for obtaining a colored derivative from the substance is necessary. Thus, a chemical reaction that is unique for the substance to be tested and that does not cause interference by other substances which may be present in the sample must be found. The reaction may require several steps of adding reagents and incubating the sample at elevated temperatures until the reaction is completed. Most reactions require that the protein first be removed from the plasma by adding a precipitating reagent and filtering the sample.

In most tests, an excess of the reagents is added and the incubation is continued until the *end point* of the reaction is reached (i.e., until all of the substance has been converted into its colored derivative). In *kinetic analysis* methods, the transmittance is measured several times at fixed time intervals while the chemical reaction continues. The concentration of the substance of interest then can be calculated from the rate of change of the absorbance.

Table 13.1. THE MOST COMMONLY USED CHEMICAL BLOOD TESTS

	Test	*Normal Ranges*	*Unit*
1.	Blood urea nitrogen (BUN)	8–16	mg N/100 ml
2.	Glucose	70–90	mg/100 ml
3.	Phosphate (inorganic)	3–4.5	mg/100 ml
4.	Sodium	135–145	mEq/liter
5.	Potassium	3.5–5	mEq/liter
6.	Chloride	95–105	mEq/liter
7.	CO_2 (total)	24–32	mEq/liter
8.	Calcium	9–11.5	mg/100 ml
9.	Creatinine	0.6–1.1	mg/100 ml
10.	Uric acid	3–6	mg/100 ml
11.	Protein (total)	6–8	g/100 ml
12.	Albumin	4–6	g/100 ml
13.	Cholesterol	160–200	mg/100 ml
14.	Bilirubin (total)	0.2–1	mg/100 ml

The most commonly required tests for blood samples are listed in Table 13.1. This table also shows the units in which the test results are expressed* and the normal range of concentration for each test. Most of these tests can be performed by color reaction even though, in most cases, several different methods have been described that can often be used alternately.

For the measurement of sodium and potassium, however, a different property is utilized, one that causes a normally colorless flame to appear

*Depending on the test, the concentration is expressed in either grams or milligrams per 100 milliliters (0.1 liter) or in milliequivalents per liter, which is obtained by dividing the concentration in milligrams per liter by the molecular weight of the substance.

Figure 13.8. Flame photometer.

yellow (sodium) or violet (potassium) when their solutions are aspirated into the flame. This characteristic is used in the *flame photometer* (Figure 13.8) to measure the sodium or potassium concentration in samples. The sample is aspirated into a gas flame that burns in a chimney. As a reference, a known amount of a lithium salt is added to the sample, thus causing a red flame. Filters are used to separate the red light produced by the lithium from the yellow or violet light emitted by the sodium or potassium. As in the colorimeter, the output from the sample cell C_S is compared with a fraction of the output from a reference cell C_R. The balance potentiometer P is calibrated directly in units of sodium or potassium concentration.

For the determination of chlorides, a special instrument (*chloridimeter*) is sometimes used that is based on an electrochemical (*coulometric*) method. For this test, the chloride is converted into silver chloride with the help of an electrode made of silver wire. By an electroplating process with a constant current, the silver chloride is percipitated.

Figure 13.9. Spectrophotometer.

When all the chloride has been used up, the potential across the cell changes abruptly and the change is used to stop an electric timer, which is calibrated directly in chloride concentration.

The simple colorimeter (or filter-photometer) shown in Figures 13.6 and 13.7 has a sophisticated relative, the *spectrophotometer* shown in Figure 13.9. In this device the simple selection filter of the colorimeter is replaced by a *monochromator*. A monochromator uses a diffraction grating G (or a prism) to disperse light from a lamp that falls through an entrance slit S_1 into its spectral components. An exit slit S_2 selects a narrow band of the spectrum, which is used to measure the absorption of a sample in cuvette C. The narrower the exit slit, the narrower the bandwidth of the light, but also the smaller its intensity. A sensitive photodetector D (often a photomultiplier) is therefore required, together with an amplifier and a meter I, which is calibrated in units of transmittance or absorbance. The wavelength of the light can be changed by rotating the grating. A mirror M folds the light path to reduce the size of the instrument.

The spectrophotometer allows the determination of the absorption of samples at various wavelengths. The light output of the lamp, however, as well as the sensitivity of the photodetector and the light absorption of the cuvette and solvent, varies when the wavelength is changed. This situation requires that, for each wavelength setting, the density reading be set to zero, with the sample being replaced by a blank cuvette, usually filled with the same solvent as used for the sample. In *double-beam* spectrophotometers this procedure is done automatically by switching the beam between a sample light path and a reference light path, generally with a mechanical shutter or rotating mirror. By using a computing circuit, the readings from both paths are compared and only the ratio of the absorbances (or the difference of the densities) is indicated.

Certain chemicals, when illuminated by light with a short wavelength in the ultraviolet (UV) range, emit light with a longer wavelength. This phenomenon is called *fluorescence.* Fluorescence can be used to determine the concentration of such chemicals using a *fluorometer,* which, like the photometer, can be either a *filter-fluorometer* or a *spectrofluorometer,* depending on whether filters or monochromators are used to select the excitation and emission wavelengths.

13.4. AUTOMATION OF CHEMICAL TESTS

Even though most chemical tests basically consist of simple steps like pipetting, diluting, and incubating, they are rather time-consuming and require skilled and conscientious technicians if errors are to be avoided. Attempts to replace the technicians by an automatic device, however, were

Figure 13.10. Continuous flow analyzer (simplified).

not very successful at first. The first automatic analyzer that found wide acceptance and that is still used at most hospitals in the *Autoanalyzer,* the principle of which is shown in Figure 13.10.

The basic method used in the Autoanalyzer departs in several respects from that of standard manual methods. The mixing, reaction, and colorimetric determination take place, not in an individual test tube for each sample but sequentially in a continuous stream. The sampler feeds the samples into the analyzer in time sequence. A proportioning pump, which is basically a simple peristaltic pump working simultaneously on a number of tubes with certain ratios of diameters, is used to meter the sample and the reagent. Mixing is achieved by injecting air bubbles. The mixture is incubated while flowing through heated coils. The air bubbles are removed, and the solution finally flows through the cuvette of a colorimeter or is aspirated into the flame of a flame photometer. An electronic ratio recorder compares the output of the reference and sample photocells. The recording shows the individual samples as peaks of a continuous transmittance or absorbance recording. The samples of a "run" are preceded by a number of standards that cover the useful concentration range of the test. The concentration of the samples is determined from the recording by comparing the peaks of the samples with the peaks of the standards. In this way the effects of errors (e.g., incomplete reaction in the incubator) are eliminated because they affect standards and samples in the same way.

Suitable adaptations of almost all standard tests have been developed for the Autoanalyzer system. The removal of protein from the plasma is achieved in the continuous-flow method with a *dialyzer* (not shown in Figure 13.10), which consists of two flow channels separated by a cellophane membrane that is impermeable to the large protein molecules, but not to the smaller molecules. The smallest model of the Autoanalyzer performs a single test at a rate up to 120 samples per hour. Large later models (one of which is shown in Figure 13.11) perform up to 12 different tests on each of 90 samples per hour. The results of these tests are directly provided in the form of a "chemical profile," drawn by a recorder on a preprinted chart. By the use of additional equipment, the results may also be provided as a digital output signal for recording on a storage medium, like punch cards or paper tape, or may be usable for direct computer processing.

A major problem with the continuous-flow process is the "carryover" that can occur when a sample with an excessively high concentration is followed by a sample with normal or low concentration. Methods of "carryover" correction are available.

Although the continuous-flow analyzer was the first to find wide acceptance, numerous other analyzers that use discrete samples are now available. Some of these analyzers perform all tests in test tubes mounted on a carousel-type carrier, or a chain belt, with the test tubes being rinsed after the completion of the analysis.

Figure 13.11. Technicon Autoanalyzer SMA II System. (Technicon **Autoanalyzer** and SMA II are registered trademarks of Technicon Instruments, Tarrytown, NY by permission.)

Figure 13.12. Automatic Clinical Analyzer. (a) The unit itself-test packs are entered in the U-shaped tray at the left, while the packages with large numbers contain the diluents. (b) Test pack containing liquid and solid reagents in the arrow-shaped compartments. (Courtesy of E.I. Du Pont de Nemours and Company Inc. Automatic Clinical Analysis Division, Wilmington, DE.)

All automatic analyzers of this type use syringe-type pumps to dispense the sample and to add the reagents. After incubation the sample is aspirated into a colorimeter cuvette, where its absorbance is measured.

Discrete sample analyzers as well as continuous-flow analyzers require that all reagents be available in the proper dilution. One automatic analyzer uses a principle that always assures the correct quantities. In this analyzer (Figure 13.12) all reagents for a given test are sealed in premeasured quantities in dry form in compartments of a plastic pouch. The package also carries a machine-readable code which identifies the particular test. The patient sample in a carrier and pouchpacks for the tests to be run on that sample are inserted together. The analyzer identifies the test from the machine-readable code and injects the necessary amount of sample together with a suitable diluent into each test pack. The reagents are released by breaking the walls of their compartments, and are mixed with sample and diluent. After incubation the absorbance of the solution is measured directly in the transparent plastic pouch using a special colorimeter which forms the pouch into an optical cell with a defined path length.

Another type of analyzer, illustrated in Figure 13.13, processes a number of samples simultaneously by means of a fast-spinning disk which

Figure 13.13. Rotochem II Parallel Fast Analyzer (Courtesy of American Instrument Company, Silver Springs, MD.)

contains reagent and sample chambers and cuvettes. The transfer of sample and reagent to the cuvette and the mixing of both is accomplished by centrifugal force. The absorbance of the solutions is measured by one colorimeter which measures all samples in sequence while the rotation of the disk carries them through the colorimeter lightbeam. This arrangement makes the centrifugal analyzer especially useful for the kinetic analysis methods mentioned in Section 13.3.

A basic problem with automatic analyzers is the positive identification of samples. In early devices the small sample cups were identified only by their position in the sample tray and the technician loading the samples had to prepare a "load list" for this purpose. Machine-readable methods of sample identification are now available and greatly reduce the likelihood of mixups.

Many modern automatic analyzers utilize electronic data processing by built-in mini- or microcomputers to calibrate the system. They also convert absorbance measurements into concentration values and print out the results of the tests. The role of the computer in the clinical chemistry laboratory is described in some detail in Chapter 15.

14

X-Ray
and Radioisotope
Instrumentation

In 1895 Conrad Röntgen, a German physicist, discovered a previously unknown type of radiation while experimenting with gas-discharge tubes. He found that this type of radiation could actually penetrate opaque objects and provide an image of their inner structures. Because of these mysterious properties, he called his discovery *X rays*. In many countries X rays are referred to as *Rontgen rays* in honor of their discoverer, who received a Nobel prize in 1901 for his work.

Soon after the discovery of X rays, their importance as a tool for medical diagnosis was recognized. Later it was found that X rays could also be used for therapeutic purposes. Both applications of X rays are the domain of the medical specialty known as *radiology*. X-ray machines were the first widely used electrical instruments in medicine. In fact, hospitals still spend more money for the purchase of X-ray equipment than for any other type of medical instrumentation.

One year after Röntgen's discovery, Henry Becquerel, the French physicist, found a similar type of radiation emanating from samples of uranium ore. Two of his students, Pierre and Marie Curie, traced this radiation to a previously unknown element in the ore, to which they gave the name *radium*, from the Latin word *radius*, the ray. The process by which radium and certain other elements emit radiation is called *radioactive decay,* whereas the property of an element to emit radiation is called *radioactivity.*

14.1 BASIC DEFINITIONS

One of the characteristics of the radiation originating in the X-ray tube or in radioactive materials is that it ionizes the gases through which it travels. Therefore, the term *ionizing radiation* is used to differentiate between this type of radiation and other, *nonionizing* types of radiation, such as radio waves, light, and infrared radiation.

Many man-made radioisotopes are now available along with the X-ray tube and radium as sources of radiation. The ability of this radiation to penetrate materials that are opaque to visible light is utilized in numerous techniques in medical diagnosis and research. The ionizing effects of radiation are also used for the treatment of certain diseases, such as cancer. The use of radiation for treatment of diseases has become an important subfield of medicine, called *radiation therapy,* which is discussed briefly in Section 14.5.

Another related topic is computerized axial tomography. While this technique involves X rays, its principles are primarily computer-related. For this reason it is discussed in detail in Chapter 15 as a computer application.

There are three different types of radiation, each with its own distinct properties. More than one type of radiation can emanate from a given sample of radioactive material. The properties of the three types of radiation are defined below.

Alpha rays are positively-charged particles that consist of helium nuclei and that travel at the moderate velocity of 5 to 7 percent of the velocity of light. They have a very small penetration depth, which in air is only about 2 in.

Beta rays are negatively-charged electrons. Their velocity can vary over a wide range and can almost reach the velocity of light. Their ability to penetrate the surrounding medium depends on their velocity, but generally it is not very great. Both alpha and beta rays, when traveling through a gaseous atmosphere, interact with the gas molecules, thereby causing ionizing of the gas.

Gamma rays and *X rays* are both electromagnetic waves that have a much shorter wavelength than radio waves or visible light. Their wavelengths can vary between approximately 10^{-6} and 10^{-10} cm, corresponding to a

Figure 14.1. Part of the electromagnetic spectrum showing the location of the X rays and gamma rays.

frequency range of between 10^{10} and 10^{14} MHz, with the X rays at the lower and the gamma rays at the higher end of this range. The ability of these rays to penetrate matter depends on their wavelengths, but it is much greater than that of the alpha and beta rays. Gamma rays do not interact with gases directly but can cause ionization of the gas molecules via photoelectrons released when the rays interact with solid matter.

Gamma rays are usually not characterized by their frequency but by their energy, which is proportional to the frequency. This relationship is expressed in the Planck equation:

$$E = hf$$

where E = energy, ergs

h = Planck's constant = 6.624×10^{-27} erg sec

f = frequency, hertz

The energy of radiation is usually expressed in electron volts (eV), with 1 eV = 1.602×10^{-12} erg.

Figure 14.1 shows the position of gamma rays and X rays within the spectrum of electromagnetic waves.

14.1.1. Generation of Ionizing Radiation

X rays are generated when fast-moving electrons are suddenly decelerated by impinging on a target. An X-ray tube is basically a high-vacuum diode with a heated cathode located opposite a target anode (Figure 14.2). This diode is operated in the saturated mode with a fairly low cathode temperature so that the current through the tube does not depend on the applied anode voltage.

The intensity of X rays depends on the current through the tube. This current can be varied by varying the heater current, which in turn controls the cathode temperature. The wavelength of the X rays depends on the target material and the velocity of the electrons hitting the target. It can be varied by varying the target voltage of the tube. X-ray equipment for diag-

Figure 14.2. X-ray tube, principle of operation.

nostic purposes uses target voltages in the range of 30 to 100 kV, while the current is in the range of several hundred milliamperes. These voltages are obtained from high-voltage transformers that are often mounted in oil-filled tanks to provide electrical insulation. When ac voltage is used, the X-ray tube conducts only during one half-wave and acts as its own rectifier. Otherwise high-voltage diodes (often in voltage-doubler or multiplier configurations) are used as rectifiers. For therapeutic X-ray equipment, where even higher radiation energies are required, linear or circular particle accelerators have been used to obtain electrons with sufficiently high energy. When the electrons strike the target, only a small part of their energy is converted into X rays; most of it is dissipated as heat. The target, therefore, is usually made of tungsten, which has a high melting point. It may also be water- or air-cooled, or it may be in the form of a motor-driven rotating cone to improve the dissipation of heat. The electron beam is concentrated to form a small spot on the target. The X rays emerge in all directions from this spot, which therefore can be considered a point source for the radiation.

Radioactive decay is the other source of nuclear radiation, but only a very small number of chemical elements exhibit natural radioactivity. Artificial radioactivity can be induced in other elements by exposing them to neutrons generated with a cyclotron or in an atomic reactor. By introducing an extraneous neutron into the nucleus of the atom, an unstable form of the element is generated that is chemically equivalent to the original form (*isotope*). The unstable atom disintegrates after some time, often through several intermediate forms, until it has assumed the form of another, stable element. At the moment of the disintegration, radiation is emitted, the type and energy of which are characteristic of a particular decay step in the process. The time after which half of the original number of radioisotope atoms have decayed is called the *half-life*. Each radioisotope has a characteristic half-life that can be between a few seconds and thousands of years.

Radioisotopes are chemically identical to their mother element. Chemical compounds in which a radioisotope has been substituted for its mother element are thus treated by the body exactly like the nonradioactive form. With the help of the emitted radiation, however, the path of the substance can be traced and its concentration in various parts of the organism determined. If this procedure is to be done in vivo, the isotope must emit gamma radiation that penetrates the surrounding tissue and that can be measured with an extracorporeal detector. When radioactive material is introduced into the human body for diagnostic purposes, great care must be taken to ensure that the radiation dose that the body receives is at a safe level. For reasons explained below, it is desirable that the radioactivity be as great as possible during the actual measurement. For safety reasons, however, the activity should be reduced as fast as possible as soon as the measurement is completed. In certain measurements, the radioactive material is excreted from the body at a rapid rate and the activity in the body decreases quickly. In most measurements, this "biological decay" of the introduced radioactivity occurs much too slowly. In order to remove the source of radiation after the measurement, isotopes with a short half-life must be used. However, there is a dearth of gamma-emitting isotopes of elements naturally occurring in biological substances that have a half-life of suitable length. The radioisotopes most frequently used for medical purposes are listed in Table 14.1. Iodine 131 is the only gamma-emitting isotope of an element that occurs in substantial quantities in the body. H-3 (tritium) and carbon 14 are beta emitters; hence their concentration in biological samples can be measured only in vitro because the radiation does not penetrate the surrounding tissue.

Table 14.1. RADIOISOTOPES

Isotope	Radiation	Half-Life
^{3}H	Beta	12.3 days
^{14}C	Beta	5570 years
^{51}Cr	Gamma	27.8 days
^{99m}Tc	Gamma	6 hours
^{131}I	Gamma	8.07 days
^{198}Au	Gamma	2.7 days

14.1.2. Detection of Radiation

Pierre and Marie Curie discovered that radioactivity can be detected by three different physical effects: (1) the activation it causes in photographic emulsions, (2) the ionization of gases, and (3) the light flashes the radiation causes when striking certain minerals. Most techniques used today are still based on the same principles. Photographic films are the most commonly used method of visualizing the distribution of X rays for diagnostic purposes. For the visualization of radioisotope concentrations in biological samples, a photographic method called *autoradiography* is used. In this technique thin slices of tissue are laid on a photographic plate and left in contact (in a freezer) for extended time periods, sometimes for months After processing, the film shows an image of the distribution of the isotope in the tissue.

When the gas ions caused by radiation are subjected to the forces of an electric field between two charged capacitor plates, they move toward these plates and cause a current flow. Above a certain voltage, all ion pairs generated reach the plates, and further increases of the voltage cause no additional increase of the current (saturation). The current flow (normally very small) can be used to measure the intensity of the radiation. This device is called an *ionization chamber*.

The number of ion pairs generated depends on the type of radiation. The number is greatest for alpha and lowest for gamma radiation. If the voltage is increased beyond a certain value, the ions are accelerated enough to ionize additional gas molecules (gas amplification, *proportional counter*). If the voltage is increased even further, a point can be reached at which any initial ion pair causes complete ionization of the tube (*Geiger counter*). Further increase of the voltage, therefore, does not increase the current (plateau). The ion generation, however, is self-sustaining and must be terminated, usually by reducing the voltage briefly. The Geiger counter cannot discriminate between the different types of radiation, but it has the advantage of providing large output pulses.

The physical configuration of the various detectors based on the principle of gas ionization can actually be the same. The mode of operation, as shown in Figure 14.3, is determined solely by the operating voltage applied to the device.

Another type of device related to the Geiger counter is the *spark chamber*, which consists of an array of opposed electrodes that have a voltage applied between them that by itself is not high enough to cause a discharge. The ionization caused by the passage of radiation, however, triggers a spark that momentarily discharges the circuits of the two electrodes between which it occurs. The spark can be detected either by photographic methods or by the sound waves that it produces.

Certain metal salts (e.g., zinc sulfide) show fluorescence when irradiated with X rays or radiation from radioisotopes. When observed under a microscope under favorable circumstances, the minute light flashes (scintillations) caused by individual radiation events can actually be seen. In earlier days these scintillations were used to measure radioactivity by simply counting them. Both scintillation and fluorescence, however, are light events of such low intensity that they can be seen only with eyes that are well adapted to the dark. Only through use of electronic devices for the detection and visualization of low-level light has their usefulness been increased to such an extent that today most isotope instrumentation is based on this principle.

Figure 14.3. Detection of nuclear radiation by the ionization of gas between two capacitor plates. The curve shows the logarithm of the current pulse amplitude as a function of the applied voltage for a constant rate of nuclear disintegrations generating either beta or gamma radiation.

14.2. INSTRUMENTATION FOR DIAGNOSTIC X RAYS

The use of X rays as a diagnostic tool is based on the fact that various components of the body have different densities for the rays. When X rays from a point source penetrate a body section, the internal structure of the body absorbs varying amounts of the radiation. The radiation that leaves the body, therefore, has a spatial intensity variation that is an image of the internal structure of the body. When, as shown in Figure 14.4, this intensity distribution is visualized by a suitable device, a shadow image is generated that corresponds to the X-ray density of the organs in the body section.

Figure 14.4. Use of X rays to visualize the inner structure of the body.

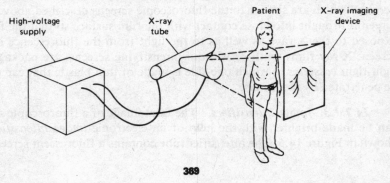

Bones and foreign bodies, especially metallic ones, and air-filled cavities show up well on these images because they have a much higher or a much lower density than the surrounding tissue. Most body organs, however, differ very little in density and do not show up well on the X-ray image, unless one of the special techniques described later is used.

14.2.1. Visualization of X Rays

X rays normally cannot be detected directly by the human senses; thus, indirect methods of visualization must be used to give an image of the intensity distribution of X rays that have passed through the body of a patient. Three different techniques are in common use.

14.2.1.1. Fluoroscopy. Rontgen actually discovered X rays when he noticed that certain metal salts glowed in the dark when struck by the radiation. The brightness of this *fluorescence* is a function of the radiation intensity, and cardboard pieces coated with such metal salts were first used exclusively to visualize X-ray images. Early *fluoroscopes* were simply cardboard funnels, open at the narrow end for the eyes of the observer, while the wide end was closed with a thin cardboard piece that had been coated on the inside with a layer of fluorescent metal salt. The fluoroscopic image obtained in this way is rather faint, however, and the X-ray intensity necessary to obtain a reasonably bright image is of such a magnitude that it can be harmful to both the patient and the observer. If the radiation intensity is reduced to a safer level, the fluoroscopic image becomes so faint that it must be observed in a completely darkened room and after the eyes of the observer have adapted to the dark for 10 to 20 minutes. Because of these inconveniences, direct fluoroscopy now has only limited use.

14.2.1.2. X-ray films. Although X rays have a much shorter wavelength than visible light, they react with photographic emulsions in a similar fashion. After processing in a developing solution, therefore, a film that has been exposed to X rays shows an image of the X-ray intensity. The sensitivity of this effect can be increased by the use of *intensifying screens,* which are similar to the fluoroscopic screens described above. The screen is brought into close contact with the film surface so that the film is exposed to the X rays as well as to the light from the fluorescence of the screen. X-ray films, with or without intensifying screens, are packaged in light-tight *cassettes* in which one side is made of thin plastic that can easily be penetrated by the X rays.

14.2.1.3. Image intensifiers. The faint image of a fluoroscopic screen can be made brighter with the help of an electronic *image intensifier,* as shown in Figure 14.5. The intensifier tube contains a fluorescent screen, the

Cine- or
video camera

Movable mirror, shown in
position for visual observation

Output
screen

Observer

Adjustable mirror

Image intensifier
tube

Fluorescent screen
backed by photo cathode

Position of
x-ray source

Figure 14.5. X-ray image intensifier for visual observation and
recording of the picture with a cine (movie) camera or with a video
tape recorder—diagram simplified.

surface of which is coated with a suitable material to act as a photocathode.
The electron image thus obtained is projected onto a phosphor screen at the
other end of the tube by means of an electrostatic lens system. The resulting
brightness gain is due to the acceleration of the electrons in the lens system
and the fact that the output image is smaller than the primary fluorescent
image. The gain can reach an overall value of several hundred, and not
only allows the X-ray intensity to be decreased but makes it possible to
observe the image in a normally illuminated room. The intensifying tube,
however, is rather heavy and requires a special suspension. For chest or
pelvic examinations with the patient in a supine position, the screen on
which the intensified image appears is high above the patient and requires
a system of lenses and mirrors to present the image to the radiologist, who
normally stands right next to the patient. For this reason, a TV camera is
now used frequently to pick up the intensified image, which can then be

observed on conveniently placed TV monitors. This TV picture can also be recorded on a TV tape recorder. Similarly, a movie camera can be used to record directly the intensified X-ray image during an examination.

14.2.2. X-ray Machines

In order to obtain an X-ray image from a certain part of the body, the region to be examined must be positioned between the X-ray tube and the imaging device, as shown in Figure 14.4 for a chest X ray. Similar to a light that throws the shadow of an object on a wall, the X-ray tube projects the "shadow" of the structures inside the body on the imaging device. In order for the X-ray image to be a sharp and well-defined replica of these structures, the part of the body being X rayed must be as close as possible to the imaging device. The X-ray tube, on the other hand, should be as far away as possible.

With mobile X-ray machines, such as the one shown in Figure 14.6(a), the cassette with the X-ray film is usually placed directly beneath the patient. The X-ray tube is mounted on an arm and can be adjusted to the desired height. "Aiming" of the tube is simplified by a small light that projects the shadow of cross hairs along the axis of the X-ray beam. Mechanical shutters can be adjusted to limit the size of the beam to the area over which an X ray is to be taken.

In stationary X-ray machines the support arm for the X-ray tube is mounted on the wall or ceiling of the examination room in such a way that its height can be adjusted and the direction of the beam can be changed. For chest X rays, a holder for the film cassette is mounted adjustably on a wall of the room. For most other X rays, the cassette is inserted in the top of an adjustable table while the X-ray tube is placed above the patient, who lies on the table in a suitable position. With image intensifiers, however, the tube is normally below the table while the intensifier is positioned above the patient. In some X-ray machines the X-ray tube and image intensifier are mounted at either end of a C-shaped structure in such a way that they face each other. Figure 14.6(b) shows this arrangement in a mobile X-ray machine.

The high voltage for the operation of the X-ray tube is provided from a transformer, often mounted in an oil-filled enclosure, which is connected to the tube housing by a pair of heavy cables. The control panel of an X-ray machine normally provides for three different controls. The tube voltage, expressed in kilovolts-peak (kVP), determines the hardness or penetration power of the X-ray beam. The beam current, expressed in milliamperes, determines the intensity of the X-ray beam. The third control simply determines the time (expressed in seconds or fractions of a second) that the beam is turned on for X-ray photos. Battery-powered mobile X-ray machines,

(a)

Figure 14.6. (a) Mobile X-ray machine. (Courtesy of General Electric Company, Medical Systems Division, Milwaukee, WI.) (b) Mobile X-ray unit (with image intensifier and television monitor). The box below the video monitor is a video disc recorder which permits the recording and playback of X-ray images. (Courtesy of Picker Corporation, Cleveland, OH.)

(b)

however, may not have a time adjustment. The control settings necessary to obtain an X-ray photo of a given part of the body are usually determined from tables, but they may have to be corrected for obese or bony patients.

14.3.   SPECIAL TECHNIQUES

The previous section described the general principle of obtaining X-ray images, but often special techniques must be used to obtain usable images from certain body structures.

14.3.1. Grids

As mentioned before, some of the X rays entering the body of a patient are actually scattered and no longer travel in a straight line. If the body section examined is very thick and if the X-rayed area is large, the scattered X rays can cause a blurring of the X-ray image. This effect can be reduced by the use of a *grid* or a *Bucky diaphragm* (named after Gustav Bucky, its inventor). This device consists of a grid-like structure made of thin lead strips that is placed directly in front of the X-ray film. Like a venetian blind that lets sun rays through only when they strike parallel to the slats of the blind, the grid absorbs the scattered X rays while those traveling in straight lines can pass. In order to keep the grid from throwing its own shadow on the film, it may have to be moved by a motorized drive during the exposure of the film.

14.3.2. Contrast Media

While foreign bodies and bone absorb the X rays much more readily than soft tissue, the organs and soft tissue structures of the body show very little difference in X-ray absorption. In order to make their outlines visible on the X-ray image, it may be necessary to fill them with a *contrast medium* prior to taking the X-ray photo. In the *pneumoencephalogram,* the ventricles of the brain are made visible by filling them with air, which absorbs X rays less than the surrounding brain structures. Similarly, the structures of the gastro-intestinal tract can be made visible with the help of *barium sulfate,* given orally or as an enema, which has a higher X-ray absorption than the surrounding tissue. Other body structures and organs can also be visualized by filling them with suitable contrast media.

14.3.3. Angiography

In angiographic procedures, the outlines of blood vessels are made visible on the X-ray image by injecting a bolus of contrast medium directly into the bloodstream in the region to be investigated. Because the contrast medium is rapidly diluted in the blood circulation, an X-ray photo or a series of such photos must be taken immediately after the injection. This procedure is often performed automatically with the help of a power-operated syringe and an electrical cassette changer.

14.3.4. Cardiac Catheterization

Cardiac catheterization is a technique used primarily to diagnose valve deficiencies, septal defects, and other conditions of the heart characterized by hemodynamic changes. For this purpose, a special catheter is inserted through an artery, vein, or occasionally, directly through the chest wall into the heart. Under fluoroscopic control (with an image intensifier), the catheter is manipulated until its tip is in the desired position within the heart. By means of the catheter, intracardiac pressures can be measured in various parts of the heart that show characteristic changes if the heart valves are either narrowed or do not close completely. Septal defects can be detected by withdrawing blood samples from various heart chambers and measuring the oxygen concentration of the samples. Similarly, pumping efficiency can be assessed by measuring pressures within the ventricles at various points of the cardiac cycle. By injection of an indicator through the catheter the cardiac output can be measured. By the injection of a contrast medium through a suitably placed cardiac catheter (*selective angiography*), the vascular structures of the heart, including the coronary arteries (*coronary arteriography*), can be visualized. Catheterization in general is discussed in more detail in Chapter 6.

14.3.5. Three-Dimensional Visualization

A basic limitation of X-ray images is the fact that they are two-dimensional presentations of three-dimensional structures. One organ located in front of or behind another organ therefore frequently obscures details in the image of the other organ. In *stereoradiography* two X-ray photos are taken from different angles, which, when viewed in a stereo viewer, give a three-dimensional X-ray image. In *tomography* (from the Greek word *tomos*, meaning slice or section) the X-ray photo shows the structure of only a thin slice or section of the body. Several photos representing slices taken at different levels permit three-dimensional visualization. Tomographic X-ray photos can be obtained by moving the X-ray tube and the film cassette in opposite directions during the exposure of the film. This procedure causes the image of the structures above and below a certain plane to be blurred by the motion, whereas structures in this plane are imaged without distortion. Special tomography machines that scan body sections with a thin X-ray beam and that determine the X-ray absorption with a radiation detector have been developed. The image of the section is reconstructed from a large number of such scans with the help of a digital computer (see Chapter 15).

14.4. INSTRUMENTATION FOR THE MEDICAL USE OF RADIOISOTOPES

The radiation exposure during X-ray examinations occurs only during a very short time interval. In diagnostic methods involving the introduction of radioisotopes into the body, on the other hand, the exposure time is much longer, and therefore the radiation intensity must be kept much smaller in order not to exceed a safe radiation dose. For this reason, the techniques used for radiation detection and visualization with radioisotopes differ greatly from those used for X rays. Radioiosotope techniques are all based on actually counting the number of nuclear disintegrations that occur in a radioactive sample during a certain time interval or on counting the radiation quanta that emerge in a certain direction during this time. Because of the random nature of radioactive decay, any measurement performed in this way is afflicted with an unavoidable statistical error. When the same sample is measured repeatedly, the observed counts are not the same each time but follow a gaussian (normal) distribution. If the mean number of counts observed is n, the standard deviation of this distribution curve will be the square root of n. The concentration of radioactive material in an unknown sample can be determined by comparing the count with that of a known standard. A much greater accuracy is obtained if the number of disintegrations counted for the measurement is high. Higher counts can be obtained either by counting over a longer time interval or by increasing the activity of the sample, both ways being limited in medical applications in which the radioactivity is measured inside the body.

Almost all nuclear radiation detectors used for medical applications utilize the light flashes caused by radiation in a suitable medium. Such *scintillation detectors* (also called *scintillation counters*) for gamma rays use a crystal made from thallium-activated sodium iodide, which is in close contact with the active surface of a photomultiplier tube. Each radiation quantum passing the crystal causes an output pulse at the photomultiplier, the amplitude of which is proportional to the energy of the radiation. This property of the scintillation detector is used to reduce the *background*, (counts due to natural radioactivity) by means of a *pulse-height analyzer*. This is an electronic circuit that passes only pulses within a certain amplitude range. The limits of this circuit are adjusted in such a way that only pulses from the radioisotope used can pass, whereas pulses with other energy levels are rejected. Figure 14.7 shows two types of scintillation detectors used for the determination of the concentration of gamma-emitting radio-isotopes in medical applications. In the *well counter,* the scintillation crystal has a hole into which a test tube with the sample is inserted. In this configuration almost all radiation from the sample passes the crystal and is counted while a lead shield reduces the background count.

Figure 14.7. Scintillation detectors for gamma radiation. (a) Well counter for in vitro determinations; (b) Detector with lead collimator for in vivo determinations.

For activity determinations inside the body, a *collimated detector,* also shown in Figure 14.7, is used. In this detector, a lead shield around the scintillation crystal has holes arranged in such a way that only radiation from a source located at one particular point in front of the detector can reach the crystal. Only a very small part of the radiation coming from this source, however, passes the crystal. This detector, therefore, is much less sensitive than the well counter type.

Figure 14.8 shows the other building blocks that constitute a typical instrumentation system for medical radioisotope measurements. The pulses from the photomultiplier tube are amplified and shortened before they pass through the pulse-height analyzer. A timer and gate allow the pulses that occur in a set time interval to be counted by means of a *scaler* (decimal counter with readout). A *rate meter* (frequency meter) shows the rate of the pulses. Its reading can be used in aiming the detector toward the location of maximal radioactivity and to set the pulse-height analyzer to where it passes all pulses from the particular isotope used.

Figure 14.8. Block diagram of an instrumentation system for radioisotope procedures.

An automatic system for the measurement of radioactivity in "in vitro" samples is shown in Figure 14.9. The automatic sample changer arm (right) obtains test tubes containing the samples from a carousel and drops them into a counting well. The number of radioactive disintegrations measured over a preselected time interval is printed out on the printer shown on the left side. A background correction can be made if desired.

The principle of the collimated scintillation detector can be used to visualize the spatial distribution of radioisotopes in a body organ. In a *radioisotope scanner* the detector is slowly moved over the area to be examined in a zigzag fashion. Attached to the mounting arm of the detector is a recording mechanism that essentially produces a plot of the distribution of the radioactivity. In early scanners this recorder was a solenoid-operated printing mechanism that was connected to the output of a binary divider

Figure 14.9. Automatic system for measurement of radioactivity in in-vitro samples. (Courtesy of Ames Co., Division of Miles Laboratory Inc., Elkhart, IN.)

and that produced a dot after a certain number of detector pulses had occurred. The density of dots along a scanning line reflected the amount of radioactivity, and when observed from a distance, the completed scan resembled a halftone picture. Interesting medical details are often manifested in rather small differences of the activity, which are not readily visible in this simple kind of scan presentation.

Such variations can be made more easily visible by use of contrast-enhancement methods, which usually employ a photographic recorder. In this recorder, a flashing light leaves a dot on an X-ray film. While the light source is triggered from the output of a digital divider, its intensity is also modulated by a rate meter circuit and, therefore, also depends on the radioactivity. The rate-meter signal is manipulated by amplification and zero suppression so that a small range of variation in radioactivity occupies the entire available density range of the X-ray film. A similar contrast enhancement can be achieved with the mechanical dot printer by an attachment. This device moves a multicolored ink ribbon under the printer head in accordance with the output from a rate meter and thus reflects small changes in radioactivity by changes of the color of the dots. A basic problem with radioisotope scanners is that the detector must travel very slowly in order to give a high-enough count rate for detecting small variations in activity.

Figure 14.10. (a) Radioisotope camera. (b) Radioisotope camera in use. (Courtesy of Searle Radiographics Division of Searle Diagnostics, Inc., Des Plaines, IL.)

Therefore, the scan of a larger organ can take a long time. For this and other reasons, scanners of this type are being replaced by *radioisotope cameras,* a portable model of which is shown in Figure 14.10. Figure 14.10(a) is a close-up view of the machine and Figure 14.10(b) shows the machine in use in a hospital. Instead of the smaller moving crystal of the scanner, this type of device has one large, stationary scintillation crystal. The position of a light flash in this crystal is determined by means of a resistor matrix from the output signals of an array of several photomultiplier tubes mounted in contact with the rear surface of the crystal. The detection of a nuclear event at a certain point in the crystal causes a light flash at the corresponding location on the screen of a cathode-ray tube, which is photographed with a Polaroid camera or with a special camera that uses X-ray film. Computers or computer techniques are being increasingly utilized to store the signals from the radioisotope camera and to process images in order to enhance the details. Different types of collimators are used in this camera, depending on the geometry of the organ to be examined.

Scans of the thyroid gland can be obtained fairly easily with iodine 131. They show cysts as areas of reduced activity and possible malignant tumors as "hot nodules" with increased activity compared to the rest of the gland. Other organs are less-easily visualized and require the use of contrast enhancement in the scanner or camera and the administration of large doses of short-lived radioisotopes. The logistics of obtaining such isotopes can be simplified by use of technetium 99m, which, although it has a half-life of only 6 hours, is the decay product of molybdenum 99, which has a half-life of 66 hours. The molybdenum 99 is contained in a special device aptly called a "cow" because the technetium 99m is "milked" from it by *eluting* it—letting a buffer solution trickle through the device. These short-lived radioisotopes do not occur naturally in the body, and, unlike iodine, the organs of the body do not have a natural selectivity to these elements. Physical effects, such as variations in blood flow, account for differences in the isotope distribution that outline the organs. The organs that can be visualized include the lungs, brain, and liver.

Despite the substantial technical effort involved in obtaining X-ray pictures or radioisotope scans, a very experienced physician is required to interpret the results. Techniques to apply computer image processing to this field are also finding increasing applications, especially with cameras.

Hydrogen and carbon, the two elements that constitute the largest percentage of all organic substances, have useful radioisotopes that are only beta emitters. With these radioisotopes, many natural and synthetic substances, including chemicals, nutrients, and drugs, can be made radioactive and their pathways in the organism can be traced. The radioactivity of these isotopes, however, can be measured only in vitro, and special detectors have to be used. For older methods, the sample is placed in a *planchet,* a round, flat dish made of aluminum or stainless steel, in which the solvent is evaporated. In a *planchet counter* [shown in Figure 14.11(a)] the planchet becomes part of a Geiger–Müller tube. The thin layer in which the sample is spread and its close contact with the collection electrodes result in a fairly high counting efficiency for beta radiation. The counting cell is continuously purged by a flow of gas that removes ionization products.

For the soft beta radiation from tritium, a radioactive isotope of hydrogen, however, the sensitivity of the planchet counter is marginal and *liquid scintillation counters* are now normally used instead. In these devices the sample is placed in a small counting vial, where it is mixed with a solvent containing chemicals that scintillate when struck by beta rays. The vial is then placed in a detector [Figure 14.11(b)], in which it is positioned between two photomultiplier tubes. The light signal picked up is very weak,

Figure 14.11. Detectors for beta radiation: (a) Planchet or gas flow counter; (b) Liquid scintillation counter.

(a)

(b)

and erroneous counts from tube noise must be reduced by a coincidence circuit, which passes only pulses that occur at the outputs of both tubes simultaneously. The remainder of the circuit is similar to the gamma measurement system shown in Figure 14.7. The low activities often encountered in measurements of this type sometimes require very long counting times. This situation has lead to the development of systems that automatically change the samples and print out the results.

14.5. RADIATION THERAPY

The ionizing effect of X rays is utilized in the treatment of certain diseases, especially of certain tumors. In dermatology very soft X rays that do not have enough penetration power to enter more deeply into the body are used for treatment of the skin. They are called *Grenz rays* (from the German word *Grenze,* meaning border) because in the spectrum they are actually at the border between the normally used X rays and the ultraviolet range (see Figure 14.1). In the therapy of deep-seated tumors, on the other hand, very hard X rays that are generated with voltages much higher than those for diagnostic X rays are used. Sometimes *linear accelerators* or *betatrons* are used to obtain electrons with a very high voltage for this purpose. Changing the direction of entry of the beam in successive therapy sessions or rotating the patient during a session reduces the radiation damage to unafflicted body parts while concentrating the radiation at the site of the tumor.

15

The Computer
In
Biomedical Instrumentation

In the relatively short time since its development, the digital computer has had a pronounced effect on almost every aspect of modern-day life. Its presence is evident in the bank, the supermarket, and at the airline ticket counter. Computerized TV games, automobiles, and microwave ovens are fast becoming commonplace. Pocket-sized calculators with enormous computational capability are now obtainable within the budget of the average student. Even so, all evidence indicates that the full impact of computer technology is yet to be realized.

Historically, the digital computer has its roots in the work of four pioneers. The first of these was Charles Babbage, a mathematics professor at Cambridge University, who devised a machine in 1812 to perform certain simple computations and originated ideas that led to the stored-program concept of automatic computation. The second was George Boole, an English mathematician who developed the logic system used in digital circuit design. The next major contribution was that of Herman Hollerith, who originated the machine-readable punched card, which was first used in the 1890 census, and became the standard form of data entry for many years. The fourth pioneer was Howard Aiken of Harvard University, who developed the first automatic-sequence-controlled calculator, proposed in 1937 and completed in 1944. Although essentially a hugh mechanical calculator, Aiken's machine led to development of several early electronic computers in the late 1940s and early 1950s which used numerous banks of vacuum tubes with extensive power and air-conditioning requirements. In the late 1950s, transistorized computers began to appear, bringing with them smaller size, lower power requirements, fewer heat problems, and more important, greater reliability and lower cost. Integrated-circuit technology continued the trend toward smaller and less expensive computers through the 1960s and led to the low-cost calculators and microprocessors which made their appearance in the late 1960s and early 1970s.

The earliest computer applications in the medical field were those related to billing and the other business aspects of running a hospital, where techniques already in use in other parts of the business world could be adopted. In the latter 1950s and early 1960s, computerized ECG and EEG analysis, pulmonary function analysis, multiphasic screening, and automated clinical laboratories began to emerge, in some cases on an experimental basis. The introduction of lower-cost minicomputers and on-line, real-time (these terms are defined in Section 15.1) computer systems in the mid-1960s made many of these applications both economically and technically feasible for clinical use. The 1960s also brought about the first computerized patient-monitoring systems, initially using large computer systems, and later, incorporating minicomputers. Experimental work with totally computerized hospital systems dates back to the late 1950s and early 1960s. This idea, in which all information generated in the hospital is handled through an integrated computer system, has yet to find widespread application among hospitals, although some systems that approach the total-hospital concept are presently in operation.

The advent of the microprocessor has markedly affected medical instrumentation, as it has most disciplines involving measurement or control. Microprocessors are now incorporated in many commercially available clinical instruments to enhance their capabilities or automate their operation. In some systems, such as certain patient monitors, microprocessors have replaced minicomputers, substantially reducing their cost.

Most medical applications of computers and microprocessors involve specific instrumentation systems; in fact, the computer often becomes an integral part of an instrument. It is therefore essential that anyone involved in the field of medical instrumentation be familiar with the basic concepts of digital computation and some of the more important medical applications. Furthermore, it is important that the biomedical engineer or technician be given an understanding of the techniques involved in interfacing a computer or microprocessor with the rest of the instrumentation system.

This chapter is intended to bring to the reader a brief background of the basic concepts of digital computation, a look into some of the more important applications of computers in medicine, and a discussion of interfacing techniques. The chapter also includes a presentation on microprocessors and their role in medical instrumentation.

15.1 THE DIGITAL COMPUTER

The modern digital computer is a special type of calculating machine capable of automatically performing a long and complicated sequence of operations as directed by a set of instructions stored within the machine. In addition to its computational ability, the computer can store and retrieve large quantities of information and can automatically alter its sequence of instructions on the basis of calculated results. The sequence of instructions required for the computer to perform a given task is called a *program.*

Digital computer technology is generally divided into two main areas of interest, the electronic circuitry and other physical equipment involved, called the computer *hardware,* and the programs with which the computer operates, called the *software.* Both hardware and software must be considered in discussing basic computer concepts.

15.1.1 Computer Hardware

Although a wide variety of digital computers can be found in biomedical applications, ranging from a one-chip microprocessor to a large multimillion-dollar computer complex, they all contain four basic elements: an *arithmetic unit* to perform the mathematical and decision-making functions, a *memory* to store data and instructions, one or more *input–output* (I/O) devices to permit communication between the computer and the outside world, and a *control unit* to control the operation of the computer. A block diagram showing the relationship of these elements is presented in Figure 15.1 where the dashed lines indicate the control functions and the solid lines show the data flow.

Under the direction of the control unit, data from the instrumentation system or from some other source enter the computer via one of the input devices. The data may be transferred directly to memory, where it is stored until needed, or through the arithmetic unit. After processing, results are either stored in the memory for future recall, or they may be presented to the outside world via one or more of the output devices.

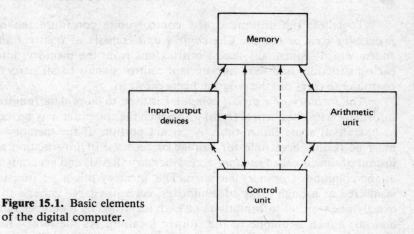

Figure 15.1. Basic elements of the digital computer.

As its name implies, the digital computer accepts, manipulates, and presents data in digital form. Although various digital codes are used, each has as its base the binary number system in which all values are represented by a set of 1s and 0s. Bistable elements are used in the computer to represent these values. Each binary digit is known as a *bit,* and the number of bits that are normally stored or manipulated together in the computer constitute the computer *word.* Computers are often designated by their word lengths. For example, a computer that handles information in 16-bit words is referred to as a 16-bit computer. Some computers work with a variable-length word, dividing each value into 8-bit segments called *bytes.* In these machines, the word length may be any number of bytes up to some limit. Also, in some machines, both alphabetic characters and decimal numbers can be coded into 6- or 8-bit groups called *characters.*

The arithmetic unit includes the circuitry that performs the computation and logic functions of the computer as well as some registers for temporarily storing the data being manipulated by that circuitry. A *register* is a set of bistable circuits capable of storing one computer word or a part of a word. The exact number and type of registers depends on the architecture of the computer. In some computers, the arithmetic unit utilizes registers physically located in the memory. One of the registers in the arithmetic unit, called the *accumulator,* is generally used to hold the results of the computation.

The circuitry that actually performs the computational and logic operations within the arithmetic unit is called the *arithmetic/logic unit* (ALU). Its functions include addition, subtraction, and the logic functions of AND, OR, and exclusive OR (XOR). Hardware multiplication and division are also provided in the ALUs of some computers, whereas others perform these operations through addition, subtraction, and shifting operations, using short sequences of instructions called *microprograms.*

Together, the arithmetic and control units constitute the *central processing unit* or (CPU). The *control unit* consists of registers and decoders which sequentially access instructions from the memory, interpret each instruction, and send appropriate control signals to all parts of the computer to carry out the program being executed.

The *memory of a digital computer* is used to store data (numbers or information in alphabetical form) with which the computer may be required to operate at some future time. A certain portion of the memory which must be readily accessible for storage or retrieval of information at any instant of time is called *random-access memory* (RAM) and generally serves as the computer's *primary memory*. This memory might be functionally visualized as a hugh array of mailboxes, each just large enough to store exactly one word of information and each identified by a number called an *address,* which is unique to the storage location. As the term "random access" implies, any address in the RAM is accessible with equal speed, regardless of the order in which information is called for. Data are *written into* storage and *read out*.

In many computers, particularly the older ones, tiny magnetic cores serve as the storage elements in the RAM. More modern computers use integrated circuits for this purpose in order to reduce size and attain higher operating speeds. Since each core or integrated-circuit element is able to hold one bit of information, each word of memory requires a number of elements equal to the word length of the computer. Thus, a 16-bit computer with 32,768 words of RAM must have 524,288 storage elements in that part of its memory.

Magnetic core memories are inherently *nonvolatile;* that is, they retain their contents without electrical power. In contrast, integrated-circuit RAMs are inherently *volatile* and lose all stored information whenever the power is removed. Such memories often have a backup battery supply to protect the memory in case of power failure. RAMs that consist of flip-flop circuits are called *static memories,* since stored data, once entered, remain intact unless power is lost until replaced by new data. Some integrated-circuit RAMs, however, use metal oxide silicon transistors that store data in the form of capacitive charges. These devices are called *dynamic* memories because the charges must be continually refreshed in order to retain the stored information.

A basic characteristic of the modern digital computer is that the programs required for each job to be done are internally stored within the memory of the computer. Generally, a portion of RAM is used for this purpose, permitting the programs to be changed as required. However, in some computers, and nearly all microprocessors, all or a portion of the programs for fixed operations or control functions may be stored in a *read-only memory* (ROM). A ROM also provides random access, but its contents cannot be changed during the normal operation of the computer. ROMs, which are also integrated-circuit memories, are generally lower in cost than RAMs; and like RAMs, they can be fabricated by *large-scale integration* (LSI) techniques in which a large number of elements are packed on a single chip. They also permit very fast access times. Most ROMs are programmed at the time of their manufacture, which requires that the ROM be replaced in order to change the program. A special type of ROM, called a *programmable read-only memory* (PROM) is available for applications in which it may be necessary to occasionally alter the program. Like ROMs, PROMs are fixed-program devices; however, with special equipment, their contents can be changed by their users. Special versions of the PROM are the erasable *programmable read-only memory* (EPROM), in which the memory can be erased by exposure to ultraviolet light and reprogrammed electrically, and the *electrically alterable read-only memory* (EAROM), which permits changes by means of electrical inputs. All these devices require special equipment, called *PROM programmers* or *burners,* to alter the program content.

The amount of random access storage (RAM and ROM) a computer can have is limited by the cost of these memories. The size of a computer's primary memory is generally dictated by the amount of information that must be readily accessible at a given time, and it varies with the particular application for which it is used. Additional information, often in vast quantities, may be stored in a *secondary memory,* which is less costly but requires longer access time. Both magnetic tapes and disks are used for this purpose.

A *disk memory* consists of one or more disks mounted in a *disk drive.* Each disk looks very much like a metal phonograph record coated on both sides with a magnetic material. Some types of disks are removable, whereas others remain a permanent part of the disk drive and cannot be removed. A set of read/write heads is provided in the drive for each disk surface. Data are arranged in circular tracks around the disk, which is constantly rotated at high speed by the drive. To access a given address on the disk, the heads must move radially to the designated track and the disk must rotate to the point at which the address is beneath the heads. The actual time required to reach a given location, usually a number of milliseconds, depends on how far the heads and disk must move. Once a location has been reached, however, a block of data, consisting of a large number of words, can be transferred very rapidly to or from the primary memory, where it can be accessed randomly. Fixed-disk systems generally have shorter access times than those with removable disks.

A less expensive form of disk storage which has achieved considerable popularity, particularly in small computer systems, is the *diskette* or *floppy disk,* a very thin oxide-coated Mylar disk, slightly under 8 in. diameter, with a hole in the center like a phonograph record. The term "floppy" is used because these disks are flexible in contrast to the rigid construction of conventional disks. Each diskette is enclosed in a protective envelope, within which it rotates during use. Because they are so thin, the diskettes require very little storage space. Floppy disks are slower than conventional disks and can store less data per disk, but their small size and low cost tend to compensate for these limitations.

Another form of secondary memory is one or more *digital magnetic tape drives* connected to the computer. Data are stored on an oxide-coated plastic tape similar to that used in analog instrumentation or home stereophonic tape recorders. Nine parallel read/write heads record a finely packed sequence of 8-bit characters along the tape. A ninth bit, called a *parity* bit, is added to each character for error-detection purposes. In this manner extremely large quantities of data can be stored on a single reel of tape. To gain access to a particular set of data on the tape, however, the tape must be wound to the location of the data. This process may take several seconds or even minutes, but once the location of the data has been reached, information can be transferred at a very high rate. This characteristic makes the use of tape most practical in applications where large, continuous blocks of data can be written into or read out of the tape and transferred to or from the primary memory.

Cassette tapes can also be used for data storage, but are slower and hold much less data than the conventional (reel-to-reel) tapes described above. Even so, they are often used with microprocessors or small computer systems because of their compact size and lower cost. A slightly larger (and also more expensive) *tape-cartridge system* is also sometimes used with small computers.

Two newer forms of digital memory, *magnetic bubble memory* (MBM) and *charge-coupled devices* (CCD), are beginning to appear on the scene. Both invented at Bell Laboratories at about the same time, these memories fill a gap in speed and cost between integrated-circuit RAMs and magnetic disks. They are also similar in principle in that they are both *sequential-access memories,* in which strings of bits circulate through one or more designated pathways. A given word can be accessed only when the beginning of that word circulates past a readout point. These memories are much faster than disks, however, because the circulation of data does not involve mechanical movement of the storage medium.

In magnetic bubble memories, microscopic domains of magnetic polarization, called *bubbles,* are generated sequentially in a thin magnetic film on the surface of a garnet chip and circulated by a rotating magnetic field. Patterns of Permalloy metal are deposited on the film to define the pathways through which the bubble domains move. Bubbles are generated by pulsing current through a microscopic one-turn loop just above the magnetic film. In a typical arrangement, one bit of data is introduced every

10 μsec. The presence of a bubble during a 10-μsec period constitutes a logic 1, whereas the absence of a bubble during that period constitutes a 0. Data are read out by means of an array of detector elements that change their resistance when bubbles pass under them. By organizing data into blocks and utilizing a combination of major and minor loops, maximum access time for any specified block of data is 1 msec, which is 8 to 100 times the speed of a disk. Since they have no moving parts, MBAs have much higher reliability and lower error rate than disks. MBMs are nonvolatile and thus require no special provision to preserve data in case of power failure. Their cost is about the same per bit as that of floppy disk or movable-head rigid disk storage. Because of their higher speed, MBMs are likely to replace disks as secondary storage in some future computer systems.

Charge-coupled devices (CCDs) are considerably faster than bubble memories, but are also more expensive. The elements of a CCD memory are somewhat similar to those of a dynamic integrated-circuit random-access memory in which data are stored in the form of small capacitive charges. However, in the CCD memory, these charges are shifted from one element to the next, along a designated path, through a silicon chip, upon receipt of each clock pulse. The output of each path is recirculated back to the input to provide continuous circulation of a string of bits. CCD memories may have a number of such paths, each typically containing 64 or more bits. The charges are refreshed as they pass through a special circuit for this purpose in each path. Although a given bit can be accessed only when it circulates past the readout, entire words or groups of words can be carried in parallel paths and accessed in microseconds (or less). Thus, their access times are short enough to make CCD memories useful as primary memories in certain applications as well as for more-rapid-access mass storage. Their lower cost, which is only about one-fourth that of an integrated-circuit RAM, makes them attractive contenders in both areas. Unlike bubble memories, CCD memories are volatile and can lose their contents when power is removed, unless a protective battery supply is provided.

Technologies associated with both MBMs and CCDs are constantly improving, with the promise that the near future will bring greater packing densities and lower costs in both areas. Another new technology, *electron-beam addressable memories* (EBAM), is also emerging. This type of memory, in which large quantities of data are stored as electrostatic charges on elements of a target of silicon dioxide or some similar material, will permit faster access than CCDs at a relatively low cost per bit. Data are written onto the target and read out by means of a high-resolution electron beam that can be directed to any portion of the array.

The versatility of a computer is largely determined by the various *input-output* (I/O) devices attached thereto. This portion of the system, which is the computer's only means of communicating with its users, is also its interface with the medical instrumentation system with which it works. Some of the more commonly used I/O systems include equipment to read and punch cards and/or paper tape, record and play back digital magnetic tapes or disks, accept input directly from a keyboard, and provide a typewriter or line-printer output. In its application with biomedical instrumentation, the I/O equipment might also include an analog-to-digital converter to convert data from analog form into the digital (usually binary) form required for computer input, a digital-to-analog converter to provide an analog representation of the output for display or control purposes, or a cathode-ray-tube display. Analog-to-digital and digital-to-analog conversion, plus other aspects of interfacing the digital computer with biomedical instrumentation, are discussed in detail in later sections of this chapter.

Figure 15.2. Optical character recognition (OCR) reader for computer entry (Courtesy of ECRM Inc., Bedford, MA.)

A new, emerging form of input device is *optical character recognition* (OCR) equipment, capable of reading information directly from a typewritten page. The OCR unit shown in Figure 15.2 can read text in single-, double-, or triple-space type from any of three character fonts that can be used on any Selectric typewriter.

Input–output equipment can either be *on-line* (connected to a computer) or *off-line* (not connected, but used in preparation of data for later computer input). It can either be *local* (at the same location as the computer) or *remote* (at some other location and either directly wired to the computer or connected through telephone lines). Remote equipment might be located in the same building as the computer or may be several thousand miles away.

Although the above-described components are essentially common to all computers, their implementation can assume a wide variety of forms, ranging from a large-scale computer of the type shown in Figure 15.3 to a microcomputer of the type shown in Figure 15.4. *Microcomputers* are small low-cost computers generally built around microprocessors (see Section 15.2).

Large-scale computers of the type shown in Figure 15.3, often costing millions of dollars, are designed to process large amounts of data at high speeds, usually for a sizable number of users, either in a batch-processing

Figure 15.3. Large-scale digital computer installation (Courtesy of IBM Corp.)

Figure 15.4. Microcomputer (top), Microcomputer board (center), and Microprocessor (bottom). (Courtesy of Data General Corporation, Westboro, MA.)

or time-sharing mode. *Batch processing* is a term used to define a method of operation in which all data for a given problem must be entered into the computer before processing begins. Once the data have been entered, the entire computational resources of the computer are devoted to that problem. When available, the results are printed out or otherwise presented to the user, and the computer begins work on the next problem. In most systems of this type, the results from a previous problem may be printed out while the current problem is being processed. At the same time, data for the next job may be entering the computer.

In contrast, many of the larger computers utilize some form of time sharing. *Time sharing* is a method of computer operation in which a number of users at various locations can use a computer simultaneously. Each user submits data and receives results via his own terminal connected to the computer either directly or via a telephone line. Although it may appear that the computer is working on a large number of jobs and processing many sets of data simultaneously, it is really sharing its time among the users, sequentially alloting a certain amount of time to each. The division of time depends upon the problems being solved and a previously determined priority schedule. Provided that the number of users is not excessive, the high operating speed of the computer allows it to service each user as rapidly as if he alone were using the machine.

The user's *terminal* is his interface with the computer. It can range from a simple teletypewriter to a very elaborate input–output system, perhaps including an analog-to-digital converter for interfacing with an instrumentation system. A typical terminal with keyboard entry and cathode-ray-tube (CRT) display is shown in Figure 15.5.

Computers are often programmed to communicate with their users in an *interactive* or *conversational mode,* allowing the users to exchange messages with the computer as though they were communicating with a person operating a keyboard at the other end of a line. Interactive programs are able to guide the user through the various steps involved in requesting information and obtaining results, and thus are suitable for situations where access is provided to physicians, nurses, or other hospital personnel unfamiliar with computer languages or conventional methods of computer operation.

Communication between the computer and a remote terminal is generally by telephone line. For this purpose data are placed on an audio-frequency *carrier* within the voice-frequency range. The modulator-demodu-

Figure 15.5. Computer remote terminal with keyboard and cathode-ray tube (CRT) display. (Courtesy of IBM Corporation.)

lator device by which the data are encoded on the carrier and by which received data are decoded is called a *modem* (a derivation combining the terms MODulator and DEModulator). The modem may be of a type that connects directly to the telephone line and applies the modulated carrier signal electrically, or it may be equipped with an acoustical coupler in which a conventional telephone receiver–transmitter cradle may be placed. The telephone line may be leased specifically for transmission of data, or it may be an ordinary telephone line normally used for voice conversation.

As an alternative to using a remote terminal on a large time-shared computer, a hospital or other medical facility may have one or more smaller computers of its own. These smaller computers are generally known as *minicomputers,* and the very smallest, *microcomputers.* Actually, the definition is usually based on cost and physical size rather than the amount of storage or complexity of the CPU. Minicomputers generally range in price from about $1000 to $25,000 for the basic unit. Most minicomputer systems include perpherals, which may add considerably to the cost. Although they are small and relatively inexpensive, modern minicomputers can be extremely fast and powerful and can provide large storage capability. Minicomputers can also have time-sharing capability. Thus, a minicomputer may be able to service a number of remote terminals around the hospital.

Although there may be some overlap, a *microcomputer* generally costs less than $1000, and incorporates a microprocessor for its CPU. Microprocessors are discussed in Section 15.2. Microcomputers are generally smaller and have less capability than minicomputers, but with ever-changing technology, some microcomputers compare favorably in many ways with some of the smaller minis.

Generally, minicomputers and microcomputers are used *on-line* and often become a part of the instrumentation system with which they serve. In many applications, they operate in *real time,* an arrangement in which the computer is able to process data as rapidly as it is received.

15.1.2. Computer Software

In a general sense, the term *software* is defined to include all the programs used by a computer system, as well as documentation and other nonhardware items supplied by manufacturers to facilitate the purchaser's efficient operation of the equipment. The software cost for a given system is usually much greater than that of the hardware involved.

There are two basic types of software: (1) *system software,* supplied by the computer manufacturer for managing the operation of the system, translating programs, performing diagnostic checks, and so on, and (2) *application software,* for carrying out the specific functions involved in the user's application. The system programs are usually specific to the computer involved, whereas application programs are most often written in a form that can be used on different kinds of computers.

The set of basic operations a computer is able to perform is called its *repertoire* or *instruction set.* The set of symbolic instructions and rules for formatting and combining these instructions, called *syntax,* constitutes a *programming language.* The language used internally by the computer itself is called *machine language,* and consists of a numeric code for each operation in the computer's repertoire. Although application programs could be written in machine language, long lists of operation codes would have to be memorized in order to write them. Instead, computers generally have system programs that accept mnemonic instructions, such as "ADD" or "SUB," and convert each to its machine language equivalent. These programs are called *assemblers,* and the mnemonic language is called an *assembly language.* Assembly language programming is much easier for programmers to use than machine language, but it is still specific to a given type of computer. That is, a program written in assembly language for one computer cannot be expected to be used on a different kind of computer. Assembly language has a one-to-one relationship with machine language in that the program must include a mnemonic statement for every step the computer is to perform. One exception is a *macroassembler,* which permits a symbolic macroinstruction to be substituted for a sequence of instructions. Another advantage of assembly language is that it permits the use of *symbolic addressing* of memory locations rather than absolute addressing, which is required in machine language. With *symbolic addressing,* the programmer assigns a name to a specified memory location rather than its absolute numerical address and allows the computer to determine the actual address to be used.

To further aid the programmer, most computers have additional software, called *compilers* and *interpreters,* which accept instructions in languages that are more problem-oriented than assembly language, and convert them into machine language. In most cases, a single statement in one of these high-level languages initiates a sequence of machine-language instructions, sometimes rather lengthy, thus reducing the length and complexity of the necessary programs. In addition, such languages involve terminology, symbols, and operations with which the user is already familiar. For example, instructions to carry out mathematical operations are written in the form of equations.

Although a compiler and an interpreter both translate high-level languages into machine languages, there is a basic difference. A *compiler* goes through an entire program after it has been entered into the computer and translates every instruction before execution is begun. On the other hand, an interpreter translates the high-level program a step at a time and executes each step as it proceeds.

There are a number of high-level languages, some suited to specific types of applications. Among the more important of these are FORTRAN (an abbreviation of FORmula TRANslation), COBOL (COmmon Business-Oriented Language), and BASIC (Beginners' All-purpose Instruction Code). Compilers and/or interpreters for these and many other languages are available for most computers, especially the larger ones.

The system software that manages the operation of the computer includes programs that control the flow of data into and out of the computer and between primary and secondary memory, and assure that all the necessary operations are carried out as efficiently as possible. These programs are called by such names as *supervisor, monitor, executive,* and *operating system.* In a time-sharing system, these programs also control the interaction of the computer with the various terminals it services and determine the priorities with which different functions are handled.

Application software is necessary to adapt a computer to each specific job it is to do. Some computers involved with medical instrumentation are used for many purposes and consequently require a variety of application programs, while others, particularly minicomputers and microcomputers, are *dedicated* to one specific task. If the task for which a dedicated computer is to be changed, a new set of application software must usually be entered, and often the computer must by physically disconnected from one set of instrumentation and connected to another. In many applications, particularly those related to research, application programs require frequent modification or rewriting. In contrast, dedicated computers in clinical instrumentation systems are often provided with software that remains unchanged and requires no programming on the part of the user. A computer system of this kind is called a *turnkey* system, since the user must do no more than turn it on in order to use it.

15.2. MICROPROCESSORS

The first all-electronic computer (ENIAC, completed in 1945) contained 18,000 vacuum tubes. The poor reliability of such early devices and the need to shut the computer down to replace defective tubes would have made much larger computers impractical. The invention of the transistor in 1947 removed this limitation and made possible the development of the first generation of computers which employed large numbers of (discrete) transistors and semiconductor diodes. In the mid-1950s, semiconductor technology had developed photolithographic and diffusion methods, which led to the planar transistor in 1958, followed shortly by the first integrated circuits in 1959. Since then the number of circuit components that can be integrated into a circuit chip has approximately doubled every year. The first step, in which up to about 16 gate functions (64 components) are contained in one integrated circuit, was called *small-scale integration* (SSI). SSI circuits range in complexity up to dual-flip-flops and one-bit binary adders. By about 1965, *medium-scale integration* (MSI) had evolved, making it possible to include up to 200 gate functions (1000 components) on one chip. The more complex MSI circuits include a complete 4-bit ALU (see Section 15.1.1). By about 1969 the number of components per circuit exceeded the 1000 limit. *Large-scale integration* (LSI) technology had come into existence. *Very large scale integration* (VLSI) technologies presently under development promise even greater concentrations of components on a single chip.

The logical continuation of the development that had begun with placing an ALU on a chip has now made it possible to put a complete computer central processing unit on a chip. The first device of this kind was announced in 1969. Because it was a complete CPU, albeit with somewhat limited performance, its developers coined the term *microprocessor* (sometimes abbreviated MPU or μP). Progress has since continued to the point where the performance of microprocessors now equals that of the minicomputer CPUs of a few years ago. The number of components that can be placed on one integrated-circuit microprocessor chip has greatly exceeded 18,000, the number of vacuum tubes used by the first, room-sized electronic computer in 1945.

A computer, however, contains more than just the CPU. Thus, in conjunction with microprocessors, large-scale integration has been applied to the other computer components, such as RAMs and ROMs, introduced in Section 15.1.1. Output ports for parallel as well as serial interfaces and controllers for disk drives are also now available as LSI circuit chips.

While the complexity of integrated circuits has increased dramatically over the years, their price has actually decreased. As a result, complete microcomputers are now available which are comparable not only in physical size, but also in price, to electronic controllers implemented with discrete components or small-scale-integration ICs. Their performance, however, is more nearly comparable to rack-size minicomputers, originally costing several tens of thousands of dollars. These developments have made it possible to incorporate a microcomputer as an integral part of many electronic instruments. The designers of biomedical instruments were among the first to utilize this possibility. As a result, biomedical devices have greatly benefited from this technology.

15.2.1. Types of Microprocessors

The first microprocessor introduced in 1969 was a 4-bit device with a rather limited instruction set. From this beginning, development evolved in several directions. Even when utilizing LSI chips for memories and input–output ports, a complete microcomputer normally includes at least a dozen integrated circuits in addition to the microprocessor. In a *single-chip computer*, all these components have been integrated into one circuit package! To achieve this feat, however, the size of the program ROM and the data RAM must be limited. Also, the allowable number of pins in the large IC packages (usually 40) limits the number of I/O ports.

The 4-bit design as it was used in the first microprocessor made it necessary to perform mathematical operations one decimal digit at a time. A word length of 8 bits is more common in modern microprocessors, which can operate in the (binary-coded) decimal system, two digits at a time, or with signed or unsigned binary numbers. Because the resolution of an 8-bit word is frequently insufficient, multiple-precision arithmetic may be employed. Sixteen-bit microprocessors are also available, some of which are compatible with the instruction sets of certain minicomputers. Another type of microprocessor, called a *bit-slice processor,* requires several chips to form a complete central processing unit. Each chip, called a *bit-slice unit,* contains circuitry for 2 or 4 bits. By combininng chips, words of any desired length can be used. Because bit-slice microprocessors are available in fast bipolar Schottky and ECL technologies, the central processing units of all but the largest mainframe computers can actually be implemented by such microprocessors. At the other end of the scale is the 1-bit microprocessor, which is intended to replace digital logic for control applications.

15.2.2. Microprocessors in Biomedical Instrumentation

The first biomedical instruments incorporating microprocessors began to appear on the market around 1975. While the first devices were mainly laboratory-type instruments, microprocessors are now used in all areas of biomedical instrumentation. Although microprocessors were originally advocated mainly as replacements for controllers using digital logic, it was soon found that the new technology could be extended much further. Following are some examples of the ways in which microprocessors are employed in contemporary medical instruments.

15.2.2.1. Calibration. Many instruments require zeroing and recalibration at certain time intervals, sometimes every few hours. A software or hardware timer in a microprocessor system can initiate a calibration cycle. As with manual calibration, this cycle requires the introduction of a blank and standard, each of which might be in the form of a voltage, gas or liquid. In manual calibration methods, zero and gain-control potentiometers are normally adjusted until the readout indicates the proper values. Microprocessor-equipped devices usually perform the calibration in digital form. During the calibration, offset and gain correction factors are determined and stored in memory to be applied to the measured data during the measurement.

15.2.2.2. Table lookup. In analog systems, nonlinear functions (e.g., those required for the correction of a transducer characteristic) are usually implemented by straight-line approximations. In microprocessor-equipped systems, table lookup with interpolation can be used. This procedure is less limited and more accurate and also permits the determination of parameters that are dependent on more than one variable.

15.2.2.3. Averaging. Microprocessors can easily average data over time or over successive measurements and can thus decrease statistical variations.

15.2.2.4. Formatting and printout. Because medical equipment using microprocessors usually processes data in digital form, the microprocessor can be utilized to format the data, convert the raw data into physical units, and print out the results in a form that does not require further transcribing or processing.

15.3. INTERFACING THE COMPUTER WITH MEDICAL INSTRUMENTATION AND OTHER EQUIPMENT

To operate effectively with or as part of a medical instrumentation system, a computer or microprocessor must properly interface with the various devices comprising the rest of the system. Input data must be requested and received in an acceptable form and output signals must be provided wherever control functions are required or where data must be transmitted to other equipment. Several important factors must be considered in interfacing, including the type of output data produced by each instrument, the logic and formatting requirements of the computer, the input requirements of any devices that are to receive signals from the computer, the method by which these signals are to be transmitted, and the commands required to control input–output traffic.

Many biomedical instruments with which a computer may be interfaced generate analog data in the form of voltages proportional to the variables represented. For computer entry, these analog signals must be converted into digital form. On the other hand, where the computer is required to provide analog output signals for display or control purposes, digital output data must be converted into analog form. Following a discussion of digital interfacing requirements, a brief introduction to analog-to-digital and digital-to-analog conversion is presented.

15.3.1. Digital Interfacing Requirements

Interfacing a computer with other devices that handle data in digital form involves both software and hardware. The software is usually a part of the computer's system software and is often an extension of the input–output package that controls the flow of information to and from such peripheral devices as disks and magnetic tape drives. Programs are included to monitor input lines, generate commands, identify the various sources of input data, accept each word of data as it arrives, and route it to the arithmetic unit or memory as appropriate.

Interfacing hardware is required to format the data, provide buffer registers to temporarily hold each word until it can be dealt with, and where necessary, convert input or output signals from one system of logic to another.

Formatting is the arranging of data into a form that can be accepted and recognized by the computer or device receiving computer output. It involves such factors as the number of bits to be received or sent out at a time and the way in which the bits of a word are arranged among the input or output lines. Data may be received or sent out in either *serial* or *parallel* form. In serial form, the bits of each word or character are received or sent one at a time over a single line, whereas in parallel transmission, a separate line is provided for each bit. Serial transmission is generally used where data are sent over long distances via telephone lines or for connection to Teletypewriter keyboard-printers or CRT terminals. On the other hand, most computer input–output (I/O) ports accept and produce data in parallel form, requiring a *parallel-to-serial* or *serial-to-parallel converter*. In such a converter the serial data are shifted into or out of a shift register, which is parallel-interfaced with the computer I/O port via a buffer register. A parallel-to-serial converter also generates and frames each word or character with *start* and *stop bits* which can be recognized by the receiving device. A serial-to-parallel converter uses these bits to control formatting of the parallel data.

Where the interface includes more than one digital device, a separate I/O port can be provided for each, or all the devices can be interconnected via a common set of data lines called an *an input/output data bus* or *party-line bus*. When this type of bus arrangement is used, additional interconnecting lines must be provided to address each individual device so that data are transferred to or from only one device at a time and to assure that each communicating device is properly identified to the computer.

When the digital devices with which the computer must interface can be controlled so that transfer of data always occurs in time correspondence with the computer's internal clock, the I/O operation is said to be *synchronous*. Most situations, however, require *asynchronous* input/output in which bidirectional control of the transfer may be accomplished through a process called *handshaking*. In this procedure, the computer and the I/O device exchange signals, indicating first that a valid character is on the line, ready to be received, and then that the transfer has been successfully accomplished.

Transmission of data in serial form via a telephone line requires not only that the data be converted into serial form and framed with appropriate start and stop bits, but also that the string of bits be placed on a carrier signal by a modem. The rate of data transmission is given in *baud*, the total number of bits transmitted per second, including start and stop bits. The rate for a 10-character-per-second teletype is 110 baud (a total of 11 bits is required for each 8-bit data character).

Devices with which a computer must interface may produce digital data in pure binary form, binary-coded decimal, or in some type of alphanumeric code, such as ASCII (American Standard Code for Information Interchange) or EBCDIC (Extended Binary-Coded Decimal Interchange Code). Both of these codes are used extensively in digital communication. In each code, an 8-bit character is defined for each numeral, letter of the alphabet, both upper- and lower-case, and punctuation mark..In addition, each code contains a number of special characters for control of a printing device, such as a Teletypewriter, or for identification of the beginning of a block of data. Limited-character 6- and 7-bit ASCII codes are also available and are used in some applications.

15.3.2. Analog-to-Digital and Digital-to-Analog Conversion

Whenever a digital computer must communicate with an instrumentation system that generates or requires data in analog form, the interface must include equipment to convert analog signals into digital data or numerical information in digital form into analog voltages. In the process of digitizing data, most analog-to-digital (A/D) converters incorporate digital-to-analog (D/A) conversion circuitry, as indicated below. For this reason D/A converters are discussed first.

15.3.2.1. Digital-to-analog conversion. In order to obtain a continuous analog signal from a sequence of values in digital form, a voltage must be generated proportional to the value of each digital word as it appears in the sequence. The circuitry by which this is accomplished is called a *digital-to-analog converter*.

Generation of a voltage proportional to a digital word can be accomplished in various ways. One method is illustrated in Figure 15.6, which shows the weighted resistor (summing amplifier) digital-to-analog

Figure 15.6. Weighted resistor type digital-to-analog convertor. (All switches shown in Binary "1" position.)

converter. This circuit is an operational amplifier connected as an *analog adder*. The output is the sum of the contributions of the various inputs. At each input the common input voltage is weighted or multiplied by the ratio of the feedback resistor to the associated input resistor.

For example, in the circuit shown in Figure 15.6, each bit of a 6-bit binary word controls the switch to one input. If a given bit has a value of 1, its corresponding switch places the appropriate input at a reference voltage V. If that bit has a value of 0, however, the input is set to ground (0 V). The most significant bit (labeled A in the figure) then contributes a voltage equal to V to the output of the circuit when that bit is a 1, but when that bit has a value of 0, it contributes nothing. Because the input resistor for bit B has twice the value of that for bit A, a 1 in bit B contributes exactly half the voltage of V to the output. Similarly, bit C contributes one-fourth the voltage of V, and so on down to the least significant bit, F, which, when given a value of 1, contributes only $\frac{1}{32}V$. These contributions correspond exactly to the relative values of the bits in the binary word. Thus, the output

404

of the operational amplifier is proportional to the sum of the value of all bits that have the value 1, and consequently is proportional to the value represented by the digital word. For a binary word of greater length (a greater number of bits), an additional input resistor and switch are required for each additional bit. For an n-bit word, the input resistor for the least significant bit would have a value of $2^{n-1} R$.

Figure 15.7 shows a *binary ladder circuit*. The output of the ladder circuit is connected to the input of an operational amplifier. As in the case of the analog adder, the ladder has an input corresponding to each bit of the binary word. Again, each input has a switch controlled by the value of its corresponding bit. As before, when a bit has a value of 1, its input is switched to ground. The ladder network is so arranged that each input switched to voltage V contributes a voltage to the input of the amplifier proportional to the value of the corresponding binary bit, while the output voltage of the circuit is proportional to the sum of all bits with a value of 1. All resistors are either of value R or $2R$. The accuracy of this circuit is not dependent upon the absolute value of resistors, but upon their relative values. Also, the ladder is so arranged that, regardless of the combination of switch positions, the input impedance seen by the amplifier is constant and equal to R.

Figure 15.7. Binary-ladder type digital-to-analog converter. (All switches shown in Binary "1" position.)

In the circuit shown in Figure 15.7, switch A is controlled by the most significant bit and switch F is controlled by the least significant bit. To accommodate digital words of greater length, the network can be extended to provide an input for each additional bit which contributes the correct voltage for that bit.

In both types of digital-to-analog converters, the switching is usually done by solid-state switching circuits. Although many circuit configurations of this type are in use, they all essentially accomplish the same purpose of providing the reference voltage with a digital input of 1 and ground with an input of 0.

There are several ways of estimating the value of the analog signal at the output of the converter between the occurrence of digital data points, all of which involve analog filters. The simplest, called *zero-order hold,* assumes that the signal remains constant at the level of each digital value until the next one occurs. Then it jumps immediately to the level of the new value, where it again remains until another value is received. Unless abrupt changes in the data can be expected which could result in excessive error, this method is usually used. More complex (and more expensive) methods are also available, such as *first-order hold,* in which the signal at any time is caused to change at the same rate as it did between the two previous digital data points.

15.3.2.2. Analog-to-digital conversion. An analog-to-digital converter is a device that accepts a continuous analog voltage signal as input and from that signal generates a sequence of digital words that represent the analog voltage as it varies with time. There are actually two processes involved in the *digitizing* of analog data. The first is *sampling*—the process of measuring the analog voltage at discrete points in time. The sampled voltage must then be *quantized.* Quantizing is the selection of a digital word of specified length to represent the analog voltage.

The simplest form of A/D converter involves a *voltage-to-frequency converter* and a counter. The voltage-to-frequency converter produces a sequence of output pulses at a frequency proportional to the voltage of the analog signal. The counter counts the number of pulses in a specified unit of time. The frequency range of the converter and the time period for counting are selected to provide an output count that corresponds numerically to the voltage of the analog signal.

Another simple A/D converter is called a *ramp* or *pulse-width converter.* At the beginning of each reading a capacitor is discharged and allowed to begin charging at a fixed rate, until it has reached a voltage equal to the voltage of the analog signal, as determined by an analog comparator. The output of the comparator is a pulse whose width is proportional to the analog voltage. During the duration of the pulse, a digital counter counts the output of a fixed-rate digital clock so that the count at the end of each pulse is proportional to the analog voltage at that time.

A slightly more complex but inherently more accurate type of A/D converter is a *dual-slope* or *up-down integrator converter*. In this device, the input of an analog integrator is alternately switched between the analog voltage being digitized and a constant reference voltage. As in the pulse-width converter, a capacitor is charged at a rate proportional to the analog voltage for a fixed time period, so that the height of the ramp at the end of the period is proportional to that voltage. The integrator is then switched to a reference voltage, and the capacitor discharges at a constant rate until the ramp reaches a predetermined level. The counter counts the clock output during this discharge interval, which is proportional to the analog input voltage.

All three of the A/D converters described so far are relatively inexpensive, but are too slow for any application in which the analog voltage varies at a rapid rate. Thus, for most A/D converters, faster and more accurate but also more expensive techniques are employed. In these techniques, the heart of the A/D converter is a D/A converter of a type described above. The basic arrangement is shown in block diagram form in Figure 15.8. In this figure the divider network is a binary ladder which, in conjunction with the reference supply, constitutes a D/A converter of the type shown in Figure 15.7. The flip-flop register is a set of bistable (flip-flop) circuits, each of which can represent a value of binary 0 or 1 and can thus store one bit of a binary digital word. The entire set of flip-flops that constitutes the register represents each digital word to be generated by the converter. Through the

Figure 15.8. Analog-to-digital converter incorporating digital-to-analog converter. (Copyright 1964, Digital Equipment Corporation, Maynard, MA. All rights reserved.)

level amplifiers, each flip-flop controls a corresponding input to the ladder network, and together they produce an analog output with the same voltage as that represented by the flip-flop register. At the time of sampling, this voltage is compared with the analog input voltage in an analog comparator circuit. When these two voltages differ, the bits in the flip-flop register are adjusted through appropriate gating and control circuitry until agreement is reached. At that time, the value represented by the flip-flop register is the nearest digital equivalent to the analog input voltage and is caused to appear at the output of the converter.

Although nearly all analog-to-digital converters use this comparison method of matching the value of the register with the input voltage, the methods by which the digital value of the register is adjusted to match the input signal can differ widely. The most common method is called the *successive approximation method,* in which each bit of each digital word is successively tested to determine whether its addition to the value of the register would cause the input signal to be exceeded. If not, that particular bit is set to 1. If the bit would have caused the value of the register to be greater than the input signal, then the bit is left at 0. The process begins at the bit representing the largest value (most significant bit) and continues from "left to right" down the register. The advantage of this type of system is that the conversion time is fixed and does not depend on the input signal. Furthermore, this type of converter gives a good response to large, rapid changes in input, such as might be expected with a multiplexer. To avoid changes in the input signal during the time the converter is in the process of checking each bit, a sample-and-hold circuit is often used to read the voltage at the beginning of each conversion period and to maintain that voltage during conversion period. The result is a closer approximation of the analog signal.

Important factors in selecting an analog-to-digital converter are the resolution of the quantizing process, the conversion rate, and the conversion aperture time. Also to be considered are the computer input requirements for formatting and the type of logic circuitry that the converter output must match.

The quantizing *resolution* of the converter is determined by the number of bits in the output word. An 11-bit-plus-sign word, for example, is capable of dividing the full range of the input signal into 4095 increments of level. This number includes 2047 positive increments and a similar number of negative increments, plus zero. The accuracy of any voltage reading, then, cannot exceed about 1 in 2000, or about 0.05 percent of full scale. Most physiological data do not require that degree of accuracy, however, for many transducers cannot provide accuracies much better than 1.0 percent. But since the cost of 1 or 2 additional bits of resolution is relatively low, it usually pays to provide for somewhat greater accuracy than that actually needed.

The *conversion rate* of an analog-to-digital converter depends on the conversion method used and the speed of the control circuitry. Extremely high rates of conversion are available. Shannon's sampling theorem requires that, to reproduce a periodic signal without severe distortion, the sampling rate be at least twice the highest frequency component that the system is able to pass. For nonperiodic waveforms, it is generally good practice to use a sampling rate of at least five times the highest frequency component. Obviously, the higher the sampling rate, the more accurate will be the representation of the analog signal; but higher digitizing rates mean that more data must be stored and handled by the computer. This usually results in a greater computation cost.

The *aperture time* is the period of time during which the analog signal is actually being sampled for conversion. A long aperture time might result in a change of data during the sampling interval. Most modern analog-to-digital converters have sufficiently short aperture times for the conversion rates at which they operate.

The process of sequentially taking readings from two or more analog data channels with a single analog-to-digital converter is called *time multiplexing.* If N data channels are multiplexed into a converter which operates at R conversions per second, and all channels are converted at the same rate, the conversion rate for any given channel is R/N conversions per second. This means that with multiplexing, the conversion rate of the converter must be the required conversion rate for each channel multiplied by the number of channels. If it is important that all of the channels be converted in exact time correspondence, sample-and-hold circuitry must be incorporated into the multiplexer to "hold" values until they can be digitized.

15.4. BIOMEDICAL COMPUTER APPLICATIONS

Applications of the digital computer in medicine and related fields are so numerous that even listing all of them is beyond the scope of this textbook. Most of these applications, however, utilize a few basic capabilities of the computer which provide an insight to ways in which computers can be used in conjunction with biomedical instrumentation. These basic capabilities include:

1. *Data acquisition:* The reading of instruments and transcribing of data can be done automatically under control of the computer. This not only results in a substantial saving of time and effort, but also reduces the number of errors in the data. When data are expected at irregular intervals, the computer can continuously scan all input sources and accept data when-

ever they are actually produced. If the data originate in analog form, the computer usually controls the sampling and digitizing process as well as identification and formatting of the data. In some cases, the computer can be programmed to reject unacceptable readings and provide an indication of possible trouble in the associated instrumentation. Sometimes the computer provides automatic calibration of each input source.

2. *Storage and retrieval:* The ability of the digital computer to store and retrieve large quantities of data is well known. The biomedical field provides ample opportunities to make use of this capability. In a modern hospital, large amounts of data are accumulated from many sources. These include admission and discharge information, physicians' reports, laboratory test results, and several other kinds of information associated with each patient. In addition, the hospital also generates a considerable amount of non-patient-oriented data, such as pharmacy records, inventories of all types, and accounting records. Without a computer, the storage of this vast amount of information is both space- and time-consuming. Manual retrievel of the data is tedious, and for some types of information, almost impossible. The digital computer, however, can serve as an automated filing system in which information can be automatically entered as it is generated. These files can be stored as long as necessary and updated whenever appropriate. Any or all of the information can be retrieved on command whenever desired and can be manipulated to provide output reports in tabular or graphic form to meet the needs of the hospital staff or other users.

3. *Data reduction and transformation:* The sequence of numbers resulting from digitizing an analog physiological signal such as the ECG or EEG would be quite useless if retrieved from the computer in raw form. To obtain meaningful information from such data, some form of data reduction or transformation is necessary to represent the data as a set of specific parameters. These parameters can then be analyzed, compared with other parameters, or otherwise manipulated. For example, the electroencephalogram (EEG) signal can be subjected to *Fourier transformation* to obtain a frequency spectrum of the signal. Further analysis can then be performed using the frequency-related parameters rather than the raw EEG data. The electrocardiogram (ECG) signal can also be subjected to data reduction methods, as shown in section 15.4.1, or heart rate information can be extracted for patient-monitoring purposes. Special trans-

formations are also required to reconstruct images in computerized axial tomography (see Section 15.4.4). The size and complexity of many of these transformation and data reduction problems are such that manual methods would be completely impractical.

4. *Mathematical operations:* Many important physiological variables cannot be measured directly, but must be calculated from other variables that are accessible. For example, many of the respiratory parameters described in Chapter 8 can be calculated from the results of a few simple breathing tests and gas concentration measurements. Also, the calculation of cardiac output by a dye or thermal dilution method as described in Chapter 6 can easily be done by computer. If a digital computer is connected on-line with the measuring instruments, the calculated results can often be obtained while the patient is still connected to the instruments. This not only enables the physician to conduct further tests if the results so indicate, but can also inform him immediately if any measurements were not properly made and require repetition.

5. *Pattern recognition:* To reduce certain types of physiological data into useful parameters, it is often necessary that important features of a physiological waveform or an image be identified. For example, analysis of the ECG waveform requires that the important amplitudes and intervals of the electrocardiogram be recognized and identified. Digital computer programs are available to search the data representing the ECG signal for certain predetermined characteristics that identify each of the important peaks. In Section 15.4.1 the technique by which this is accomplished is described. Somewhat different techniques are used in other pattern recognition problems, such as the identification and labelling of chromosomes, but since each type of pattern has unique features that must be identified, programming for pattern recognition is a highly specialized process.

6. *Limit detection:* In applications involving monitoring and screening, it is often necessary to determine when a measured variable exceeds certain limits. For example, in the analysis of the electrocardiogram, each important parameter of the ECG can be checked to determine whether it falls within a preestablished "normal" range. By comparison of the measured parameter with each limit of the range, the computer can indicate which parameters exceed the limit and the amount by which they deviate from normal. Using this technique, patients can be

screened to select those with ECG irregularities that should receive further attention. In most cases, the "normal" range is defined in advance, but sometimes the computer is programmed to establish normal ranges for each patient based upon the averages of repeated measures taken under specified conditions.

7. *Statistical analysis of data:* In the diagnosis of disease, it is often necessary to select one most likely cause out of a set of possible causes associated with a given set of observed symptoms, measurements, and test results. Similarly, medical research investigators must decide at times whether an observed change or condition in a person or animal is due to some treatment imposed by the researcher, or whether the result could be attributed to some other cause or just to chance alone. Both of these situations require the use of inferential statistical procedures, some of which are quite complex. Fortunately, most statistical methods lend themselves well to computer techniques, especially when large numbers of variables must be analyzed together or where data from a large number of patients are used. Even simple descriptive statistics, such as means, standard deviations, and frequency distributions can be computerized, resulting in significant savings of time and effort.

8. *Data presentation:* An important characteristic of any instrumentation and data-processing system is its ability to present the results of measurements and analyses to its users in the most meaningful way possible. By virtue of appropriate output devices, a digital computer can provide information in a number of useful forms. Table printouts, graphs, and charts can be produced automatically, with features clearly labeled using both alphabetic and numeric symbols. If the necessary computer peripherals are available, plots and cathode-ray-tube displays can also be generated. In addition to controlling the output devices, the computer can be programmed to organize the data for presentation in the most meaningful form possible, thus providing the user with a clear and accurate report of his results.

9. *Control functions:* Digital computers are capable of providing output signals that can be used to control other devices. In such applications, the computer is programmed to influence or control physiological, chemical, or other measurements from which its input data are being generated. The computer can also be used to provide feedback to the source of its data.

For example, while reading and analyzing the results of a chemical process, the computer can be made to control the rate, quantity, or concentration of reagents added to the process, or it could control the heating element of a temperature bath. By controlling these and other possible inputs, the process can be regulated to achieve desired results. In addition, the computer can be programmed to recognize certain characteristics of the measured results that would indicate possible sources of error. Sometimes other parameters are monitored in addition to the actual results to increase the sensitivity of the computer to conditions that could result in erroneous measurements. The computer can automatically compensate for some sources of error, such as a gradual drift in the baseline, by either altering the process itself or by mathematically adjusting the results before printing them out. When more serious types of error occur, the computer can alert the operator to the condition or, if necessary, can automatically stop the process.

The extent to which each of the described capabilities above can actually be utilized in a given situation depends on the available hardware and software. Obviously, some of these capabilities require greater resources than others.

Following are some specific examples of computer applications in clinical medicine and research. Although they represent only a few of the many possible ways in which computers can be used in medicine and biology, they serve to illustrate the role of each of the above-described capabilities. In each example, the computer techniques are described in conjunction with their associated biomedical instrumentation.

15.4.1. Computer Analysis of the Electrocardiogram

The use of computers for the clinical analysis of the electrocardiogram (ECG) has developed over the span of many years. There are several reasons for this. First, ECG potentials are relatively easy to measure. Second, the ECG is an extremely useful indicator for both screening and diagnosis of cardiac abnormalities. In addition, certain abnormalities of the ECG are quite well defined and can be readily identified.

Measurement of the electrocardiogram for computer analysis is essentially the same as is used for manual ECG interpretation. Most computerized systems use the 12 standard leads described in Chapter 6. There are more elaborate systems, however, that simultaneously measure three orthogonal components of the ECG vector. For some of these systems, a special orthogonal lead configuration is used.

Entry of the ECG into a digital computer requires that the analog ECG signals be converted into digital form. Although some attempts have been made to partially reduce the ECG data in analog form, nearly all presently used systems incorporate an analog-to-digital converter operating at a constant rate. The actual sampling rate depends upon the desired bandwidth of the signal to be analyzed. Sampling rates ranging from 100 readings per second up to 1000 readings per second are in current use. Analog filtering is often used ahead of the converter to eliminate noise and interference above the upper limit of the desired frequency band.

Once inside the computer, the ECG signal can be subjected to additional smoothing by means of digital filtering methods. This smoothing process eliminates high-frequency variations in the signal that might otherwise be mistaken for features of the ECG.

Pattern recognition techniques are next employed to identify the various features of the ECG. These features are shown in Figure 3.6. The most stable reference point of the ECG pattern, and one of the most reliably identified, is the downward slope between the R and S waves of the QRS complex. This slope can be characterized as the most negative peak that occurs in the first derivative of the ECG waveform. To recognize this point, the ECG signal must be differentiated to obtain a signal representing the first derivative, and the first derivative signal must be scanned to locate its most negative peaks. Other tests are then applied to both the ECG and its derivative to verify that a true RS slope has been located.

From this reference point, the computer scans the ECG data in a backward direction with respect to time to locate the positive peak just preceding the reference. This peak is identified as the R wave. The negative peak of the ECG just subsequent to the reference slope is the S wave, and the negative peak just ahead of the R wave is the Q wave.

A predetermined interval of the ECG signal prior to the QRS complex is scanned for a positive peak to locate the P wave. Actually, the P wave is often identified on the basis of both the ECG waveform and its first derivative. The T wave is identified as a peak within a predetermined interval of the ECG signal following the QRS complex. In most ECG analysis programs, identification of the various waves is based on at least two leads.

The baseline of the ECG waveform is usually defined as a straight line from the onset of the P wave in one ECG cycle to the onset of the P wave in the next cycle. The amplitude of each of the waves (P, Q, R, S, and T) is measured with respect to that baseline. Also, a few points along the S-T segment are measured to determine their deviation from the baseline. Deviations from the baseline of the ECG signal as well as characteristics of the first derivative waveform are used to locate the onset and ending times of all waves. From this information the duration of each wave and the intervals between waves are measured. The duration of the QRS complex, the P-R interval, and the S-T interval are especially significant.

Each of the measured amplitudes, durations, and intervals is a characteristic parameter of the ECG signal. Another important parameter is the heart rate (determined by measuring the time intervals between successive R waves). Each of these parameters can be averaged over several cycles with the means and standard deviations being printed out for each of the leads measured.

For screening purposes, each of the parameters can also be checked to see if it falls within a normal range for that parameter. Any parameters that lie outside the normal range are indicated on the computer-generated report. A report of this type is shown in Table 15.1. This is the result of a test run on a 36-year-old male who was presumably normal, but was found by this screening analysis to have bradycardia (slow heart rate).

Identification and other patient information is printed at the top. The mean values for the various parameters are then presented in a matrix form. The columns represent the 12 standard leads while the rows indicate the parameters. Data from lead V3 were purposely omitted to show the response of the system to missing data. Below this matrix, values for the P-R, QRS, and Q-T intervals and the heart rate for each of the leads are printed out. The heart rate varies from lead to lead because in this system each lead is measured at a different time. Calibration information for each lead and the calculated angle of the axis of the heart (see Chapter 6) for each portion of the ECG cycle are also given. At the bottom of the printout are indications of any noted abnormalities. In the example, the condition of bradycardia (heart rate below 60 beats per minute) is noted as well as the absence of data from one lead.

In more sophisticated systems for computer analysis of the ECG, additional ways of representing the ECG are derived to further aid in distinguishing an abnormal ECG from a normal one. One such representation is a three-dimensional time-variant vector derived from the simultaneous measurement of three orthogonal leads. The behavior of this vector tells much more about the electrical activity of the heart than does the instantaneous calculation of the axis angle for a given portion of the ECG cycle.

Another parameter is the *time integral* of the ECG waveform. To obtain this integral, the areas of each wave above and below the baseline are determined and the sum of the areas below the baseline (negative) is subtracted from the sum of the areas above the baseline (positive). This integral can be determined for any portion of the ECG cycle. The sum of the time integral of the QRS complex and that of the T wave is sometimes called the *ventricular gradient,* and is believed to indicate the difference in the time course of depolarization and repolarization of the ventricles. The time integrals of the three orthogonal leads can be added vectorially to obtain three-dimensional time integrals.

Some systems for computer analysis of the ECG use statistical methods in an attempt to classify ECG patterns as various types of abnormalities

Table 15.1. ECG COMPUTER ANALYSIS DATA

RUN

H456789A   13:54   11/5/70

U.S.P.H.S. CERTIFIED E.C.G. PROGRAM PROCESSED BY THE BECKMAN HEARTLINE
FOR   BECKMAN INSTRUMENTS, INCORPORATED   LOC 10
  STAT
PAT 123456789   DATE 11- 5-70   SERIAL 126   OPERATOR 5
36 YR   MALE   5 FT 11 IN   190 LBS
BP NORMAL   MEDS NONE

	I	II	III	AVR	AVL	AVF	V1	V2	V3	V4	V5	V6	
PA	.08	.13	.00	-.07	.05	.08	.05	.12		.12	.08	.07	
PD	.13	.12	.00	.08	.09	.10	.05	.10		.10	.11	.08	
Q/SA	-.07	.00	.00	-.91	-.11	.00	.00	.00		.00	.00	.00	Q/SA
Q/SD	.02	.00	.00	.06	.02	.00	.00	.00		.00	.00	.00	Q/SD
RA	.86	.97	.13	.00	.61	.58	.16	.41		.67	1.72	1.33	RA
RD	.05	.09	.05	.00	.05	.09	.02	.03		.08	.10	.09	RD
SA	-.10	.00	-.21	.00	-.08	.00	-.95	-2.64		.00	.00	.00	SA
SD	.01	.00	.02	.00	.02	.00	.05	.07		.00	.00	.00	SD
RPA	.00	.00	.07	.00	.00	.00	.00	.00		.00	.00	.00	RPA
RPD	.00	.00	.02	.00	.00	.00	.00	.00		.00	.00	.00	RPD
STO	.03	.00	.00	-.03	.03	.02	-.03	.09		.08	.01	.00	STO
STM	.03	-.01	-.02	-.01	.04	.02	.04	.29		.04	.01	.00	STM
STE	.04	.00	-.04	-.02	.06	.00	.03	.38		.08	.04	.02	STE
TA	.28	.27	.07	-.30	.24	.19	-.15	1.15		.61	.43	.34	TA
PR	.16	.18	.00	.21	.15	.19	.17	.19		.19	.18	.18	PR
QRS	.08	.09	.09	.06	.09	.09	.07	.10		.08	.10	.09	QRS
QT	.38	.39	.43	.37	.39	.39	.38	.39		.39	.40	.41	QT
RATE	60	71	61	55	59	58	56	54		62	53	56	RATE
CODE	3	2	2	3	2	2	3	3	A	3	2	2	CODE
CAL	99	99	99	99	99	99	99	99		99	99	99	CAL

AXIS IN	P	QRS	T	Q	R	S	STO		ST-T	QRS-T
DEGREES	53	47	28		37	253	23		05	19

        MSDL APPROVED VERSION   •
        D 41-42-25-11   •
1131 RATE UNDER 60   • BRADYCARDIA
     1 LEAD NOT MEASURED   •
                                   • ATYPICAL ECG
                                   • ------------- M.D.

TIME 1 SECS.

or as being normal. Obviously, the more information available about the ECG, the better will be the discriminating ability of the computer programs. Multivariate statistical analysis techniques are sometimes employed, both for one-dimensional and three-dimensional data. Because of the wide inter-personal variation even among normals, accurate computer classification is difficult.

15.4.2   The Digital Computer in the Clinical Chemistry Laboratory

The modern clinical laboratory includes various types of automated instruments for the routine analysis of blood, urine, and other body fluids and tissues. Some of these devices are described in Chapter 13. While automated equipment can be used for most laboratory tests, there are still many determinations which are performed manually, either because of insufficient volume for certain tests or because satisfactory automated tests have not yet been devised. As a result, data from the clinical laboratory are generated in many forms, many of which require manual transcription of the test results.

In the chemistry laboratory, Autoanalyzers and other types of automated clinical chemistry equipment produce charts on which the test results are recorded. To produce laboratory reports which eventually become a part of the patients' records, data must be transcribed from these charts and combined with results from manually performed tests. Care must be taken to assure that data are accurately transcribed and that each test result is associated with the correct patient information.

To accommodate the large output of test results from the automated clinical chemistry equipment and to assimilate those data with patient information and the results of manually performed tests, a number of clinical chemistry laboratories have installed computer systems for data acquisition and processing. Computers of various sizes including micro processors, can be used in such systems, depending upon the extent to which the computer participates in the operation of the laboratory. In a highly automated system, the computer accepts test requisitions, prepares lists for blood drawing, schedules the loading of sample trays, reads test results, provides on-line quality control of the process, assimilates data, performs calculations, prepares reports, and stores data for possible comparison with future test results.

In a typical computerized system such as those discussed in Section 13.4, the medical staff may order tests directly via a remote terminal on the hospital ward or by use of machine-readable requisition forms which are automatically read by computer input equipment in the laboratory. From this requisition information, the computer schedules the drawing of blood by printing out blood drawing lists and preprinted specimen labels. These labels, which may be machine-readable, contain identification information to be used for all tests, automated and manual, from a given patient during that day. As the specimens arrive in the laboratory, the computer prepares a loading list which assigns a specific sample position in the analyzer loading tray for each test.

Patient information is entered into the computer either at the time the patient is admitted to the hospital or when the medical staff orders tests. This information is usually entered by keyboard, either from a remote terminal or in the laboratory.

Once a test run is begun, the output readings of all automated instruments are automatically entered into by the computer. Entry is usually accomplished by means of retransmitting slide wires attached to the recorder pens which produce analog voltages proportional to the output of each instrument. These analog voltages are sampled and converted to digital form by means of a time multiplexer and an analog-to-digital converter. The computer is programmed to recognize legitimate peaks as they arrive and to reject questionable or improperly shaped peaks. The computer also performs the necessary calculations to convert the value of each measured peak into medically useful units. By virtue of its position in the sequence of measured peaks or machine-readable ID labels, each test result is identified and associated with the correct patient. Control samples, placed randomly (by computer assignment) throughout the run, are used to periodically check the calibration of the system. By monitoring these control samples and the measured values from patient samples, the computer is able to perform "on-line quality control." In some cases, the computer can automatically correct the output values for drift and certain other types of error. In case of severe error, the computer may provide a warning to the operator, who may then choose to stop the test because of equipment malfunction.

The computer, after assimilating data from all automatically performed tests, may also receive results from manually performed tests. These manual test results would be entered by keyboard or via machine-readable data sheets specially prepared for each type of test. Once all test results have been received, credibility checks can be run to search for any impossible or unlikely combinations of results or any impossible changes in a given patient's test results from one day to the next. After the data have been checked and verified, the computer provides a physician's report, either in printed form or on a cathode-ray-tube terminal. This terminal can either be located in the laboratory, on the patient's ward, or in the physician's office. In addition, the computer might incorporate the test results into a patient filing system, so that whenever desired, the physician can request a profile of test results for a given patient over a specified number of days. Such a profile allows the physician to note changes in a patient's condition over time.

Another feature of most clinical laboratory computer systems is the capability of handling emergency requests. Such emergencies often require that a specimen of blood or urine be entered into the system ahead of routine samples. When patient identification is controlled by the position of a sample in the sample tray of the automated instrument, changes in sample positions to accommodate emergency needs must also be made known to the computer, either by keyboard notification of each change or by some automatic means of reading sample cup labels.

Provision must also be made for a physician to obtain results of a specific test before other tests on that patient have been completed and prior to the normal reporting of results. The inquiry is usually made by keyboard, either at the computer or from a remote terminal. Results of that specific test, if available, are given at the same terminal. If the test has not been completed at the time of the inquiry, the physician is so notified.

15.4.3. The Digital Computer in Patient Monitoring

Instrumentation systems for monitoring patients in intensive- and coronary-care units are described in Chapter 7. In recent years, especially since the advent of the microprocessor, an increasing number of patient-monitoring systems include some form of digital computer.

The type of computer involved and the extent of its role in the overall patient monitoring system may vary widely. In some systems, a small computer, usually a microprocessor, is used to store a limited amount of data and control a nonfade display of the ECG and other variables in an analog system. The waveforms either move across the screen with uniform brightness or remain stationary until replaced by new information, which appears to sweep across the screen and replace the old trace. Computer-controlled displays of this type usually include on-screen digital readouts of such parameters as systolic and diastolic blood pressures and heart rate.

In another type of computerized patient-monitoring system, the computer is simply attached to a conventional analog patient monitor to store and analyze information. Except for the interface through which the computer receives its data, the two systems are completely independent. A computer failure would have no effect whatever on the monitoring of patients. Waveform and trend plots are displayed on cathode-ray screens which are separate from the basic patient-monitoring system.

More often, the computer is an integral part of the patient-monitoring system and, in addition to storing and analyzing data, takes over many of the functions otherwise performed by analog circuitry, such as the filtering of signals to remove noise and artifacts and the controlling of alarms in case of an emergency. Some of the more recent systems utilize microprocessors for this purpose. The PDS 3000 shown in Figures 7.6 and 7.7 (Chapter 7) is a system of this type.

In a few very large hospitals, the patient monitoring system is integrated into a more extensive computer system in which patient records, laboratory test results, pharmacy records, and related information are combined with the ongoing data obtained from the patient monitor. Such systems may also tie in with the operating suite, cardiac catheterization laboratory, and other special diagnostic laboratories. By bringing together data from many sources, the computer can provide more complete information to assist the medical staff in their diagnoses and in monitoring the treatment of patients.

As stated in Chapter 7, the physiological variables typically measured by a patient-monitoring system include the ECG, temperature, a means of obtaining respiration rate, and often arterial and central venous blood pressures. Blood gas and pH measurements are also sometimes included. In a computerized system, the computer generally controls the collection and logging of data from their various sources to assure that readings are taken at the required intervals and properly recorded. Even where the computer is merely an adjunct to a conventional analog monitoring system, this data-acquisition function is required. Since most of the measured variables occur in analog form, control of an A/D converter is also involved. Digital filtering techniques are usually employed to smooth the data for display.

Computerized patient-monitoring systems generally involve most of the basic functions listed and described at the beginning of Section 15.4. Data acquisition and logging and the basic storage and retrieval functions have already been discussed. Data reduction and transformation techniques and mathematical operations are employed extensively in the calculation of a number of parameters, many of them indirect. The derived parameters usually include heart rate, respiration rate, systolic and diastolic blood pressures, and mean arterial and venous pressures. Other parameters, such as cardiac output, stroke volume, blood gas values, urine output, and various lung volumes and capacities are also sometimes calculated. Pattern-recognition techniques are utilized in the detection of arrhythmias and combinations of conditions that may require special attention. Limit detection and statistical analysis are used in checking the validity of data, monitoring for alarm conditions, and comparing results with normal values. The computer is also very much involved in the presentation and display of data. In addition to providing nonfade display of ECG and other raw data, the system may also produce many forms of graphical display, including histograms, trend plots, and plots showing the relationship of two or more variables. In some cases, the computer can also be used to control the infusion of blood or medication, based on the measured values of affected variables. For example, it can monitor a patient's urine output and actuate a pump to infuse a diuretic agent whenever the output falls below a predetermined quantity.

15.4.4. Computerized Axial Tomography (CAT) Scanners

A highly acclaimed application of the digital computer to clinical medicine is *computerized axial tomography (CAT)*. This procedure, which combines X-ray imaging (see Chapter 14) with computer techniques, permits visualization of internal organs and body structures with greater definition and clarity than could ever be attained by conventional methods. Although X rays have been in use since their discovery in 1895 and the reconstruction methods used in axial tomography date back to 1917, a practical combination of these techniques could not be achieved until the availability of the modern computer.

The basic principles involved in conventional X-ray imaging are discussed in Chapter 14, in which it is pointed out that the X-ray photograph is literally a shadow of all organs and structures in the path of the rays. If two radiopaque objects lie, one behind the other, in the X-ray path, as shown in Figure 15.9, the smaller of the two may be completely hidden by the larger. To partially circumvent this problem, a method of *linear tomography* was developed in which the X-ray source and film are simultaneously moved in opposite directions, as shown in Figure 15.10. For any given combination of source and film velocities, there will be one single plane perpendicular to the path of the rays in which objects will appear to remain stationary with respect to the film during the movement. In contrast, the shadows of objects at all other distances from the source will move on the film and produce a blur. In Figure 15.10, the sphere lies in the plane that appears stationary, whereas the cube does not. The shadow of the sphere is therefore reinforced as the X-ray vantage point is changed.

The principle of obtaining X-ray images from a number of vantage points is also used in computerized axial tomography, but in a different way. As the name implies, the vantage points for *axial tomography* are taken around the axis of the body. Instead of sending X rays through the entire portion of the body to be visualized, a very narrow pencil-like X-ray beam scans a single slice perpendicular to the body's axis. By scanning two or more such slices, a three-dimensional representation can be produced. Rather than obtaining an image on an X-ray film, the intensity of the X rays, after penetrating the body, is measured by means of one or more sodium iodide, xenon, or calcium chloride crystal detectors, which scintillate in proportion to the intensity (see Chapter 14). The scintillation light is measured by photomultiplier tubes. In the original computerized axial tomography (CAT) scanners, the source of the pencil-like beam was mechanically moved across the region of the slice, as shown in Figure 15.11. At the same time, the detector moved linearly in parallel with the source to receive a signal whose variations with respect to time represented the density pattern across the slice from one vantage point. The mechanism containing the source and

Figure 15.9. Conventional X-ray imaging of two objects, one behind the other.

Film

X-ray source

Figure 15.10. Linear tomography. X-ray source and film move simultaneously in opposite directions. Plane, in which small sphere lies, appears stationary on film.

Film

X-ray source

detector were then rotated about the axis of the body to a new vantage point, from which another scan of the slice was made. Scans were taken from 180 such vantage points, 1° apart. Data from each scan were fed into a computer, which combined the density pattern and reconstructed the anatomical density of the two-dimensional slice. By repeating this process for several slices, a detailed three-dimensional representation could be obtained. The early instruments usually scanned two slices at a time, this process requiring about 5 minutes. Because the region to be scanned had to remain stationary for this length of time, such scans were limited to the brain and other structures of the head, which could be kept immobilized in the necessary position by water bags.

Figure 15.11. Scanning pattern of early computerized axial tomography (CAT) scanners. X-ray source and detector move simultaneously in linear parallel paths to measure density through slice. Entire unit rotates about body to obtain scans from 180 vantage points, 1° apart.

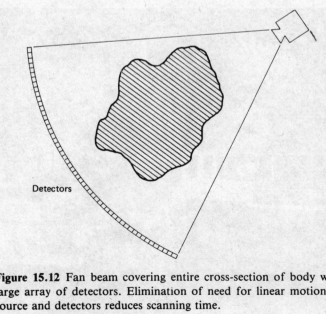

Figure 15.12 Fan beam covering entire cross-section of body with large array of detectors. Elimination of need for linear motion of source and detectors reduces scanning time.

To reduce scanning time, modern CAT scanners use X-ray sources that produce fan beams and multiple detectors to simultaneously measure the density across a wider portion of the slice. The fastest instruments have a fan beam that covers the entire width of the slice, as shown in Figure 15.12. Several hundred detectors are required to measure the density pattern of the slice with sufficient resolution to meet clinical needs. Greater scanning speed is also obtained by taking scans from fewer vantage points around the body. One commercial system, for example, uses only 15 scans, 12° apart; another uses 18 scans, 10° apart. Using these techniques, the time for complete scanning of a slice has been reduced to as little as 2½ seconds. Scanners with 100-msec scan times are under development. A modern instrument of this type is shown in Figure 15.13. Some instruments offer a choice of two scanning rates, permitting a trade-off between speed and resolution.

The higher scanning rates now available permit scanning of all sections of the body, since a patient can be asked to hold his or her breath and lie completely still for the few seconds necessary to complete a procedure. By synchronizing scans with the ECG, it is even possible to reconstruct slices of the heart in various phases of the cardiac cycle.

Figure 15.13. Modern computerized axial tomography (CAT) scanner (Courtesy of EMI Medical Inc., Northbrook, IL.)

Figure 15.14. Reconstructed image of slice through brain. (a) Non-contrast CT scan of the mid-brain demonstrating the third ventricle, frontal horns of the lateral ventricles, and quadrageminal cistern. (b) Quadrant magnification of scan in (a). (Courtesy of EMI Medical Inc., Northbrook, IL.)

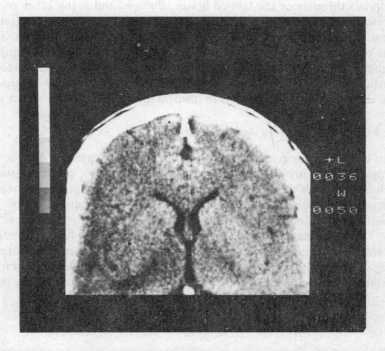

In the computer the cross section to be reconstructed is divided into tiny picture elements called *pixels*. The greater the number of pixels, the greater the resolution. An image of 180 × 180, or a total of 32,400 pixels, is typical. Each pixel is given a value proportional to the X-ray density of that element.

Several different mathematical techniques can be used to construct an image from the set of density patterns obtained during the individual scans. Most involve Fourier transformations and some require iterative operations, both of which are well suited to computer techniques. Digital spatial filters are usually employed to remove the blurring effects of the shadows created by more dense regions. In the final result, each pixel of the computer-generated image is given a degree of brightness proportional to its X-ray density. Figure 15.14 is an example of a reconstructed image of a slice through the brain. Figure 15.15 shows an image of the abdominal region. In some systems, the contrast between regions of different density can be enhanced by assigning each level of brightness a different color on a color TV monitor. This process, called *color enhancement,* provides a further aid in the detection of tumors and other abnormalities that might go unnoticed in a black-and-white display.

Because the CAT scanner can provide information about internal organs and body structures unobtainable by any other available means, and with radiation exposure to the patient no greater than that of conventional X-ray photographs, this instrument brought about a revolution in diagnostic radiology. Its popularity has resulted in scanners being installed in numerous hospitals throughout the United States, Europe, and many other parts of the world. The number of these installations and their high cost (ranging from $250,000 to nearly $1,000,000) have drawn criticism from those who fear technology as a contributor to increasing medical costs. Attempts to regulate the number of scanners on the basis of population have received considerable support. Nonetheless, this instrument is widely regarded as one of the major developments in medical instrumentation in recent years.

15.4.5. Other Computer Applications

The examples discussed in the previous sections represent only a small sample of the many ways in which computers are used in medical instrumentation. Although the proliferation of computers and microprocessors has extended into almost all types of medical instrumentation, a few more specific applications should be mentioned.

In the pulmonary function laboratory, pulmonary function tests and arterial blood gas analysis are often computerized. Measured values of lung volumes, vital capacity, flow rates, FEVs, blood gas levels, and related variables are compared with predicted normal values, based on the height,

Figure 15.15. Reconstructed image of abdominal slice. (a) CT scan at the mid-renal level; Normal study; Contrast filled renal pelvis is well demonstrated; The infundibula are clearly visualized bilaterally. The vena-cava and aorta are also visible. (b) CT scan of the same patient at a slightly higher level; Shows the lower aspect of the gall bladder and tip of the spleen; Both kidneys are well demonstrated with contrast noted in the collecting system; The left renal vein can be seen in its entirety extending anterior to the aorta and entering the inferior vena-cava. (Courtesy of EMI Medical Inc., Northbrook, IL.)

weight, and age of the patient. Variables not directly measurable are calculated and results may be interpreted for the physician. In some systems,
each set of measurements is compared with data from previous analyses
for determination of trends.

An extension of computerized ECG analysis are various computer-
assisted systems for exercise. In such systems preliminary data are gathered
to establish a preexercise cardiac template and to search for any contra-
indications to exercise for the patient. During the exercise, the ECG is monitored to determine the changes in a number of specific features of the waveform and to detect various exercise end-point indicators, such as attainment
of a target heart rate, supraventricular tachycardia, a predetermined amount
of S-T depression, and certain PVC patterns.

The cardiac catheterization laboratory provides another area in which
the computer is able to make a significant contribution. Intracardiac blood
pressures and pressure gradients across heart valves, vascular resistance
values, and other parameters of importance to the physician in locating and
defining cardiovascular abnormalities are measured or calculated using data
from one or more catheters within the chambers of the heart. With an
on-line computer, results can be obtained almost immediately, giving the
physician the assurance that the catheter is in the desired location and often
eliminating the need for the patient to return for a repeat of the test.

The success of computerized axial tomography to obtain detailed X-ray
images of slices of the body (Section 15.4.4) has led to the development
of similar techniques for other forms of imaging. A promising example is
emission computerized tomography, an application of computerized
tomographic techniques to nuclear medicine, which permits detailed visualization of the distribution of radioisotopes throughout the body. As explained in Chapter 14, radioactive isotopes of certain elements can be used
to trace the metabolism, pathways, and concentrations of these elements.
Through emission computerized tomography, the physician can be provided
a detailed three-dimensional distribution map of an isotope which has been
injected into the body and allowed to distribute itself. The three-dimensional
image is created by taking a number of slice scans, similar to the X-ray
slice images obtained by CAT scanner. The instrumentation for emission
computerized tomography is more complicated, however. In one configuration the body or section of the body to be imaged is surrounded by 66
sodium iodide detectors, 11 on each side of a hexagonal array. The detectors
are scanned sequentially and coincident pulses on opposite sides of the
hexagon are detected and counted. The entire array is rotated through 60°
during the course of a normal scan. The count of coincident events for each
pair of detectors is fed into a computer which, using techniques similar to
those employed in CAT scanners, produces a radioactivity map of each slice
scanned.

Computerized tomographic methods are being developed for ultrasonic imaging of the heart and abdominal organs. Computer techniques are also involved in *zeugmatography,* a new noninvasive imaging method utilizing the measurement of *nuclear magnetic resonance* (NMR). The benefits to be obtained from these and other new computer applications in medical technology must yet be assessed in light of their costs before their clinical significance can be determined.

16

Electrical Safety
of
Medical Equipment

Each year in the United States about 100,000 people are killed in accidents. About half the fatal accidents occur in motor vehicles, about 20 percent involve falls, and only about 1 percent of the fatalities are caused by electric current, including lightning. The majority of accidental electrocutions occur in industry or on farms. The statistics, which consider medical facilities to be industries, do not specifically show how many of these accidents occur in hospitals, but the number is probably not large. Most electrical accidents, however, are not fatal, but incidents in which staff members or patients receive nonfatal electrical shocks are much more common than the fatality statistics show.

Over the years electrical and electronic equipment has found increasing use in the hospital. Little attention was paid at first to the hazards that this proliferation might create. Some sensational reports published around 1970 on *microshock hazard,* which supposedly had killed a large number of patients in intensive-care units, suddenly drew attention to this subject. While the reports on microshock accidents were frequently anecdotal and no concise statistical analysis ever seems to have been published, growing concern about electrical hazards nevertheless resulted in numerous regulations and standards which attempted to improve electrical safety in the hospital. While some of the requirements have come under attack for unnecessarily increasing the cost of health care, this development has definitely contributed to improved design of electrical and electronic equipment for hospital use.

16.1 PHYSIOLOGICAL EFFECTS OF ELECTRICAL CURRENT

Electrical accidents are caused by the interaction of electric current with the tissues of the body. For an accident to occur, current of sufficient magnitude must flow through the body of the victim in such a way that it impairs the functioning of vital organs. Three conditions have to be met simultaneously [see Figure 16.1(a)]: two contacts must be provided to the body (arbitrarily called first and second contacts), together with a voltage source to drive current through these contacts. The physiological effects of the current depend not only on their magnitude but also on the current pathway through the body, which in turn depends on the location of the

Figure 16.1. The electrical accident. (a) The three necessary conditions. (b) The generalized model where R_F is the fault or leakage resistance, R_{C1} and R_{C2} are first and second contact resistance, R_B is body resistance and R_R is the ground return resistance.

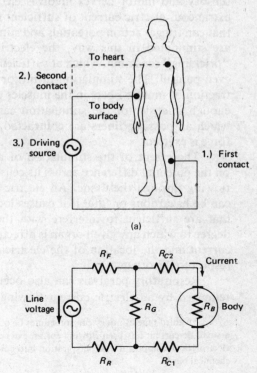

first and second contacts. Two particular situations have to be considered separately: when both contacts are applied to the surface of the body and when one contact is applied directly to the heart. Because the current sensitivity of the heart is much higher in the second case, the effect of current applied directly to the heart is often referred to as *microshock,* while in this context the effect of current applied through surface contacts is called *macroshock.*

Figure 16.1(b) is a generalized model of an electrical accident and will be referred to later in the chapter in various appropriate sections.

Basically, electric current can affect the tissue in two different ways.* First, the electrical energy dissipated in the tissue resistance can cause a temperature increase. If a high enough temperature is reached, tissue damage (burns) can occur. With household current, electrical burns are usually limited to localized damage at or near the contact points, where the density of the current is the greatest. In industrial accidents with high voltage, as well as in lightning accidents, the dissipated electrical energy can be sufficient to cause burns involving larger parts of the body. In *electrosurgery,* the concentrated current from a radio-frequency generator with a frequency of 2.5 or 4 MHz is used to cut tissue or coagulate small blood vessels.

Second, as shown in Chapter 10, the transmission of impulses through sensory and motor nerves involves electrochemical action potentials. An extraneous electric current of sufficient magnitude can cause local voltages that can trigger action potentials and stimulate nerves. When sensory nerves are stimulated in this way, the electric current causes a "tingling" or "prickling" sensation, which at sufficient intensity becomes unpleasant and even painful. The stimulation of motor nerves or muscles causes the contraction of muscle fibers in the muscles or muscle groups affected. A high-enough intensity of the stimulation can cause tetanus of the muscle, in which all possible fibers are contracted, and the maximal possible muscle force is exerted.

The extent of the stimulation of a certain nerve or muscle depends on the potential difference across its cells and the local density of the current flowing through the tissue. An electric current flowing through the body can be hazardous or fatal if it causes local current densities in vital organs that are sufficient to interfere with the functioning of the organs. The degree to which any given organ is affected depends on the magnitude of the current and the location of the electrical contact points on the body with respect to the organ.

Respiratory paralysis can also occur if the muscles of the thorax are tetanized by an electric current flowing through the chest or through the

---

*A third type of injury can sometimes be observed under skin electrodes through which a small dc current has been flowing for an extended time interval. These injuries are due to electrolytic decomposition of perspiration into corrosive substances and are, therefore, actual chemical burns.

respiratory control center of the brain. Such a current is likely to affect the heart also, because of its location.

The organ most susceptible to electric current is the heart. The peculiar characteristics of its muscle fibers cause it to react to electric current differently than other muscles. When the current density within the heart exceeds a certain value, extra systolic contractions first occur. If the current density is increased further, the heart activity stops completely but resumes if the current is removed within a short time. This type of response, however, appears to be limited to a fairly narrow range of current density. An even further increase in current density causes the heart muscle to go into fibrillation. In this state the muscle fibers contract independently and without synchronism, a situation that fails to provide the necessary gross contraction. When the fibrillation occurs in the ventricles (ventricular fibrillation) the heart is unable to pump blood. In human beings (and other large mammals) ventricular fibrillation does not normally revert spontaneously to a normal heart rhythm. Ventricular fibrillation and resulting cessation of blood circulation is the cause of death in the majority of fatal electrical accidents. It can be converted to a regular heart rhythm, however, by the application of a defibrillating current pulse of sufficient magnitude. Such a pulse, applied from a defibrillator (see Section 7.6), causes a momentary contraction of many or all muscle fibers of the heart, which effects a synchronization of their activity. If, in an accidental situation, the heart receives enough current to tetanize the entire myocardium and assuming the current is removed in time, the heart will revert to normal rhythm after cessation of the current.

The magnitude of electric current required to produce a certain physiological effect in a person is influenced by many factors. Figure 16.2 shows the approximate current ranges and the resulting effects for 1-second exposures to various levels of 60-Hz alternating current applied externally to the body. For those physiological effects that involve the heart or respiration, it is assumed that the current is introduced into the body by electrical contact with the extremities in such a way that the current path includes the chest region (arm-to-arm or arm-to-diagonal leg).

For most people, the perception threshold of the skin for light finger contact is approximately 500 μA, although much lower current intensities can be detected with the tongue. With a firm grasp of the hand, the threshold is about 1 mA. A current with an intensity not exceeding 5 mA is generally not considered harmful, although the sensation at this level can be rather unpleasant and painful. When at least one of the contacts with the source of electricity is made by grasping an electrical conductor with the hand, currents in excess of about 10 or 20 mA can tetanize the arm muscles and make it impossible to "let go" of the conductor. The maximum current level a person can tolerate and still voluntarily let go of the conductor is called his *let-go current level*. Ventricular fibrillation can occur at currents

Figure 16.2. Physiological effects of electrical current from 1-second external contact with the body (60 Hz ac).

The labels within the figure, from top to bottom:

SEVERE BURNS
and physical injury

10 A — Sustained myocardial contraction (followed by normal heart rhythm if current is removed in time)

Danger of respiratory paralysis

1 A — DANGER of ventricular fibrillation

100 mA —

Pain, fatigue, possible physical injury

← Maximum "let go" current

10 mA —

← Accepted safe level (5 mA)

1 mA —

500 μA — ← Threshold of perception

above about 75 mA, while currents in excess of about 1 or 2 A can cause contraction of the heart, which may revert to normal rhythm if current is discontinued in time. This condition may also be accompanied by respiratory paralysis.

Data on these effects are rare for obvious reasons and are generally limited to accidents in which the magnitude of the current could be reconstructed, or to experimentation with animals. From the data available it appears that the current required to cause ventricular fibrillation increases with the body weight and that a higher current is required if the current is applied for a very short duration. From experiments in the current range of the perception threshold and let-go current, it is known that the effects of the current are almost independent of frequency up to about 1000 Hz. Above that limit, the current must be increased proportionally with the frequency in order to have the same effect. It can be assumed that, at higher current levels, a similar relationship exists between current effects and frequency.

In the foregoing considerations, the electrical intensity is always described in terms of electric current. The voltage required to cause the current flow depends solely on the electrical resistance that the body offers to the current. This resistance is affected by numerous factors and can vary from a few ohms to several megohms. The largest part of the body resistance is normally represented by the resistance of the skin. The inverse of this resistance, the skin conductance, is proportional to the contact area and also depends on the condition of the skin. Intact, dry skin has a conductivity of as low as 2.5 μ v cm^2. This low conductivity is caused mainly by the horny, outermost layer of the skin, the epithelium, which provides a natural protection against electrical danger. When this layer is permeated by a conductive fluid, however, the skin conductivity can increase by two orders of magnitude. If the skin is cut, or if conductive objects like hypodermic needles are introduced through the skin, the skin resistance is effectively bypassed. When this situation occurs, the resistance measured between the contacts is determined only by the tissue in the current path, which can be as low as 500 Ω. Electrode paste used in the measurement of bioelectric potentials (see Chapters 4, 6, and 10) reduces the skin resistivity by electrolyte action and mechanical abrasion. Many medical procedures require the introduction of conductive objects into the body, either through natural openings or through incisions in the skin. In many instances, therefore, the hospital patient is deprived of the natural protection against electrical dangers that the skin normally provides. Because of the resulting low resistance, dangerously high currents can be caused by voltages of a magnitude that normally would be rendered safe by the high skin resistance.

In certain medical procedures, a direct contact to the heart may even be established. This contact can occur in three different ways:

1. Electrically conductive catheters are inserted through a vein into the heart to apply stimulating signals from an externally worn pacemaker. Such pacing catheters provide a connection with a resistance of only a few ohms. Patients with such catheters are normally located in the coronary-care or intensive-care unit of the hospital.

2. Fluid-filled catheters provide a conductive pathway only incidentally because the insulating catheter wall retains the current in the conductive fluid that fills the catheter lumen. These catheters provide a current path with a much higher resistance than that of a pacing catheter (0.1 to 2 MΩ, depending on the size and length of the catheter). Fluid-filled catheters are used for a number of medical procedures. For cardiac catheterization—normally performed in a specially equipped X-ray suite—pressures in the heart are measured and blood samples are withdrawn through similar catheters. Similarly, dyes or saline solution are injected and blood samples are withdrawn to determine the cardiac output (see Chapter 6), a procedure that is sometimes even performed at the bedside of patients. In (selective) angiocardiography, catheters are used to inject a radiopaque dye into the heart or the surrounding blood vessels to facilitate their visualization on a series of X-ray photos, often taken in rapid succession (see Chapter 14). This procedure is often performed in the regular X-ray suite.

3. While in the procedures described, a conductive path is created either intentionally or incidentally, a contact to the heart can also be established accidentally without the physician being aware of that fact. This situation can occur when an electrical device (e.g., a thermistor catheter, which is supposed to be insulated, see Chapter 6) has an insulation failure, or when a fluid-filled catheter is inadvertently positioned inside the heart rather than in one of the major veins.

Information on the current necessary to cause ventricular fibrillation when applied directly to the heart was obtained mainly from experiments with dogs, since human data are very limited. While fibrillation has occasionally been observed at currents as low as 20 μA, in most cases the necessary current is much higher.

16.2. SHOCK HAZARDS FROM ELECTRICAL EQUIPMENT

An example of a typical hospital electric-power-distribution system, is shown in somewhat simplified form in Figure 16.3. From the main hospital substation, the power is distributed to individual buildings at 4800 V, usually through underground cables. A stepdown transformer in each building has a secondary winding for 230 V that is center-tapped and thus can provide two circuits of 115 V each. This center tap is grounded to the earth by a connection to a ground rod or water pipe near the building's substation. Heavy electrical devices, such as large air conditioners, ovens, and X-ray machines, operate on 230 V from the two ungrounded terminals of the transformer secondary. Lights and normal wall receptacles receive 115 V through a black "hot" wire from one of the ungrounded terminals of the transformer secondary and a white "neutral" wire that is connected to the grounded center tap, as shown in Figure 16.3.

In order to be exposed to an electrical macroshock hazard, a person must come in contact with both the hot and the neutral conductors simultaneously, or with both hot conductors of a 230-V circuit. However, because

Figure 16.3. Electric power distribution system (simplified).

437

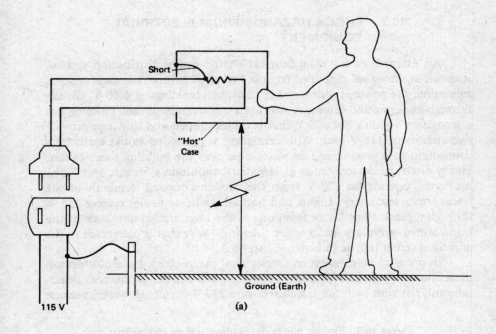

Short

"Hot"
Case

115 V

Ground (Earth)

(a)

Figure 16.4. Ground shock hazards.

Short

Ground
Wire

Ground (Earth)

(b)

the neutral wire is connected to ground, the same shock hazard exists between the hot wire and any conductive object that is in any way connected to ground. Included would be such items as a room radiator, water pipes, or metallic building structures. In the design of electrical equipment, great care is taken to prevent personnel from accidentally contacting the hot wire by the use of suitable insulating materials and the observation of safe distances between conductors and equipment cases. Through insulation breakdown, wear, and mechanical damage, however, contact between a hot wire and an equipment case can accidentally occur.

Figure 16.4(a) shows the scenario of such an accident. A defect in the equipment has caused a short between the hot wire of the line cord and the (conductive) equipment case, placing the case at a potential of 115 V ac with respect to ground. A user whose body is in contact with ground (the first contact of Figure 16.1) will be placed in jeopardy when a (second) contact between his body and the case of the faulty equipment is established. The generalized model for electrical accidents, shown in Figure 16.1(b), permits a more detailed analysis of the situation. The model represents a network consisting of a voltage source and six resistances. The *fault resistance* (or leakage resistance), R_F, represents the short between the hot conductor and the case of the equipment. The *first and second contact resistance,* R_{C1} and R_{C2}, represent, respectively, the resistances of the first and second contacts to the body of the accident victim. Together with the *body resistance,* R_B, they form the resistance of the current path through the victim's body. The *grounding resistance,* R_G (which in Figure 16.4 is infinitely large), is connected in parallel with the current path through the body. The *ground return resistance,* R_R, is essentially the resistance between ground and the center tap of the transformer shown in Figure 16.3. This resistance is normally very small.

An electrical accident can occur when the six resistances shown in the figure assume any combination of values such that the resulting current through the body of the victim reaches a dangerous magnitude. All measures taken to reduce the probability of electrical accidents are, in effect, attempts to manipulate the value of one or more of the resistances.

16.3. METHODS OF ACCIDENT PREVENTION

In order to reduce the likelihood of electrical accidents, a number of protective methods have evolved. Some are used universally, some are required in areas that are generally considered especially hazardous, and still others have been developed essentially for use in hospitals.

16.3.1. Grounding

The protection method used most frequently is proper *grounding* of equipment. The principle of this method is to make the grounding resistance R_G in Figure 16.1(b) small enough that for all possible values of the fault resistance R_F, the majority of the fault current bypasses the body of the victim and the body current remains at a safe level even if contact and body resistances are small. The practical implementation of this method is shown in Figure 16.4(b), where the metal case of the equipment is connected to ground by a separate wire. In cord-connected electrical equipment this ground connection is established by the third, round, or U-shaped contact in the plug. If a short occurs in a device whose case has been grounded in this way, the electric current flows through the short to the case and returns to the substation through the ground wire. Ideally, the short circuit will result in sufficient current to cause the circuit breaker to trip immediately. This action would remove the power from the faulty piece of equipment and thus limit the hazard.

Protection by grounding, however, has several shortcomings. Obviously, it is effective only as long as a good ground connection exists. Experience has shown that many receptacles, plugs, and line cords of the conventional type do not hold up under the conditions of hospital use. Many manufacturers now make available *Hospital Grade* receptacles and plugs which are designed to pass a strict test required by the Underwriters Laboratory for devices to qualify for this specification. Hospital Grade plugs and receptacles are marked by a green dot.

A second disadvantage is that in the case of a short, protection is provided by removing the power from the defective device by tripping the circuit breaker. This action, however, also removes the power from all other devices connected to the same branch circuit. In a hospital setting, one defective device could disable a number of other devices, which might include life-saving instruments.

16.3.2. Double Insulation

In double-insulated equipment the case is made of nonconductive material, usually a suitable plastic. If accessible metal parts are used, they are attached to the conductive main body of the equipment through a separate (protective) layer of insulation in addition to the (functional) insulation that separates this body from the electrical parts.

The intention of this method is to assure that the fault resistance R_F is always very large. Double-insulated equipment need not be grounded, and therefore it is usually equipped with a plug that does not have a ground pin. Equipment of this type must be labeled "Double Insulated." Double insulation is now widely used as a method of protection in hand-held power tools and electric-powered garden equipment such as lawn mowers. However, double insulation is of only limited value for equipment found in a hospital environment. Unless the equipment is also designed to be waterproof, the double insulation can easily be rendered ineffective if a conductive fluid such as saline or urine is spilled over the equipment or if the equipment is submerged in such a fluid.

16.3.3. Protection by Low Voltage

In the generalized accident model of Figure 16.1(b) it was assumed that the voltage source was the line voltage (115 or 230 V ac). If, instead, another voltage source were used, and if the voltage of this source could be made small enough, the body resistance R_B would be sufficient to limit the body current to a safe value, even if the fault and contact resistances become very small. One way of creating this situation is to operate the equipment from batteries. Aside from its lower voltage there is the additional advantage that battery-operated equipment does not have to be grounded. Normally, battery operation is limited to small devices such as flashlights and razors, but occasionally equipment as large as portable X-ray machines may use this method of protection. A low operating voltage can also be obtained by means of a step-down transformer. In addition to lowering the voltage the transformer provides isolation of the supply voltage from ground. Where power requirements are small, the transformer can be made an integral part of the line plug, a design now frequently employed in small electronic equipment as well as in such medical devices as ophthalmoscopes and endoscopes.

16.3.4. Ground-Fault Circuit Interrupter

Statistical evidence indicates that most electrical accidents are of the type in which the body of the victim provides a conductive path to ground, as shown in Figure 16.4. Normally all current that enters a device through the hot wire returns through the neutral wire. However, in the case of such an accident, part of the current actually returns through the body of the victim and through ground. In the *ground fault circuit interrupter,* the difference between the currents in the hot and neutral wires of the power line is monitored by a differential transformer and an electronic amplifier. If this difference exceeds a certain value, usually 5 mA, the power is interrupted by a circuit breaker. This interruption occurs so rapidly that, even in the case of a large current flow through the body of a victim, no harmful effects are encountered.

Figure 16.5. Current limiters. (a) Input circuit of older ECG machine or ECG monitor; (b) The same circuit modernized by the addition of current limiters; (c) Electrical characteristics of current limiter.

16.3.5. Isolation of Patient-Connected Parts

Many types of medical equipment require that an electrical connection be established to the body of the patient, either to measure electrical potentials, such as in ECG machines, or to apply electrical signals, such as in electrical pacemakers. These electrical connections, however, could also serve as a path for dangerous electrical currents should the equipment malfunction. For example, in older ECG machines and patient monitors, it was common practice to connect one of the patient leads (the RL lead) to a power-line ground. This effectively grounded the patient and established one of the two connections necessary for an electrical accident. Modern technology makes it possible to design circuits that isolate the patient leads from ground. For patient leads that connect to an amplifier, this isolation is most commonly achieved by the use of an isolated input amplifier, as shown in Figure 16.5. This type of amplifier is completely isolated from the rest of the equipment, with the power provided through a low-capacitance transformer. A second transformer is used to couple the amplified signal to the rest of the equipment. Because signal transformers are difficult to design for the frequency range of biological signals, a modulation scheme is normally employed. The amplifier shown in the figure uses amplitude modulation of the carrier signal used to provide power for the isolated amplifier. Other designs use frequency modulation.

Figure 16.6. Input circuit of modern ECG machine or ECG monitor with isolated patient leads achieved by the use of a carrier amplifier.

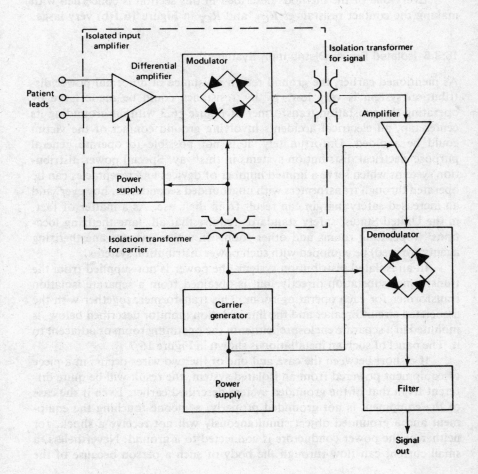

Occasionally, isolation protection is provided by connecting a *current limiter* into each patient lead. The characteristics of these devices are shown in Figure 16.6. For low currents these devices act as resistors, but when a certain current level is approached they change their characteristics and prevent the current from exceeding a predetermined limit. Although current limiters are less desirable than isolated amplifiers, they are nevertheless used where many patient leads have to be protected, such as in EEG machines.

In biomedical devices that provide electrical energy to the body of a patient, such as pacemakers or electrosurgical devices, protection is achieved by isolating the patient leads from ground. In pacemakers, this is now normally accomplished by using only battery-operated types. Modern electrosurgical devices use output transformers to isolate patient leads.

Every one of the methods described in this section is concerned with making the contact resistances R_{C1} and R_{C2} in Figure 16.1(b) very large.

16.3.6 Isolated Power Distribution Systems

As mentioned earlier, the ground return resistance of a normal power distribution system is very low. If this resistance could be made large by operating the substation transformer of Figure 16.3 without grounding its center tap, all electrical accidents involving ground contact of the victim could be avoided. Unfortunately, it is not possible to operate general purpose electrical distribution systems in this way. Special power distribution systems which serve a limited number of devices and receptacles can be operated through transformers with ungrounded secondaries, however, and an increased safety margin can result from their use. As a matter of fact, in the United States, safety standards require that all "anesthetizing locations" (operating rooms and other rooms in which gaseous anesthetizing agents are used) be equipped with such power distribution systems.

In an isolated distribution system, the power is not supplied from the transformer substation directly, but is obtained from a separate isolation transformer for each operating room. This transformer, together with the associated circuit breaker and the line isolation monitor described below, is mounted in a separate enclosure, either in the operating room or adjacent to it. The panel of such an installation is shown in Figure 16.7.

If a short between the case and one of the two wires occurs in a piece of equipment powered from an isolated system, the result will be quite different from that of the grounded system described earlier. Even if the case of the equipment is not grounded properly, someone touching the equipment and a grounded object simultaneously will not receive a shock, for neither of the power conductors is connected to a ground. Nevertheless, a small current can flow through the body of such a person because of the

Figure 16.7. Panel of isolated power distribution system. (Courtesy of Sorgel Electric Corporation, subsidiary of Square D Company, Oshkosh, WI.)

capacity between the conductors of the system and ground. This current, however, will be of a magnitude of at most 1 or 2 mA, which may be perceived without being harmful. If the equipment in which the short occurs is properly grounded, this *leakage current* will return through the ground connection. In this case, however, the short in the faulty equipment effectively grounds one of the conductors of the isolated distribution system. As a result, the isolated system is changed back to a grounded distribution system and all the protection provided by the isolated system is obviated. In order to provide a warning in the event that this situation occurs, isolated power systems employ *line isolation monitors* (LIM). This device alternately checks the two wires of the distribution system for isolation from ground. The degree of isolation, expressed as the *risk current* or *fault hazard current,* is indicated on an electric meter.

In addition to the meter, two warning lamps are provided. When the system is adequately isolated, a green lamp (sometimes labeled "SAFE") will be on. If the isolation begins to deteriorate or if a short occurs between one of the wires and ground anywhere in the system, a red lamp (sometimes labeled "HAZARD") will light up. At the same time, an acoustical alarm will begin to sound. This hazard alarm merely indicates that the system has lost its protective properties. It still requires a second fault before an actual hazard can arise. If the alarm occurs while an operation is in progress, it is therefore possible to complete the procedure before attempting to find the cause of the alarm. For this situation, the line isolation monitor has a button with which the acoustical alarm can be silenced. Even if the acoustical alarm is turned off, the red warning lamp remains on, indicating the continued presence of an alarm condition. The line isolation monitor also has a button that allows it to be tested for proper functioning. Pressing this button simulates a short.

Receptacles powered from an isolated system are not always the common three-prong type but may be a special locking type, shown in Figure 16.8.

Figure 16.8. Locking plug for isolated power distribution system. (Courtesy of Veterans Administration Biomedical Engineering and Computing Center, Sepulveda, CA.)

In addition to the isolated distribution system, a special high-quality grounding system is also required for all anesthetizing locations. This system not only protects the patient and staff by shunting all leakage currents to the ground but is also necessary for the proper functioning of the line isolation monitor. The special grounding system is called an *equipotential grounding system* because it keeps all metallic objects in the area that could possibly come in contact with staff or patients at the same electrical potential. For this purpose, not only the enclosures of electrical equipment but also all other metal objects—operating tables, anesthesia machines, and instrument tables—that might come in contact with electrical equipment must be interconnected by the grounding system. Portable items of this kind may require the use of separate ground wires connected to a common grounding point near the head of the operating table. Special bayonet-type plugs are used on this ground wire. Similar equipotential grounding systems are also required in intensive-care units. Such a system is shown in Figure 16.9.

Figure 16.9. Principle of an equipotential grounding system in one room or cubicle of an intensive care or cardiac care unit.

Appendices

A

Medical Terminology and Glossary

A.1. MEDICAL TERMINOLOGY

One of the problems of an interdisciplinary field is that of communication between the disciplinary components that make up the field. Engineers and technicians have to learn enough physiology, anatomy, and medical terminology to be able to discuss problems intelligently with members of the medical profession.

The typical technical person faces enough difficulty with language, but when confronted with medical terminology, his or her problems are compounded. However, with a few simple rules, medical terminology can be understood more easily. Most medical words have either a Latin or Greek origin, or, as in engineering, chemistry, and physics, the surnames of prominent researchers are used.

Most words consist of a root or base which is modified by a prefix or suffix or both. The root is often abbreviated when the prefix or suffix is added.

The following list gives some of the more common roots, prefixes, and suffixes.

PREFIXES

a	without or not	*mal*	bad
ab	away from	*medio*	middle
ad	to, toward	*mes*	middle
an	absence of	*meta*	beyond, over
ante	before	*micro*	small
antero	in front	*ortho*	straight; correct
anti	against	*para*	beside
bi	two	*patho*	disease
brady	slow	*peri*	outside, around
dia	through	*poly*	many
dys	difficult, painful	*pseudo*	false
endo	within	*quadri*	fourfold
epi	upon	*retro*	backward
eu	well, good	*sub*	beneath
ex	away from	*supra*	above
exo	outside	*tachy*	fast
hyper	over	*trans*	across
hypo	under or less	*tri*	three
infra	below	*ultra*	beyond
intra	within	*uni*	single, one

ROOTS

aden	gland	*gaster*	stomach
arteria	artery	*haemo* or *hemo*	blood
arthros	joint	*hepar*	liver
auris	ear	*hydro*	water
brachion	arm	*hystera*	womb
hronchus	windpipe	*kystis (cysto)*	bladder
cardium	heart	*larynx*	throat
cephalos	brain	*myelos*	marrow
cholecyst	gallbladder	*nasus*	nose
colon	intestine	*nephros*	kidney
costa	rib	*neuron*	neuron
cranium	head	*odons*	tooth
derma	skin	*odynia*	pain
enteron	intestine	*optikas*	eye
epithelium	skin	*os*	bone
esophagus	gullet	*osteon*	bone
ostium	mouth, orifice	*pyretos*	fever
otis	ear	*ren*	kidney
pes	foot	*rhin*	nose

pharynx	throat	*rhythmos*	rhythm
phlebos	vein	*spondylos*	vertebra
pleura	chest	*stoma*	mouth
pneumones	lungs	*thorax*	chest
psyche	mind	*trachea*	windpipe
pulmones	lungs	*trophe*	nutrition
pyelos	pelvis	*vene*	vein
pyon	pus	*vesica*	bladder

SUFFIXES

algia	pain	*emia*	blood
centeses	puncture	*iasis*	a process
clasia	remedy	*itis*	inflammation
ectasis	dilatation	*oma*	swelling, tumor
ectomy	cut	*sclerosis*	hardening
edema	swelling		

ia is also used as a suffix in many combinations and it indicates a state or condition.

Examples of how the words are formed are easily illustrated. Arteriosclerosis means hardening of the arteries. The heart is the *cardium* and the loose sac in which it is contained is called the *pericardium* (outside the heart). If the pericardium is diseased, it is called *pericarditis*. Note that some letters are dropped or changed for the new word, but the construction is easily recognizable.

Another example would be the root *trophe,* literally meaning nutrition. The prefix *a* means absence of, and *hyper* means over. Therefore, *atrophy* is to waste away, and *hypertrophy* is to enlarge.

English usage is sometimes peculiar and utilizes the Greek and Latin words together. An example is the kidney—*ren* in Latin and *nephros* in Greek. We talk about kidney function as *renal* function, but inflammation of the kidney is *nephritis*.

Descriptions for relative position are frequently used in medical usage. These are:

anterior	situated in front of; forward part of.
distal	away from the center of the body.
dorsal	a position more toward the back of an object of reference.
frontal	situated at the front.
inferior	situated or directed below.
lateral	a position more toward the side of flank.
proximal	toward the center of the body.
sagital	relating to the median plane of the body or any plane parallel to it.
superior	situated or directed above.

A.2. MEDICAL GLOSSARY

Throughout this book many biomedical words have been used which are possibly unfamiliar to the reader. To help achieve a better understanding, the following glossary of medical terms is presented in alphabetical order for easy reference. There are many sources for these definitions, including the authors' own interpretation, but among well-known reference books used are various Webster's dictionaries (G. & C. Merriam Co., Springfield, Mass.) and *Dorland's Illustrated Medical Dictionary,* 25th ed. (W. B. Saunders Company, Philadelphia, 1974).

A

acetylcholine- a reversible acetic acid ester of choline having important physiological functions, such as the transmission of a nerve impulse across a synapse.

acidosis- a condition of lowered blood bicarbonate (decreased pH).

afferent- conveying toward the center or toward the brain.

alkalosis- a condition of increased blood bicarbonate (increased pH).

alveoli- air sacs in the lungs formed at the terminals of a bronchiole. It is through a thin membrane (0.001 mm thick) in the alveoli that the oxygen enters the bloodstream.

anaerobic- growing only in the absence of molecular oxygen.

anoxic- oxygen insufficient to support life.

aorta- the great trunk artery that carries blood from the heart to be distributed by branch arteries through the body.

aortic valve- outlet valve from left ventricle to the aorta.

apnea- absence of breathing.

arrhythmia- an alteration in rhythm of the heartbeat either in time or force.

arteriole- one of the small terminal twigs of an artery that ends in capillaries.

artery- a vessel through which the blood is pumped away from the heart.

atrioventricular- located between an atrium and ventricle of the heart.

atrium- an anatomical cavity or passage; especially a main chamber of the heart into which blood returns from circulation.

auscultation- the act of listening for sounds in the body.

autonomic- acting independently of volition; relating to, affecting, or controlled by the autonomic nervous system.

axon- a usually long and single nerve-cell process that, as a rule, conducts impulses away from the cell body of a neuron.

B

baroreceptors- nerve receptors in the blood vessels, especially the carotid sinus, sensitive to blood pressure.

bifurcation- branching, as in blood vessels.

bioelectricity- the electrical phenomena that appear in living tissues.

brachial- relating to the arm or a comparable process.

bradycardia- a slow heart rate.

bronchus- either of two primary divisions of the trachea that lead, respectively, into the right and the left lung; broadly, bronchial tube.

bundle of His- a small band of cardiac muscle fibers transmitting the waves of depolarization from the atria to the ventricles during cardiac contraction.

C

cannula- a small tube for insertion into a body cavity or blood vessel.

capacity, functional residual- the volume of gas remaining in the lungs at the resting expiratory level. The resting end-expiratory level is used as the baseline because it varies less than the end-inspiratory position.

capacity, inspiratory- the maximal volume of gas that can be inspired from the resting expiratory level.

capillaries- any of the smallest vessels of the blood-vascular system connecting arterioles with venules and forming networks throughout.

cardiac- pertaining to the heart.

cardiac arrest- standstill of normal heartbeat.

cardiology- the study of the heart, its action and diseases.

cardiovascular- relating to the heart and blood vessels.

catheter- a tubular medical device inserted into canals, vessels, passageways, or body cavities, usually to permit injection or withdrawal of fluids or to keep a passage open.

cell- a small, usually microscopic, mass of protoplasm bounded externally by a semipermeable membrane, usually including one or more nuclei and various nonliving products, capable (alone or interacting with other cells) of performing all the fundamental functions of life, and of forming the least structural aggregate of living matter capable of functioning as an independent unit.

cerebellum- a large, dorsally projecting part of the brain especially concerned with the coordination of muscles and the maintenance of bodily equilibrium.

cerebrum- the enlarged anterior or upper part of the brain.

computerized axial tomography- a technique combining x-ray and computer technology for visualization of internal organs and body structures.

coronary artery and sinus- vessels carrying blood to and from the walls of the heart itself.

cortex- the outer or superficial part of an organ or body structure; especially the outer layer of gray matter of the cerebrum and cerebellum.

cortical- of, relating to, or consisting of the cortex.

cranium- the part of the head that encloses the brain.

cytoplasm- the protoplasm of a cell exclusive of that of the nucleus.

D

defibrillation- the correction of fibrillation of the heart.

defibrillator- an apparatus used to counteract fibrillation (very rapid irregular contractions of the muscle fibers of the heart) by application of electric impulses to the heart.

dendrite- any of the usual branching protoplasmic processes that conduct impulses toward the body of a nerve cell.

depolarize- to cause to become partially or wholly unpolarized.

diastole- a rhythmically recurrent expansion, especially the dilatation of the cavities of the heart as they fill with blood.

diastolic- of or pertaining to the diastole (e.g., diastolic blood pressure).

dicrotic- having a double beat; being or relating to the second expansion of the artery that occurs during the diastole of the heart (hence dicrotic notch in the blood pressure wave).

dyspnea- difficulty in breathing.

E

ECG- abbreviation for electrocardiogram.

echocardiogram- an ultrasonic record of the dimension and movement of the heart and its valves.

ectopic- located away from the normal position.

EEG- abbreviation for electroencephalogram.

efferent- conveying away from a center.

electrocardiogram- a record of the electrical activity of the heart.

electrocardiograph- an instrument used for the measurement of the electrical activity of the heart.

electrode- a device used to interface ionic potentials and currents.

electroencephalogram- the tracing of brain waves made by an electroencephalograph.

electroencephalograph- an instrument for measuring and recording electrical activity from the brain (brain waves).

electrolyte- a nonmetallic electric conductor in which current is carried by the movement of ions.

electromyogram- the tracing of muscular action potentials by an electromyograph.

electromyograph- an instrument for measurement of muscle potentials.

electromyography-- the recording of the changes in electric potential of muscle.

electrophysiology- the science of physiology in its relations to electricity; the study of the electric reactions of the body in health.

embolus- an abnormal particle (air, clot, or fat) circulating in the blood.

embryo- a human or animal offspring prior to emergence from the womb or egg; hence, a beginning or undeveloped stage of anything.

EMG- abbreviation for electromyography.

epilepsy- any of a variety of disorders marked by disturbed electrical rhythms of the central nervous system, typically manifested by convulsive attacks, usually with clouding of consciousness.

expiratory reserve volume- that volume capable of being expired at the end-expiratory level of a quiet expiration.

external respiration- movement of gases in and out of lungs.

extracellular- situated or occurring outside a cell or the cells of the body.

extracorporeal- situated or occurring outside the body.

extrasystole- premature contraction of the heart independent of normal rhythm.

F

fibrillation- spontaneous contraction of individual muscle fibers; specifically, nonsynchronized activity of the heart.

fluoroscopy- process of using an instrument to observe the internal structure of an opaque object (as the living body) by means of X rays.

forced expiratory flow- ($FEF_{200-1200}$) the average rate of flow for a specified portion of the forced expiratory volume, usually between 200 and 1200 ml (formerly called maximum expiratory flow rate).

forced expiratory volume- (qualified by the subscript indicating time interval in seconds, FEV_T—e.g., FEV_{10})- the volume of gas exhaled over a given time interval during the performance of a forced vital capacity. FEV can be expressed as a percentage of the forced vital capacity ($FEV_{T\%}$).

forced midexpiratory flow ($FEF_{25-75\%}$)- the average rate of flow during the middle half of the forced expiratory volume.

forced vital capacity- (FVC)- the maximum volume of gas that can be expelled as forcefully and rapidly as possible after maximum inspiration.

functional residual capcity- *see* Capacity, functional residual.

G

galvanic- uninterrupted current derived from a chemical battery.

ganglion- any collection or mass of nerve cells outside the central nervous system that serves as a center of nervous influence.

H

heart block- a delay or interference of the conduction mechanism whereby impulses do not go through all or a major part of the myocardium.

heparin- an acid occurring in tissues, mostly in the liver. It can be produced chemically and can make the blood incoaguable if injected into the bloodstream intravenously.

hyperventilation- abnormally prolonged, rapid deep breathing or overbreathing.

hypoventilation- decrease of air in the lungs below the normal amount.

hypoxia- lack of oxygen.

I

infarct- an area of necrosis in a tissue or organ resulting from obstruction of the local circulation by a thrombus or embolus.

inferior vena cava- main vein feeding back to the heart from systemic circulation below the heart.

inspiratory capacity- *see* Capacity, inspiratory.

inspiratory reserve volume- maximal volume of gas that can be inspired from the end-inspiratory position.

ion- an atom or group of atoms that carries a positive or negative electric charge as a result of having lost or gained one or more electrons.

ischemic- a localized anemia due to an obstructed circulation.

isoelectric- uniformly electric throughout; having the same electric **potential,** and hence giving off no current.

isometric- having the same length: a muscle acts isometrically when it applies a force without changing its length.

isotonic- having the same tone: a muscle acts isotonically when it changes length without appreciably changing the force it exerts.

isotropic- exhibiting properties with the same values when measured along axes in all directions.

K

Korotkoff sounds- sounds produced by sudden pulsation of blood being forced through a partially occluded artery and heard during auscultatory blood pressure determination.

L

latency- time delay between stimulus and response.

lobe- a somewhat rounded projection or division of a body organ or part.

lumen- the cavity of a tubular organ or instrument.

lung capacity, total- the amount of gas contained in the lung at the end of maximal inspiration.

M

maximal breathing capacity- same as maximal voluntary ventilation.

maximal voluntary ventilation- the volume of air that a subject can breathe with maximal effort over a given time interval.

membrane- a thin layer of tissue that covers a surface or divides a space or organ.

metabolism- the sum of all the physical and chemical processes by which the living organized substance is produced and maintained.

mitral stenosis- a narrowing of the left atrioventricular orifice.

mitral valve- valve between the left atrium and ventricle of the heart.

motor- a muscle, nerve, or center that effects or produces movement.

myelin- the fat-like substance forming a sheath around certain nerve fibers.

myocardium- the walls of the chamber of the heart which contain the musculature that acts during the pumping of blood.

myograph- an apparatus for recording the effects of a muscular contraction.

N

necrosis- death of tissue, usually as individual cells, groups of cells, or in small localized areas.

nerve- a cord-like structure that conveys impulses from one part of the body to another. A nerve consists of a bundle of nerve fibers either efferent or afferent or both.

neuron- a nerve cell with its processes, collaterals, and terminations—regarded as a structural unit of the nervous system.

nodes of Ranvier- nodes produced by constrictions of the myelin sheath of a nerve fiber at intervals at about 1 mm.

O

oxyhemoglobin- a compound of oxygen and hemoglobin formed in the lungs—the means whereby oxygen is carried through the arteries to the body tissues.

P

partial pressure of oxygen in air- the pressure of the oxygen contained in air. Since air is about 21 percent oxygen, partial pressure is 21 percent of 760 mm of mercury, or 159 mm Hg. That is, oxygen needs can be supplied by pure oxygen at 159 mm Hg, which is equivalent to breathing air at 760 mm Hg P_{O_2} (at sea level).

perfuse- to pour over or through.

permeate- to pass through the pores or interstices.

plethysmography- the recording of the changes in the volume of a body part as modified by the circulation of the blood in it.

pneumograph- an instrument for recording the thoracic movements or volume change during respiration.

prosthesis- an artificial substitute for a missing or diseased part.

pulmonary- relating to, functioning like, or associated with the lungs.

pulmonary atelectasis- lung collapse.

pulmonary minute volume (pulmonary ventilation)- volume of air respired per minute = tidal volume × breaths/min.

pulse pressure- the difference between systolic and diastolic blood pressure (usually about 40 mm Hg).

R

radioisotope- an isotope that is radioactive, produced artifically from the element by the action of neutrons, protons, deuterons, or alpha particles in the chain-reacting pile or in the cyclotron. Radioisotopes are used as tracers or indicators by being added to the stable compound under observation, so that the course of the latter in the body (human or animal) can be detected and followed by the radioactivity thus added to it. The stable element so treated is said to be "labeled" or "tagged."

residual capacity- *see* Capacity, residual functional.

residual volume- air left in the lungs after deep exhale (about 1.2 liters).

respiratory center- the center in the medulla oblongata that controls breathing.

respiratory quotient- ratio of volume of exhaled CO_2 to the volume of consumed O_2 (0.85).

S

semilunar pulmonary valve-   outlet valve from the right ventricle into the pulmonary artery.

sinoatrial node-   the pacemaker of the heart—a microscopic collection of atypical cardiac muscle fibers which is responsible for initiating each cycle or cardiac contraction.

sphygmomanometer-   an instrument for measuring blood pressure, especially arterial blood pressure.

spirometer-   an instrument for measuring the air entering and leaving the lungs.

stenosis-   narrowing of a duct or canal.

stroke volume-   amount of blood pumped during each heartbeat (diastolic volume of the ventricle minus the volume of blood in the ventricle at the end of systole).

superior vena cava-   main vein feeding back to the heart from systemic circulation above the heart.

synapse-   the point at which a nervous impulse passes from one neuron to another.

systemic-   pertaining to or affecting the body as a whole.

systole-   the contraction, or period of contraction, of the heart, especially that of the ventricles. It coincides with the interval between the first and second heart sound, during which blood is forced into the aorta and the pulmonary trunk.

systolic-   of or pertaining to systole (e.g., systolic blood pressure).

T

tachycardia-   relatively rapid heart action.

thorax-   the part of the body of man and other mammals between the neck and the abdomen.

thrombus-   a clot of blood formed within a blood vessel and remaining attached to its place of origin.

tidal volume-   volume of gas inspired or expired during each quiet respiration cycle.

tissue-   an aggregation of similarly specialized cells united in the performance of a particular function.

trachea-   the main trunk of the system of tubes by which air passes to and from the lungs.

tricuspid valve-   the valve connecting the right atrium to the right ventricle.

V

vasoconstriction-   narrowing of the lumen of blood vessels, especially as a result of vasomotor action.

vasodilation-   dilation or opening of blood vessel by vasomotor action.

vasomotor-   having to do with the musculature that affects the caliber of a blood vessel.

ventricle-   a chamber of the heart which receives blood from a corresponding atrium and from which blood is forced into the arteries.

ventricular fibrillation- convulsive nonsynchronized activity of the ventricles of the heart.

venule- a small vein; especially one of the minute veins connecting the capillary bed with the larger systemic veins.

vital capacity- volume of air that can be exhaled after the deepest possible inhalation.

B

Physiological Measurements Summary

B.1. BIOELECTRIC POTENTIALS

Electrocardiogram (ECG or EKG). A record of the electrical activity of the heart. Electrical potentials: 0.1 to 4 mV peak amplitude. Frequency response requirement: dc to 100 Hz. Used to measure heart rate, arrhythmia, and abnormalities in the heart. Also serves as timing reference for many cardiovascular measurements. Measured with electrodes at the surface of the body.

Electroencephalogram (EEG). A record of the electrical activity of the brain. Electrical potentials: 10 to 100 μV peak amplitude. Frequency requirement: dc to 100 Hz. Used for recognition of certain patterns, frequency analysis, evoked potentials, and so on. Measured with surface electrodes on the scalp and with needle electrodes just beneath the surface or driven into specific locations within the brain.

Electromyogram (EMG). A record of muscle potentials, usually from skeletal muscle. Electrical potentials: 50 μV to 1 mV peak amplitude. Required frequency response: 10 to 3000 Hz. Used as indicator of muscle action, for measuring fatigue, and so on. Measured with surface electrodes or needle electrodes penetrating the muscle fibers.

Other bioelectric potentials

1. Electroretinogram—a record of potentials from the retina.
2. Electrooculogram—a record of corneal-retinal potentials associated with eye movements.
3. Electrogastrogram—a record of muscle potentials associated with motility of the GI tract.
4. Individual nerve action potentials—potentials generated by information being transmitted by the nervous system.

B.2. SKIN RESISTANCE MEASUREMENTS

Galvanic skin response (GSR). Measurements of the electrical resistance of the skin and tissue path between two electrodes. A variation of resistance from 1000 to over 500,000 Ω. Variations are associated with activity of the autonomic nervous system. Used to measure autonomic responses. Principle behind "lie detection" equipment. Variations occur with bandwidth from 0.1 to 5 Hz. Measured with surface electrodes.

Basal skin resistance (BSR). Same as GSR, except that the BSR is a measure of the slow baseline changes instead of the variations caused by the autonomic system. Frequency-response requirements: dc to 0.5 Hz.

B.3. CARDIOVASCULAR MEASUREMENTS

Blood pressure measurements

1. *Arterial:* Pressure variations from 30 to 400 mm Hg. Pulsating pressure with each heart beat. Frequency-response requirements: dc to 30 Hz. Measured at various points in the arterial circulatory system. Measured directly by implanted pressure transducer; transducer connected to catheter in bloodstream, or manometer; indirectly by sphygmomanometer, and so on.
2. *Venous:* Pressure variations from 0 to 15 mm Hg. An almost static pressure with some variations with each heart beat. Frequency-response requirements: 0 to 30 Hz. Measured at various points in the venous circulatory system. Measured

by manometer, implanted pressure transducer, or external transducer connected to catheter.

Blood volume measurements

1. *Systemic volume:* Measure of total blood volume in the system. Measured by injection of an indicator such as a dye and subsequent measurement of indicator concentration.
2. *Plethysmograph measurement:* A measure of local blood volume changes in limbs or digits. This is an actual change in volume measured as a displacement change in a closed cup or tube. Volume pulsations occur at rate of heart beat. Required frequency response: dc to 40 Hz. Can also be measured indirectly with photoelectric device or tissue impedance measurement. Used to measure effectiveness of circulation, and in pulse-wave velocity measurements.

Blood flow measurements. A measure of the velocity of blood in a major vessel. In a vessel of a known diameter, this can be calibrated as flow and is most successfully accomplished in arterial vessels. Range is from -0.5 to $+1650$ ml/sec. Required frequency response: dc to 50 Hz. Used to estimate heart output and circulation. Requires exposure of the vessel. Flow transducer surrounds vessel. Methods of measurement include electromagnetic and ultrasonic principles.

Ballistocardiogram. Slight movement of body due to forces exerted by beating of the heart and pumping of blood. Patient placed on special platform. Movement measured by accelerometer. Required frequency response: dc to 40 Hz. Used to detect certain heart abnormalities.

Pulse and cardiovascular sound measurements

1. *Pulse pressure measurements:* Pressure variations at surface of the body due to arterial blood pulsations. Used for timing of pulse waves, pulse-wave velocity measurements, and as an indirect indicator of arterial blood pressure variations. Required frequency response: 0.1 to 40 Hz. Measured by low-frequency microphone or crystal pressure pickup.
2. *Heart sounds:* An electrically amplified version of the sounds normally picked up by the conventional stethoscope. Frequency response: 30 to 150 Hz. Picked up by microphone.

3. *Phonocardiogram:* A graphic display of the sounds generated by the heart and picked up by a microphone at the surface of the body. Frequency response required is 5 to 2000 Hz. Measured by special crystal transducer or microphone.
4. *Vibrocardiogram:* A measure of the movement of the chest due to the heart beat. Frequency response required: 0.1 to 50 Hz. Special pressure or displacement transducer placed on the appropriate point on the chest.
5. *Apex cardiogram:* A measurement of the pressure variations at the point where the apex of the heart beats against the rib cage. Frequency response required: 0.1 to 50 Hz. Measured with special pressure sensitive-microphone or crystal transducer.

B.4. RESPIRATION MEASUREMENTS

Respiration flow measurements. A measurement of the rate at which air is inspired or expired. Range: 250 to 3000 ml/sec, peak. Frequency response: 0 to 20 Hz. Used to determine breathing rate, minute volume, depth of repiration. Measured by pneumotachometer or as the derivative of volume measurement.

Respiration volume. Measurement of quantity of air breathed in or out during a single breathing cycle or over a given period of time. Frequency response required: 0 to 10 Hz. Used for determination of various respiration functions. Measure by integration of respiration flow-rate measurements or by collection of expired air over a given period. Indirect measurement by belt transducer, impedance pneumograph, or whole-body plethysmograph.

B.5. TEMPERATURE MEASUREMENTS

Systemic temperature. A measure of the basic temperature of the complete organism. Measured by thermometer, rectal or oral, or by rectal or oral thermistor probe.

Local skin temperature. Measurement of the skin temperature at a specific part of the body surface. Measured by thermistors placed at the surface of the skin, infrared thermometer or thermograph.

B.6. PHYSICAL MOVEMENTS

Various measurements of *displacement, velocity, force,* or *acceleration*. Measured by transducers sensitive to the parameter desired or derived indirectly from related parameters. Special measurement of movement by ultrasound techniques.

B.7. BEHAVIORAL CHARACTERISTICS

Measurement of response of organism to various stimuli. Responses measured may be any of the above, or may be subjective. Includes such measures as speech, visual and sound perception, tactile perception, smell, and taste. Measuring devices include generation of the appropriate stimulus as well as transducers for the various responses.

C

SI Metric Units
and Equivalencies ·

SI Unit	Quantity	Equivalency
degree Celsius	temperature	degree centigrade
		⅝ (degree Fahrenheit − 32°)
gram	mass	0.03527 ounce
hertz	frequency	cycles per second
kilogram	mass	2.2 pounds
kilopascal	pressure	7.5 mm Hg
liter	fluid volume	1.06 quarts
meter	length	3.28 feet
meter per second	velocity	39.37 inches per second
newton	force	0.2247 pound force

D

Problems and Exercises

D.1. INTRODUCTION

This book is both a reference and a textbook. In the latter function, problems and exercises are needed to aid the student. In a book of this nature, which is primarily descriptive, quantitative problems are not as necessary as in the usual technical book. A few have been provided, but most of these exercises are designed to test the student's knowledge of the key portions of the text, and provide an opportunity to expand on it. The problems are relatively short and do not include long essay-type questions. Such questions are left to the instructor to pose.

Chapter 1

1.1. There are many factors to consider in the design and application of a medical instrumentation system. Discuss what you think are the 10 most important and state why.

1.2. The book lists a number of qualities important to a medical instrumentation system. Suggest one additional quality not listed and state your reasons.

1.3. How would you state the sensitivity characteristics of the following instruments?
   (a) An electrocardiograph to give a 2-in. deflection on a recorder for a 2-mV peak reading.
   (b) An electroencephalograph to give a 1.5-cm deflection for a 50-μV peak reading.
   (c) A thermistor-temperature measuring system to record body temperature at a normal value, plus or minus 5 percent, on a 3-in. scale.

1.4. Check elsewhere in this book or in other references for the required frequency response of:
   (a) An electromyogram.
   (b) Blood flow measurements.
   (c) Phonocardiogram.
   (d) Plethysmogram.

1.5. Discuss the possibility of other errors not listed in Section 1.3.

1.6. By using the table of roots, prefixes, and suffixes in Appendix A, determine what the following medical names mean:
   (a) Periodontitis.
   (b) Bradyrhythmia.
   (c) Tachycardia.
   (d) Endoesophagus.
   (e) Exostosectomy.
   (f) Hepatitis.
   (g) Dysentery.
   (h) Epidermitis.

1.7. Name six body functions and relate them to a field or topic normally studied as an engineering-type subject—for example, cardiovascular system and fluid mechanics.

1.8. The text lists three basic differences that contribute to communication problems between the physician and the engineer. What are they? How can they be overcome? Can you think of any others?

1.9. Discuss the major differences encountered between measurements in a physiological system as distinct from a physical system.

1.10. What are the objectives of a biomedical instrumentation system?

1.11. Explain the difference between in vivo and in vitro measurements.

1.12. Name the major physiological systems of the body.

1.13. What specific features might be incorporated into an instrument designed for clinical use as opposed to one designed for research purposes?

1.14. In designing an instrumentation system for measurement of physiological variables, which of the components shown in Figure 2.1 should be determined first? Why? Which would you next determine?

1.15. Draw a diagram showing the hydraulic (cardiovascular) system of the body, using the terminology common to the engineering analogy given in this chapter.

Chapter 2

2.1. Discuss four different types of transducers, explaining what they measure and the principles involved.

2.2. What do you understand by the term "gage factor"?

2.3. Discuss the relationship among displacement, velocity, acceleration, and force.

2.4. Explain the difference between isometric and isotonic transducers.

2.5. What is a mercury strain gage? Describe its operation and list as many biomedical applications as you can.

2.6. Which of the following types of physical transducers, in basic form, are capable of a direct measurement of displacement and which are primarily velocity transducers?
(a) Potentiometer transducer.
(b) Piezoelectric crystal.
(c) Differential transformer.
(d) Bonded strain gage.
(e) Unbonded strain gage.
(f) Capacitance transducer.
(g) Induction-type transducer.

2.7. You have invented a device that changes its resistance linearly as a function of ozone in a sample of air (smog). Draw a transducer-type circuit excited by an audio oscillator and explain how it would operate and how you would use it.

2.8. What is the difference between an active and a passive transducer?

2.9. When a student takes courses in physics, the topics usually include the concepts of mechanics, heat, light, sound, electricity, and magnetism. For each of these topics, specify a transducer which belongs in that field and discuss the basic energy form and how transduction is effected.

2.10. Invent a new transducer. Explain the energy form you wish to use and what you would transduce to. Later you may wish to adapt your new transducer to a biomedical application, but you should read a few more chapters first.

Chapter 3

3.1. Draw an action potential waveform and label the amplitude and time values.

3.2. Explain polarization, depolarization, and repolarization.

3.3. What is a biopotential? Name six types of biopotential sources.

3.4. Explain the electrical action of the sinoatrial node.

3.5. Do you think the electroencephalogram is subject to frequency discrimination? Explain.

3.6. How are the potentials in muscle fibers measured, and what is the record called that is obtained therefrom?

3.7. How does an evoked EEG response differ from a conventional electroencephalogram?

Chapter 4

4.1. Name the three basic types of electrodes for measurement of bioelectric potentials.

4.2. For a patient, which type of electrode would be the least traumatic?

4.3. Why are microelectrodes sometimes needed?

4.4. What are the problems involved in using flat electrodes in terms of interference or high impedance between electrode and skin? How could you help eliminate this problem?

4.5. What do you understand by the term "reference electrode"?

4.6. What is a glass electrode used for?

4.7. What is an ear-clip electrode used for?

4.8. Why are the partial pressure of oxygen and the partial pressure of carbon dioxide useful physical parameters? Explain briefly how each can be measured.

4.9. Calculate the potential difference across a membrane separating two very dilute solutions of a monovalent ion, one concentration being 100 times as great as the other. Assume a body temperature of 37 °C.

4.10. What is the major advantage of floating-type skin surface electrodes?

4.11. What is the hydrogen ion concentration of blood with a pH of 7.4?

Chapter 5

5.1. A patient has a cardiac output of 4 liters/min, a heart rate of 86 beats per minute, and a blood volume of 5 liters. Calculate the stroke volume and the mean circulation time. What is the mean blood velocity in the aorta (in feet per second) when the vessel has a diameter of 30 mm?

5.2. Explain the operation of the heart and the cardiovascular system briefly. Draw an analogous electric circuit and show how Ohm's law and Kirchoff's laws could apply in the analog.

5.3. Develop a time-phase diagram showing the correlation of the mechanical pumping of the heart, including the opening of the valves, with the electrical-excitation events.

5.4. Draw the waveshape of blood pressure on a time base and explain it. What is the dicrotic notch?

5.5. What is the difference in the information contained in a phonocardiogram and an electrocardiogram?

5.6. In a harmonic analysis of the following waveforms, what range of frequencies could be expected in the human being?
(a) The ECG.
(b) The phonocardiogram.
(c) The blood pressure wave.
(d) The blood flow wave.

5.7. Would you expect blood flow to obey Bernoulli's equation, even with reservations? Explain why.

5.8. If a person stands up, does his blood pressure increase? Why?

5.9. If a person eats a large meal, does his heart rate increase? Why?

5.10. What part of the cardiovascular system normally contains the greatest volúme of blood?

5.11. Define systole and diastole.

Chapter 6

6.1. Draw an electrocardiogram (in lead II), labeling the critical features. Include typical amplitudes and time intervals for a normal person.

6.2. A differential amplifier has a positive input terminal, a negative input terminal, and a ground connection. ECG electrodes from a patient are connected to the positive and negative terminals, and a reference electrode is connected to ground. A disturbance signal develops on the patient's body. This will appear as a voltage from the positive terminal to ground and a similar voltage from the negative terminal to ground. How does the differential amplifier amplify the ECG signal while not essentially amplifying the disturbance signals? Draw a sketch showing the patient connected to the amplifier.

6.3. Why are the vector sums of the projections on the frontal-plane cardiac vector at any instant onto the three axes of the Einthoven triangle zero?

6.4. Explain the difference between indirect and direct measurement of blood pressure.

6.5. The "thermostromuhr" and the indicator-dilution method with cool saline as an indicator both use thermistors for detectors. What is the difference between the two methods?

6.6. For a cardiac-output determination, 5 mg of Cardiogreen was injected into a patient and a calibration mixture with a concentration of 5 mg/liter was prepared from a previously withdrawn blood sample. The calibration mixture gave a deflection of ¾ cm on the recorder used, which had a paper speed of 1 cm/sec. The area under the extrapolated curve (obtained by the Hamilton method) was 86 cm². What is the cardiac output in liters per minute? (*Answer:* 0.872 liter/min)

6.7. Explain the basic operation of the following blood pressure transducers:
(a) A resistance-bridge type.
(b) A linear variable differential transformer type.

6.8. Explain what is meant by "plethysmography"? Discuss one way to make measurements and their clinical implications.

6.9. You are to measure the blood pressure of a dog during heavy exercise on a treadmill by using a catheter-type resistance strain-gage transducer. What is the desirable frequency response for your whole system? Explain.

6.10. Laplace's law can be used for cylindrical blood vessels. Simply stated in this context, the tension in the wall of a vessel is the product of the radius and internal pressure. Given that 1 mm Hg is equivalent to approximately 1300 dynes/cm^2, find the tension in the wall of:
   (a) An aorta with a mean pressure of 100 mm Hg and a diameter of 2.4 cm. (*Answer:* 1.56×10^5 dynes/cm^2)
   (b) A capillary with a mean pressure of 25 mm Hg and a diameter of 8 μm. (*Answer:* 13 dynes/cm^2)
   (c) The superior vena cava with a mean pressure of 10 mm Hg and 3 cm diameter. (*Answer:* 19.5×10^3 dynes/cm^2)

6.11. Assume that blood flow obeys Bernoulli's equation:

$$\frac{p}{w} + \frac{v^2}{2g} + z = \text{constant}$$

where
$$p = \text{pressure}$$
$$w = \text{specific weight}$$
$$v = \text{velocity}$$
$$g = \text{gravitational constant}$$
$$z = \text{elevation head}$$

The three terms are often referred to as the pressure head, the velocity head, and the potential or elevation head, respectively. In measurements on a patient, the elevation is a constant, so the equation can be expressed as

$$p + \frac{wv^2}{2g} = \text{constant}$$

A certain type of blood pressure transducer positioned in the aorta will measure this value, but since the lateral blood pressure is simply the p term, $wv^2/2g$ represents an error. If the density of the blood, w/g, is estimated to be 1.03 grams/cm^3, and the blood is flowing at a velocity of 100 cm/sec, calculate the error in blood pressure measurement. Given 1 mm Hg is equivalent to 1330 dynes/cm^2. (*Answer:* 3.88 mm) Do you consider this to be a significant error in the aorta?

6.12. You are employed by a hospital research unit on a certain project to measure the blood pressure and blood flow in the femoral artery of an anesthetized dog lying on an operating table.
   (a) Design a system to do this by (1) describing the transducers, if any, you would use; (2) specifying all necessary instrumentation; (3) discussing surgical or medical methods used to ensure that your physiological measurements are taken correctly—for example, catheterization, implantation, and so on. Draw block diagrams to illustrate.
   (b) How would you zero and calibrate your blood pressure measurements?

6.13. Blood shows certain conductive properties. Discuss an instrument that uses this property.

6.14. Discuss the advantages and disadvantages of four types of blood pressure transducers that can either be implanted or placed in the bloodstream through a catheter.

6.15. Draw a simplified model using block diagrams to show how the brain, pressoreceptors, and hormonal secretion could control the heart rate. Use the brain and the heart as your feed-forward loop and other parameters as feedback loops.

6.16. Why is the impedance plethysmograph sometimes called a pseudo-plethysmograph?

6.17. Explain the difference between a phonocardiogram and a vibrocardiogram. How do transducer requirements differ for these two measurements?

6.18. What is meant by mean arterial pressure? How do you measure it?

6.19. Discuss the automatic and semiautomatic methods of measuring blood pressure. Can you suggest any modifications?

6.20. What is the difference between a single-lumen catheter and a multiple-lumen "floatation" catheter?

6.21. Discuss measurement of blood pressure and possible errors due to trauma or other psychological effects on the patient.

6.22. What are the relative merits of dyes and cold saline methods in cardiac output measurements?

Chapter 7

7.1. Design a coronary-care hospital suite. Show all rooms in a layout plan. Illustrate all your instrumentation systems by block diagrams.

7.2. Discuss warning devices to be used in intensive-care units.

7.3. Explain the operation of a pacemaker and why it is needed.

7.4. What do you understand by fibrillation? How do you correct for it? Draw a circuit of a direct-current defibrillator.

7.5. What part of the electrocardiogram is the most useful for determining heart rate? Explain.

7.6. A certain patient-monitoring unit has an input amplifier with a common-mode rejection ratio of 100,000:1 at 60 Hz. At other frequencies, the common-mode rejection ratio is 1000:1. Do you consider these ratios adequate for monitoring the ECG? Explain.

7.7. Discuss possible causes of a patient-monitoring system falsely indicating an excessive high heart rate.

7.8 What is a "demand" pacemaker and when is it used?

7.9. What is the difference between a "bouncing ball" and nonfade display? Discuss their relative merits.

7.10. Discuss instrumentation and methods for rapid diagnosis and repair of instrumentation in an intensive-care unit.

7.11. What equipment would you need in a diagnostic catheterization laboratory?

7.12. Design the cardiology department of a small hospital to include facilities for intensive-care monitoring, surgery, and diagnostics. Specify all the equipment and instrumentation necessary, including the possibility of emergencies.

Chapter 8

8.1. Using the correct anatomical and physical terms, explain the process of respiration, tracing the taking of a breath of air through the mouth to the using of the oxygenated blood in the muscle of an athlete's leg.

8.2. How many lobes are there in the lungs? Explain.

8.3. Boyle's law is an important law in physics. How does it relate to the breathing process? (*Hint: PV* is a constant at a constant temperature.)

8.4. What is the difference between death by carbon monoxide poisoning and death by strangulation? Explain.

8.5. Define the important lung capacities and explain them.

8.6. A person has a total lung capacity of 5.95 liters. If the volume of air left in the lungs at the end of maximal expiration is 1.19 liters, what is his vital capacity? (*Answer:* 4.76 liters)

8.7. If the volume of air expired and inspired during each respiratory cycle varies from 0.5 to 3.9 liters during exercise, what is this value called and what does it mean?

8.8. During a typical day, a person works for 8 hours, rests for 4 hours, walks for 1 hour, eats for 2 hours, and sleeps for 9 hours. How many pounds of oxygen would he consume during the whole day? (During sleep and rest he can be assumed to consume 0.05 pound/hour; during eating, this figure will double; during walking, consumption will triple; and during work it will quadruple.) (*Answer:* 2.6 pounds)

8.9. Explain the operation of a pulmonary measurement indicator.

8.10. Since the lungs contain no musculature, what causes them to expand and contract in breathing?

8.11. For what measurements can a spirometer be used? What basic lung volumes and capacities cannot be measured with a spirometer? Why?

Chapter 9

9.1. What do you understand by the term "noninvasive methods"?

9.2. Explain the difference between a thermistor and a thermocouple in temperature measurement.

9.3. Discuss how temperature is controlled in the body by the brain.

9.4. Explain the technique of thermography. Comment on its usefulness.

9.5. Why is skin surface temperature lower than systemic temperature measured orally?

9.6. What are the important characteristics to be considered in selecting a thermistor probe for a specific medical application?

9.7. Discuss the properties of ultrasound and how ultrasound can be used for diagnostics.

9.8. What do you understand about the following terms?
(a) Doppler effect.
(b) Half-value layer.
(c) Acoustic impedance.
(d) Attenuation constant.

9.9. What are the four basic modes of transmission of ultrasound? Describe each briefly.

9.10. What is meant by "ultrasonic imaging"?

9.11. What is echoencephalography?

9.12. Discuss the applications of ultrasound in medicine. Can you suggest some possible applications that are not discussed in the chapter?

9.13. A patient has a heart problem that seems to suggest mitral valve stenosis. Discuss the transducer you would specify to perform a diagnosis.

9.14. Compare ultrasonic diagnosis with X-ray diagnosis discussed in Chapter 14.

9.15. Discuss the relative differences between high- and low-frequency ultrasound.

9.16. An ultrasonic imaging system is capable of operating at both 5 and 12.5 MHz. What is the advantage of being able to select between two frequencies? Under what circumstances would you use each?

9.17. What is range-gated pulsed Doppler ultrasound? Describe at least two possible applications.

Chapter 10

10.1. What is the difference between afferent and efferent nerves?

10.2. Explain the difference between a motor nerve and a sensory nerve.

10.3. How does the action of the sympathetic nervous system differ from that of the parasympathetic system? Quote an example from a body system.

10.4. What is a neuronal spike? Draw a typical spike showing amplitude and duration.

10.5. What is a 10–20 electrode placement system and with what bioelectric instrument is it used?

10.6. Discuss some possible uses of electromyography.

10.7. Draw a sketch of a neuron and label the cell body, dendrite, axon, and axon hillock.

10.8. What are the nodes of Ranvier and what useful purpose do they serve?

10.9. Explain the way in which a neuronal spike is transmitted from one neuron to another.

10.10. What are graded potentials?

10.11. Explain the function of:
(a) The cerebral cortex.
(b) The cerebellum.
(c) The reticular activation system.
(d) The hypothalamus.

10.12. What is a spinal reflex, and how is it related to the functions of the brain?

10.13. If the same neuronal spike were measured intracellularly and extracellularly, what would be the difference between the two measurements?

10.14. What are the differences in amplification and bandwidth requirement of amplifiers for ECG, EMG, and EEG?

Chapter 11

11.1. You want to determine what concentration of salt in water can be detected by the human taste sense. How would you set up the experiment?

11.2. For a "differential response" experiment, an animal box contains two lamps and one bar. The positive reinforcement is food, dispensed by a magnetic feeder, the negative reinforcement is electric shock. Devise a simple programming circuit, using relays, that causes positive reinforcement when the animal presses the bar while either light is on and negative reinforcement if the animal presses the bar while both lights are on. Bar pressing while no light is on shall have no effect.

11.3. List some of the possible difficulties that might be encountered in using GSR measurements as a lie detector test.

11.4. Explain the principle of the Békésy audiometer.

11.5. What is a cumulative recorder and how it is used?

11.6. You have been assigned the task of measuring all possible responses of the autonomic nervous system. Design a system for providing various forms of stimuli that would be expected to actuate the autonomic system for measurement of each response. Describe the type of instrumentation you would use.

Chapter 12

12.1. List some advantages and disadvantages of biotelemetry.

12.2. Draw a block diagram of a system to send an electrocardiogram from an ambulance to a hospital by telemetry.

12.3. Why do you think measurements of physiological parameters on an unanesthetized animal may be more useful than those on an anesthetized one?

12.4. What do you see as some of the problems of telemetrized systems in the future?

12.5. It is desirable to monitor the temperature of a man very accurately while he is climbing a mountain and then record the data on tape for later computer analysis. You are to remain in a cabin at the foot of the mountain. Explain how you would do this accurately, and draw a block diagram of any equipment stages used in your system.

12.6. Explain how four physiological parameters can be monitored and telemetered simultaneously.

12.7. If subdermal needles connected to a telemetry transmitter are implanted into a muscle, explain how a trained physician might recognize different effects from another room by using a sense other than vision to monitor.

12.8. Design a hospital with a telemetry system, explaining why you would telemetrize the functions you have selected.

12.9. Discuss telemetry of electrocardiograms and advantages or disadvantages over a wired system for:
(a) A hospital bed patient.
(b) A convalescing patient.
(c) An athlete being measured on a treadmill.

12.10. Discuss telemetry as an emergency care tool.

12.11. What are medical transmitting frequencies? Why is it necessary to specify them?

12.12. Design a system that is capable of transmitting the ECG of a patient at home by radio to a hospital, then by telephone line to a computer center, and finally sending the data to a cardiologist to diagnose.

Chapter 13

13.1. List the most important components of the blood.

13.2. List the main types of bood tests and explain each briefly.

13.3. What do you understand by the term "blood count"?

13.4. Describe the operation of a blood counter.

13.5. Describe the colorimetric method of determining chemical concentration.

13.6. When counting red blood cells with one of the automatic counting methods described in Section 13.1, you will, by necessity, also count the white blood cells in the process. Why is the error introduced by this negligible? Why must the blood be diluted for all the automatic blood cell counters? How do the automatic cell counters avoid counting the platelets?

13.7. For a glucose determination, a standard with a known glucose concentration of 80 mg/100 ml is used. After the color reaction has taken place, this standard shows a transmittance of 38 percent. A patient sample shows a transmittance of 46 percent. What is the glucose concentration in this patient sample? Another patient sample shows a transmittance below 10 percent, which is hard to read accurately. What can be done to this sample to bring the transmittance into a more suitable range, and what correction has to be applied in the calculation?

13.8. Explain the difference between the continuous-flow method and the discrete sample method of automated clinical chemistry equipment. What are some of the shortcomings of each?

Chapter 14

14.1. In both X-ray and radioisotope procedures, potentially harmful ionizing radiation is used for diagnostic purposes. Why is the safe radiation intensity for X rays much higher than that for isotope methods?

14.2. X-ray and radioisotope methods for diagnostic purposes both make use of the tissue-penetrating properties of radiation. What is the principal difference between the two methods?

14.3. Why is the use of radioisotopes for in vivo methods limited to those isotopes that emit gamma radiation?

14.4. Describe the principle of visualizing body organs by radioisotope methods.

Chapter 15

15.1. Define each of the following terms as related to digital computation:
   (a) Word length.
   (b) Register.
   (c) Memory.
   (d) Character.
   (e) Address.
   (f) Byte.
   (g) Time sharing.
   (h) Modem.
   (i) Real time.
   (j) On line.
   (k) Software.

15.2. Describe the processes required to enter each of the following types of data into a digital computer:
   (a) numerical data written in tabular form on sheets of paper

      (b) the output of a pneumotachograph transducer

      (c) the output of a digital electronic counter

      (d) an electrocardiogram signal

15.3. A microcomputer has three types of memory: integrated-circuit RAM, integrated-circuit ROM, and floppy disk. How might each be used in biomedical instrumentation?

15.4. What role does a digital-to-analog converter play in an analog-to-digital converter?

15.5. What is the purpose of a parallel-to-serial converter? When would such a device be used?

15.6. Several applications of digital computers to medicine are given in Chapter 15. Can you suggest other possible applications?

15.7. You have been assigned the task of designing a computerized patient-monitoring system for an intensive-care unit in a medium-size community hospital. What parameters would you monitor? What role would you have the computer play? Draw a block diagram of a typical system and explain the purpose of each block.

15.8. Explain the principle of computerized axial tomography and compare its method of visualization with conventional X-ray methods.

15.9. In a high-speed CAT scanner, 20 scans are taken using a fanbeam X-ray source and an array of 350 detectors. What is the maximum number of pixels that can result from this arrangement?

Chapter 16

16.1. Name two different ways in which electricity can harm the body.

16.2. List the various effects of electrical current that occur with increasing current intensity.

16.3. What is the difference between electrical macroshock and microshock? In what parts of the hospital are microshock hazards likely to exist?

16.4. What is the basic purpose of the safety measures used with electrically susceptible patients?

16.5. Why is it so important to maintain the integrity of the grounding system for protection against microshock?

16.6. A fluid-filled catheter is used to measure blood pressure in the right atrium of the heart. Resistance of the fluid path is $1 M\Omega$. The external end of the catheter is grounded to the equipment ground of a receptacle at the left side of the patient's bed. The patient's right leg is grounded via a patient monitor to another receptacle at the right side of the patient's bed. Because of a malfunction in a vacuum cleaner, a fault current of 10 A flows through the ground wire connecting the two receptacles. What is the maximum allowable resistance for the ground wire connecting the receptacles to prevent exceeding the 10 μA safe current limit for microshock in the patient?

Bibliography

General

The following works may be considered as general references throughout the book. Other references are cited for particular chapters.

BEST, C. M. AND N. B. TAYLOR, *The Living Body, a Text in Human Physiology.* New York: Holt, Rinehart and Winston, Inc., 1971.

BEST, C. M. AND N. B. TAYLOR, *Physiological Basis of Medical Practice.* 9th ed., John K. Brobeck (ed.). Baltimore, Md.: The Williams & Wilkins Company, 1973.

BILOON, F., *Medical Equipment Service Manual.* Englewood Cliffs, N.J.: Prentice-Hall, Inc., 1978.

BRONZINI, J. D., *Technology for Patient Care.* St. Louis, Mo.; The C. V. Mosby Company, 1977.

BROWN, J. H. U., J. E. JACOBS, AND L. STARK, *Biomedical Engineering.* Philadelphia: F. A. Davis Company, 1971.

CACERES, C. A. (ed.), *The Practice of Clinical Engineering.* New York: Academic Press, 1977.

CROMWELL, L., M. ARDITTI, F. J. WEIBELL, E. A. PFEIFFER, B. STEELE, AND J. LABOK, *Medical Instrumentation for Health Care.* Englewood Cliffs, N.J.: Prentice-Hall, Inc., 1976.

Dorland's Illustrated Medical Dictionary. 25th ed. Philadelphia: W. B. Saunders Company, 1974.

EVANS, W. F., *Anatomy and Physiology, the Basic Principles.* Englewood Cliffs, N.J.: Prentice-Hall, Inc., 1971.

FLEMING, D. G., AND B. N. FEINBERG, *CRC Handbook of Engineering in Medicine and Biology.* Cleveland, Ohio: CRC Press, Inc., 1976.

GEDDES, L. A., AND L. E. BAKER, *Principles of Applied Biomedical Instrumentation,* 2nd ed. New York: John Wiley & Sons, Inc., 1975.

GRAF, R. F. AND G. J. WHALEN, *The Reston Encyclopedia of Biomedical Engineering Terms.* Reston, Va.: Reston Publishing Company, Inc., 1977.

GUYTON, A. C. *Textbook of Medical Physiology.* Philadelphia: W. B. Saunders Company, 1971.

JACOBSON, B., AND J. G. WEBSTER, *Medicine and Clinical Engineering.* Englewood Cliffs, N.J.: Prentice-Hall, Inc., 1977.

KLINE, J. (ed.), *Biological Foundations of Biomedical Engineering.* Boston: Little, Brown and Company, 1976.

MOUNTCASTLE, V. B. (ed.), *Medical Physiology,* 12th ed., Vols. I and II. St. Louis, Mo.: The C. V. Mosby Company, 1968.

RAY, C. D. (ed.), *Medical Engineering.* Chicago: Year Book Medical Publishers, Inc., 1974.

SCHMIDT-NIELSEN, K., *Animal Physiology.* Englewood Cliffs, N.J.: Prentice-Hall, Inc., 1974.

STRONG, P., *Biophysical Measurements.* Beaverton, Ore.: Tektronix, Inc., 1970.

WEBSTER, J. G. (ed.), *Medical Instrumentation, Application and Design.* Boston: Houghton Mifflin Company, 1978.

WEISS, M. D., *Biomedical Instrumentation.* Philadelphia: Chilton Book Company, 1973.

WELKOWITZ, W., AND S. DEUTSCH, *Biomedical Instruments, Theory and Design.* New York: Academic Press, 1976.

YANOF, H. M., *Biomedical Electronics,* 2nd ed. Philadelphia: F. A. Davis Company, 1972.

Chapter 2

BARTHOLOMEW, D., *Electrical Measurements and Instruments.* Boston: Allyn and Bacon, Inc., 1963.

COBBOLD, R. S. C., *Transducers for Biomedical Instruments: Principles and Applications.* John Wiley & Sons, Inc., 1974.

NORTON, H. N., *Handbook of Transducers for Electronic Measuring Systems.* Englewood Cliffs, N.J.: Prentice-Hall, Inc., 1969.

Chapter 3

BRAZIER, M. A. B., *The Electrical Activity of the Nervous System.* Baltimore, Md.: The Williams & Wilkins Company, 1968.

BURCH, G. E., AND T. WINSOR, *A Primer of Electrocardiography.* Philadelphia: Lea & Febiger, 1960.

KEELE, C. A., AND E. NEIL, *Samson Wright's Applied Physiology.* New York: Oxford University Press, inc., 1961.

SCHER, A. M., "The Electrocardiogram," *Scientific American,* 205, No. 5 (November, 1961), 132–141.

THOMPSON, R. F., *Foundations of Physiological Psychology.* New York: Harper & Row, Publishers, 1967.

Chapter 4

BAIR, E. J., *Introduction to Chemical Instrumentation.* New York: McGraw-Hill Book Company, 1962.

BATES, R. G., *Determination of pH—Theory and Practice.* New York: John Wiley & Sons, Inc., 1954.

DURST, R. A. (ed.), *Ion-Selective Electrodes.* Washington, D.C.: National Bureau of Standards Publication No. 314, 1969.

GEDDES, L. A., *Electrodes and the Measurement of Bioelectric Events.* New York: John Wiley & Sons, Inc., 1972.

HILL, O. W., AND R. S. KHANDPUR, The Performance of Transistor ECG Amplifier," *World Medical Instruments,* 7, No. 5 (May, 1969), 12–22.

MILLER, H. A., AND D. C. HARRISON (eds.), *Biomedical Electrode Technology: Theory and Practice.* New York: Academic Press, 1974.

PFEIFFER, E. A., "Electrical Stimulation of Sensory Nerves with Skin Electrodes for Research, Diagnosis, Communication and Behavioral Conditioning: A Survey," *Medical and Biological Engineering,* 6 (1968), 637–651.

Chapters 5 and 6

BURCH, G. E., AND N. P. DE PASQUALE, *Primer of Clinical Measurement of Blood Pressure.* St. Louis. Mo.: The C. V. Mosby Company, 1962.

BURCH, G. E., AND T. WINSOR, *A Primer of Electrocardiography,* 4th ed. Philadelphia: Lea & Febiger, 1960.

CAPPELEN, C. (ed.), *New Findings in Blood Flowmetry.* Olso, Norway: Universitetsforlaget, 1968.

Cardiac Output Computer. Promotional material available from Columbus Instruments, Columbus, Ohio, 1970.

ECG Measurements, Application Note AN711. Waltham, Mass.: Hewlett-Packard, Inc., Medical Electronics Division, 1970.

FLEMING, D. G., W. H. KO, AND M. R. NEUMAN, *Indwelling and Implantable Pressure Transducers.* Cleveland, Ohio: CRC Press, Inc., 1977.

FRANKLIN, D. L., "Techniques for Measurement of Blood Flow Through Intact Vessels," *Medical Electronics and Biological Engineering,* 3, (1965), 27–37.

GEDDES, L. A., *The Direct and Indirect Measurement of Blood Pressure.* Chicago: Year Book Medical Publishers, Inc., 1970.

GEE, W., et al., "Ocular Pneumoplethysmography in Carotid Artery Disease," *Medical Instrumentation,* 8, No. 4 (July–August, 1974).

The Measurement of Cardiac Output by the Dye Dilution Method. Monograph available from Lexington Instruments Corporation, Waltham, Mass., 1963.

Pressure Measurements, Application Note AN710. Waltham, Mass.: Hewlett-Packard, Inc., Medical Electronics Division, 1969.

Recommendations for Human Blood Pressure Determination by Sphygmomanometers. New York: American Heart Association, 1967.

"Recommendations for Standardization of Instruments in Electrocardiography and Vectorcardiography," AHA Subcommittee Report, *IEEE Transactions on Biomedical Engineering,* January, 1967, 60–68.

Sphygmomanometers—Principles and Precepts. Copiague, N.Y.: W. A. Baum Co., 1965.

WARBASSE, R. J., et at., "Physiologic Evaluation of a Catheter Tip Electromagnetic Velocity Probe," *American Journal of Cardiology,* 23 (March, 1969), 424–433.

ZIERLER, K. L., "Circulation Times and the Theory of Indicator Dilution Methods for Determining Blood Flow and Volume," in *Handbook of Physiology,* Sec. 2, Vol. 1, J. Field (ed). American Physiological Society, 1959, 585–615.

Chapter 7

Cardiac Pacemaking. Somerville, N.J.: Hoechst Pharmaceuticals, Inc., 1974.

"Coronary Arteriography," *Directions in Cardiovascular Medicine,* Vol. 1. Somerville, N.J.: Hoechst Pharmaceuticals, Inc., 1970.

"The Coronary Care Unit," *Directions in Cardiovascular Medicine,* Vol. 3. Somerville, N.J.: Hoechst Pharmaceuticals, Inc., 1970.

A Guide to Fetal Monitoring. Waltham, Mass.: Hewlett–Packard, Inc., 1973.

HENDRIE, W. A., "Patient Monitoring," *World Medical Instrumentation,* 7, No. 7 (July, 1969).

HILL, D. W., AND A. M. DOLAN, *Intensive Care Instrumentation,* New York: Academic Press, 1976.

KARSELIS, T., *Descriptive Medical Electronics and Instrumentation.* Thurofare, N.J.: Charles B. Slack, Inc., 1973.

KLEIN, B., *Introduction to Medical Electronics.* Blue Ridge Summit, Pa.: Tab Books, 1973.

LOWN, B., "Intensive Heart Care," *Scientific American,* 219, No. 1 (July, 1968), 19–27.

An Overview of Pacing. Minneapolis, Minn.: Medtronic Inc., 1973.

Planning a Patient Monitoring System. Waltham, Mass.: Hewlett–Packard, Inc., Medical Electronics Division, 1973.

Note: Many instrument manufacturers have published description booklets on patient-monitoring systems.

SWAN, H. J. C., W. GANZ, et al., "Catheterization of the Heart in Man with Use of a Flow-Directed Balloon-Tipped Catheter," *New England Journal of Medicine,* 283 (August 27, 1970), 447.

Chapter 8

BASS, B. H., *Pulmonary Function in Clinical Medicine.* Springfield, Ill.: Charles C Thomas, Publisher, 1964.

BELINKOFF, S., *Introduction to Inhalation Therapy*. Boston: Little, Brown and Company, 1969.

BUIST, A. S., "Clinical Significance of Pulmonary Function Tests: Early Detection of Airways Obstruction by the Closing Volume Technique," *Chest,* 64, No. 4 (1973), 495–499.

CHERNIAK, R. M., AND L. CHERNIAK, *Respiration in Health and Disease*. Philadelphia: W. B. Saunders Company, 1965.

COMROE, J. H., et al., *The Lung Clinical Physiology and Pulmonary Function Tests*. Chicago: Year Book Medical Publishers, Inc., 1963.

EGAN, D. F., *Fundamentals of Respiratory Therapy,* 2nd ed. St. Louis, Mo.: The C. V. Mosby Company, 1973.

FILLEY, G. F., *Pulmonary Insufficiency and Respiratory Failure*. Philadelphia: Lea & Febiger, 1968.

GAENSLER, E. A. AND G. W. WRIGHT, "Evaluation of Respiratory Impairment," *Archives of Environmental Health,* 12 (February, 1966).

The Riker Pulmonitor, Vol. 1 in a series of monographs on spirometry. Northridge, Calif.: Riker Laboratories.

SCHOLANDER, P. F., "Analyzer for Accurate Estimation of Respiratory Gases in One-half Cubic Centimeter Samples," *Journal of Biological Chemistry,* 167 (1947).

WOOLMER, R. F., *A Symposium of pH and Blood Gas Measurements*. Boston: Little, Brown and Company, 1959.

Chapter 9

BARNES, R. B., "Thermography of the Human Body," *Science,* 140, No. 3569 (May 24, 1963), 870–877.

BARTHOLOMEW, D., *Electrical Measurements and Instruments* Boston: Allyn and Bacon, Inc., 1963.

BENCHIMOL, A., *Non-invasive Diagnosing Techniques in Cardiology*. Baltimore, Md.: The Williams & Wilkins Company, 1977.

FEIGENBAUM, H., *Echocardiography,* Philadelphia: Lea & Febiger, 1976.

KELLY, E., (ed.), *Ultrasonic Energy*. Urbana, Ill.: University of Illinois Press, 1965.

LAWSON, R. N., AND L. L. ALT., "Skin Temperature Recording with Phosphors: A New Technique," *Canadian Medical Association Journal,* 92 (February 6, 1965), 255–260.

LINZER, M. (ed.), *Ultrasonic Imaging*. New York: Academic Press, 1979.

LION, K. S., *Instrumentation in Scientific Research*. New York: McGraw-Hill Book Company, 1959.

SEGAL, B. L., "Echocardiography, Clinical Application in Mitral Stenosis,"

Journal of the American Medical Association, 1951 (January 17, 1966), 161–166.

THOMPSON, R. F., *Foundations of Physiological Psychology.* New York: Harper & Row, Publishers, 1967.

WELLS, P. N. R., *Biomedical Ultrasonics.* New York: Academic Press, 1977.

WELLS, P. N. R., *Ultrasonics in Clinical Diagnosis.* Edinburgh: Churchill Livingstone, 1972.

WHITE, D. (ed.), *Ultrasound in Medicine.* New York: Plenum Publishing Corporation, Vol. III, 1977; also Vol. I, 1975; Vol. II, 1976.

WHITE, D. N., *Recent Advances in Ultrasound in Biomedicine.* Forest Grove, Ore.: Research Studies Press, 1977.

Chapter 10

BRAZIER, M. A. B., *The Electrical Activity of the Nervous System,* 3rd ed. Baltimore, Md.: The Williams & Wilkins Company, 1968.

THOMPSON, R. F., *Foundations of Physiological Psychology.* New York: Harper & Row, Publishers, 1967.

VENABLES, P. H., AND MARTIN, I. (eds.), *A Manual of Psycho-Physiological Methods.* New York: John Wiley & Sons, Inc., 1967.

Chapter 11

BÉKÉSY, G. V., "A New Audiometer," *Acta Oto-Laryngologica,* 34 (1947), 411–422.

GRINGS, W. W., *Laboratory Instrumentation in Psychology.* Palo Alto, Calif.: The National Press, 1954.

SCHWITZGEBEL, R. L., "Survey of Electro-mechanical Devices for Behavior Modification," *Psychological Bulletin,* 70, No. 6 (1968), 444–459.

SCHWITZGEBEL, R. L., AND R. K. (eds.), *Psychotechnology-Electronic Control of the Mind and Behavior.* New York: Holt, Rinehart and Winston, Inc., 1973.

SIDOWSKY, J. R., "Buyers Guide for the Behavioral Scientist," *American Psychologist,* 24 (1969), 309–384.

STEBBINS, W. C., "Behavioral Techniques," in *Methods in Medical Research,* Vol. 11, B. F. Rushmer (ed.). Chicago: Year Book Medical Publishers, Inc., 1966.

VENABLES, P. H., AND I. MARTIN, *A Manual of Psychophysiological Methods.* New York: John Wiley & Sons, Inc., 1967.

Note: See also the following company manuals on the programming of behavioral experiments:

Bits of Digi—An Introductory Manual to Digital Logic Packages, 4th ed. Beltsville, Md.: BRS—Foringer Division of Technical Services, Inc., 1970.

Lafayette Data Systems Operation and Program Manual. Lafayette, Ind.: Lafayette Instrument Company, 1970.

Solid State Control—A Handbook for the Behavioral Laboratory. Fogelsville, Pa.: Lehigh Valley Electronics, 1970.

Chapter 12

CROMWELL, L., "Use of Telemetry in Cardiovascular Research," in *Proceedings of the 1968 National Telemetry Conference IEEE,* Houston, Texas, April, 1968.

CROMWELL, L., "Some Advances in Techniques for Remote Monitoring of Blood Pressure, in *IEEE Conference Record, Fifth Annual Rocky Mountain Bioengineering Symposium,* Denver, Colo., May, 1968.

CROMWELL, L., "Investigation of Cardiovascular Phenomena by the Use of Biotelemetry," in *Journal of Physiology (London),* 198, No. 2 (September, 1968), 114.

CROMWELL, L., "Biotelemetry Applied to the Measurement of Blood Pressure." Doctoral dissertation, U.C.L.A., December, 1967.

FRANKLIN, D. L., R. L. VAN CITTERS, AND N. W. WATSON, "Applications of Telemetry to Measurement of Blood Flow and the Pressure in Unrestrained Animals," in L. Winner (ed.), *Proceedings of the National Telemetry Conference,* New York, 1965, 233–234

FRYER, T. B., *Implantable Biotelemetry Systems,* Washington, D.C.: NASA Publication SP-5094, 1970.

HANISH, H. M., *Biolink Telemetry Systems Application Notes.* Culver City, Calif.: Biocom, Inc., 1971.

KIMMICH, H. P. (ed.), *Biotelemetry,* Vol. 1. Basel: S. Karger, 1974 Fryer, T. B. "Power Sources for Implanted Telemetry Systems," (especially pp. 31–40; Fryer; T. B., and H. Sandler, "A Review of Implant Telemetry Systems," pp. 351–374.).

KONIGSBERG, E., "A Pressure Transducer for Chronic Intravascular Implantation," in *Fourth National Biomedical Sciences Instrumentation Symposium,* Anaheim, Calif., May, 1966.

MACKAY, R. S., *Bio-Medical Telemetry.* New York: John Wiley & Sons, Inc., 1968.

'Special Issue on Emergency Medical Services Communications," *IEEE Transactions on Vehicular Technology,* VT-29, No. 4 (November, 1976).

Chapter 13

ANNINO, J. S., *Clinical Chemistry.* Boston: Little, Brown and Company, 1964.

LEE, L. W., *Elementary Principles of Laboratory Instruments,* St. Louis, Mo.: The C. V. Mosby Company, 1970.

WHITE, W. L., M. M. ERICKSON, AND S. C. STEVENS, *Practical Automation for the Clinical Laboratory.* St. Louis, Mo.: The C. V. Mosby Company, 1965.

WILLARD, H. H., L. L. MERRITT, AND J. A. DEAN, *Instrumental Methods of Analysis,* 2nd ed. New York: Van Nostrand Reinhold, 1974.

Chapter 14

BLAHD, W. H., *Nuclear Medicine.* New York: McGraw-Hill Book Company, 1965.

"Cardiac Catheterization," *Directions in Cardiovascular Medicine,* Vol. III. Somerville, N.J.: Hoechst Pharmaceuticals, Inc., 1973.

CHASE, G. D., AND J. L. RABINOWITZ, *Principles of Radioisotope Methodology,* 3rd ed. Minneapolis, Minn.: Burgess Publishing Company, 1967.

HINE, G. H. (ed.), *Instrumentation in Nuclear Medicine.* New York: Academic Press, Vol. 1, 1967, Vol. 2, 1974.

JAUNDRELL-THOMPSON, F., AND W. J. ASHWORTH, *X-Ray Physics and Equipment.* Philadelphia: F. A. Davis Company, 1970.

JOHNS, W. E., *The Physics of Radiology.* Springfield, Ill.: Charles C Thomas, Publisher, 1961.

QUIMBY, E. H., S. FEITELBERG, AND W. GROSS, *Radioactive Nuclides in Medicine and Biology: Basic Physics and Instrumentation.* Philadelphia: Lea & Febiger, 1970.

SELMAN, J., *The Fundamentals of X-Ray and Radium Physics.* Springfield, Ill.: Charles C Thomas, Publisher, 1965.

SILVER, S., *Radioactive Nuclides in Medicine and Biology: Medicine.* Philadelphia: Lea & Febiger, 1968.

Chapter 15

BARNA, A., AND D. I. PORAT, *Introduction to Microcomputers and Microprocessors.* New York: John Wiley & Sons, Inc., 1976.

DAVID, D. O., AND B. D. PRESSMAN, "Computerized Tomography of the Brain," *Radiologic Clinics of North America,* 12, No. 2 (August, 1974), 297–313.

DAVIS, G. B., *An Introduction to Electronic Computers.* New York: McGraw-Hill Book Company, 1965.

GORDON, R., G. T. HERMAN, AND S. A. JOHNSON, "Image Reconstruction from Projections," *Scientific American,* 233, No. 4 (October, 1975), 56–68.

HAGA, E. (ed.), *Computer Techniques in Biomedicine and Medicine.* Philadelphia: Querbach Publishers, Inc., 1973.

HOESCHELE, D. F., JR., *Analog-to-Digital/Digital-to-Analog Conversion Techniques,* New York: John Wiley & Sons, Inc., 1968.

JULIUSSEN, J. E., "Magnetic Bubble Systems Approach Practical Use," *Computer Design,* October, 1976, 81–92.

JURGEN, R. K., "Electronics in Medicine," *IEEE Spectrum,* January, 1978, 68–72.

KNIGHTS, E. M., JR., (ed.), *Mini-Computers in the Clinical Laboratory.* Springfield, Ill.: Charles C Thomas Publisher, 1970.

KORN, G. A., *Microprocessors and Small Digital Computer Systems for Engineers and Scientists.* New York: McGraw-Hill Book Company, 1977.

MILHORN, H. T., JR., *The Application of Control Theory to Physiological Systems.* Philadelphia: W. B. Saunders Company, 1966.

PEATMAN, J. B., *Microprocessor-based Design.* New York: McGraw-Hill Book Company, 1977.

SIPPL, C. J., AND D. A. KIDD, *Microcomputer Dictionary and Guide.* Champaign, Ill.: Matrix Publishers, Inc., 1976.

SOUCEK, B., *Microprocessors and Microcomputers.* New York: John Wiley & Sons, Inc., 1976.

STACY, R. W., AND B. D. WAXMAN (eds.), *Computers in Biomedical Research,* Vols. I, II, III, and IV. New York: Academic Press, 1965–1974.

WELLS, P. N. T., AND J. P. WOODCOCK, *Computers in Ultrasonic Diagnosis.* Forest Grove, Ore.: Research Studies Press, 1977.

ZAKLAD, H., "Computerized Multiple X-Rays Give a New View of the Body's Interior," *Electronics,* October 14, 1976.

Chapter 16

BRUNER, J. M. R., "Hazards of Electrical Apparatus," *Anesthesiology,* 28 (1967), 396–424.

Electricity in Patient Care Facilities. Boston: National Fire Protection Association, 1973.

KEESEY, J. C., AND F. S. LETCHER, *Minimum Threshold for Physiological Responses to Flow of Alternating Electric Current Through the Human Body at Power-Transmission Frequencies.* Bethesda, Md.: Naval Medical Research Institute Research Report MR 005.08-00300B #1, September, 1969.

Manual for the Safe Use of Electricity in Hospitals. Boston: National Fire Protection Association, 1971.

National Electrical Code 1971. Boston: National FIre Protection Association, 1971.

Patient Safety, Application Note AN718. Waltham, Mass.: Hewlett–Packard, Inc., Medical Electronics Division, 1970.

PFEIFFER, E. A., "Electrical Stimulation of Sensory Nerves with Skin Electrodes for Research, Diagnosis, Communication and Behavioral Conditioning: A Survey," *Medical and Biological Engineering,* 6 (1968), 637–651.

PFEIFFER, E. A., "Plugs and Receptacles in the Hospital: A Compendium for the Clinical Engineer," *Clinical Engineering,* 2, No. 1 (1976), 46–55.

PFEIFFER, E. A., AND F. J. WEIBELL, "Safe Current Limits: Are They Too Low?" *Biomedical Safety and Standards,* 2, No. 8 (August 10, 1972), 92–94.

WEIBELL, F. J., "Electrical Safety in the Hospital—1974," *Annals of Biomedical Engineering,* 2 (1974), 126–148.

Index